British Railway Bridges & Viaducts

British Railway Bridges & Viaducts

Martin Smith

IAN ALLAN
Publishing

Half-title page :

Smardale Viaduct, 1861: Whereas some of the viaducts on the Stainmore line were eventually widened to accommodate a second track, Smardale Viaduct was built to double-track width but only ever carried a single track. The Tebay–Darlington train crossing the viaduct is hauled by a pair of Standard '3MT' 2-6-0s, Nos 77003 and 77012. *J. W. Armstrong*

Title page:

Montrose Viaduct, 1881: The structure crossed what used to be the South Arm outlet from Montrose Basin, but in this picture of 30 March 1974 the infilling of the South Arm is very evident. Class 26s Nos 26019 and 26010 cross the viaduct with the 1.15pm Aberdeen to Glasgow service. *Brian Morrison*

First published 1994

ISBN 0 7110 2273 9

Published by Ian Allan Publishing

an imprint of Ian Allan Ltd, Terminal House, Station Approach, Shepperton, Surrey TW17 8AS.
Printed by Ian Allan Printing Ltd, Coombelands House, Coombelands Lane, Addlestone, Weybridge, Surrey KT15 1HY.

Acknowledgements

Two exceptionally large 'thank-yous' are due. The first goes to my ever-patient wife, Micky, who still reckons that Isambard Kingdom Brunel was famous only because he had a funny name. The second goes to Paul Gilson, who demonstrated his computer wizardry during a long Saturday evening and, miraculously, rescued 40,000 words of text from a seemingly deceased processor disk.

The text of certain sections of this book has leant heavily on information researched and provided by: Ian S. Carr, Dr T. L. Coombs (Highland Railway Society), Mr A. M. Davies (Manchester Locomotive Society), Mr D. Duncan (Highland Railway Society), Mr D. Jackson (GNSR Association/Highland Railway Society), Keith Jones (GNSR Association), Norman Lee (LNWR Society), Stuart Rankin (G&SWR Association), John Redfearn, Marshall Shaw (North British Study Group), Alan Simpson (North British Study Group) and Bryan Wilson (Welsh Railways Research Circle). Where would we be without experts such as these?

Sincere thanks are also due to the vast legion of people who offered all sorts of advice and assistance, often in exceedingly generous helpings. They are: Carol Arrowsmith (Institution of Civil Engineers), Hugh Ballantyne, Stephen Batty, Mr D. Bromwich (Somerset Local History Library), Neil Burgess, Richard Casserley, Ray Caston (Welsh Railways Research Circle), Paul Chancellor, Mr A. J. Cooper, Steve Daly (Welsh Railways Research Circle), Elizabeth Doley (Berwick-upon-Tweed Museum), Sandy Edward, Chris Hawkins, Peter Herring, Alastair Ireland, Robin P. Jenkins (Leicestershire Record Office), Rex Kennedy, Keith Lawrence, Mr J. A. Lloyd (ScotRail), Mrs J. MacPherson, Tom McGhie (Caledonian Railway Association), Brian Morrison, Ian Nulty (Regional Railways, Swindon), Mr N. Pankhurst (Somerset & Dorset Railway Trust), Bill Peto (Great Western Society), Mr I. Rush (Network SouthEast), Eric Sawford, Mr H. G. T.Smith, Brian Stephenson, Peter Tatlow, Paul Taylor (Tyne & Wear Metro), Arnold Tortorella (G&SWR Association), Peter Waller, Ron White (Colour-Rail), and the staff at the Public Record Office and various local history libraries throughout the country.

Martin Smith
Coleford, Somerset
February 1994

Right:

Wye Bridge, rebuilt 1962: On 27 September 1962, a Cheltenham-bound train crosses the 'up' line while cranes operating on the new 'down' line span remove the paraphernalia of the Brunel's suspension bridge of 1852. *British Railways*

Bridges and viaducts are an integral part of railway infrastructure. Ever since the start of the railway era, lines have had to cross voids which, for various reasons, could not be traversed by purpose-built embankments. Road bridges had, of course, been in existence for thousands of years before the coming of the railways but horse-drawn carts, stagecoaches and pedestrians tended to weigh rather less than railway locomotives. Consequently, such bridges had had to be constructed to only relatively lightweight specifications.

The science of bridge building had to be advanced during the canal era, and many splendid 18th and 19th century aqueducts still survive today. Although the construction of aqueducts required considerable engineering skills, the loads carried by such structures were constant and evenly distributed - this was in marked contrast to the irregular and uneven stresses and vibrations created by railway locomotives and trains. For the first few decades of the railway era, the engineers who had to address such problems had no precedents from which to draw experience and, therefore, had to work beyond the bounds of contemporary knowledge. Many of the bridges and viaducts built at the very start of the railway era still stand to this day, and that is a fitting tribute to the ingenuity of their designers.

The structure which is usually acknowledged as Britain's first railway bridge is Causey Arch at Tanfield Moor in County Durham. Constructed in 1727 to carry a wooden-railed colliery line, it was built of stone and remained in use for over 100 years. Causey Arch still stands, and now has the status of a listed structure. Unsurprisingly, stone was still a popular medium for the construction of bridges and viaducts when Britain's public railway system started to develop in the 1820s, and the use of stone was perpetuated until the present century. The preferred method of construction was the arch - either singly or in multiple. The oldest railway bridge still in regular use in Britain (Skerne Bridge at Darlington, completed in 1825) is of the stone arch format.

Nevertheless, an iron bridge was first seen as early as 1825. George Stephenson's ingenious bridge over the River Gaunless in County Durham was opened to traffic in that year and remained in use until 1901. Cast iron subsequently grew in popularity as a bridge-building material, George and Robert Stephenson being among the keen proponents of the medium. Cast iron was eminently suitable for sections subjected to compression but it had limited tolerances to tension and bending, and although it became widely used in the construction of railway bridges, the collapse of a cast iron bridge at Norwood in London in 1891 finally brought

Left:
Causey Arch, 1727: Built to carry a 4ft gauge wooden-railed colliery tramway across Beckley Burn in County Durham, Causey Arch is the world's oldest surviving railway bridge. It was, incidentally, also known as 'Dawson's Bridge', the Mr Dawson in question being a prominent local landowner and industrialist. Designed and built by a local stonemason, Ralph Wood, the arch rose 35ft from the springing and was 22ft 7½in across. After more than a century of use the tramway was upgraded for use by locomotive traction, but a new alignment via an embankment was built so that locomotives did not have to cross Causey Arch. The bridge was eventually given the status of an Ancient Monument and today it carries a footpath. This picture of it nestling amid the encroaching vegetation was taken as recently as 24 March 1991. *Ian S. Carr*

Above:
Saddleworth Viaduct, 1849: For many years, stone remained a very popular medium for the construction of railway bridges and viaducts. One of the many fine examples of stone-built structures was Saddleworth Viaduct, built to carry the LNWR's Manchester–Huddersfield route across the Huddersfield Canal and the River Tame. The viaduct is situated immediately to the south of Saddleworth station (closed 7 October 1968) and, here, the 14.57 Manchester Victoria–York is seen crossing the viaduct in February 1975. *David A. Flitcroft*

Connel Bridge.

Deepdale Viaduct, 1861: The Barnard Castle–Tebay line (popularly referred to as the Stainmore line) had three splendid lattice girder viaducts which were supported by cast iron piers. The viaducts were designed by Thomas Bouch, whose working practices were subjected to close scrutiny after the fall of his Tay Bridge in 1879, but despite the eventual distrust of Bouch-designed structures, those on the Stainmore line went on to have active lives of just over 100 years. Whatever one's feelings about Bouch and his methods, his viaducts were extremely eye-catching, as evidenced by this wonderfully-detailed picture of Deepdale Viaduct, on the Stainmore line. The picture shows a pair of '4MT' 2-6-0s hauling a westbound special across the viaduct. *J. W. Armstrong*

about the recommendation that all such structures be replaced.

The logical alternative to cast iron was wrought iron, which coped with certain stresses far better than cast iron. However, wrought iron was much more expensive and so its use was often kept to a minimum. Both types of iron were eventually superseded by steel, the first bridge to be built of mild steel being the world-famous Forth Bridge, completed in 1890.

Another alternative to cast iron was timber. The use of timber for the construction of railway bridges and viaducts was not particularly widespread, although the structures designed by John and Benjamin Green for the Newcastle & North Shields Railway and, in particular, Isambard Kingdom Brunel's timber viaducts in the West Country and South Wales were widely regarded as masterpieces in their own right. Numerous timber structures were also constructed for, among others, the North Western Railway and the Caledonian Railway, but these are frequently overlooked.

Timber was a relatively inexpensive and readily available material and, furthermore, the construction of a bridge or viaduct in timber was a comparatively swift procedure. It was, of course, fully appreciated by all concerned that timber structures had finite life expectancies and would, sooner or later, have to be replaced by more durable structures. However, the initial cheapness and speed of

Connel Ferry Bridge, 1903: The best-known steel-built cantilever bridge on Britain's railway network was, of course, the Forth Bridge. A smaller steel cantilever bridge carried not only the Connel Ferry–Ballachulish branch, but also a road across Loch Etive. This highly-distinctive bridge is discussed in a little more detail later on in this book. *Bucknall Collection/Ian Allan Library*

construction were in many cases very attractive selling points. It is, however, arguable that even Brunel would have been surprised by the lifespans of some of his timber viaducts; one built to his design in Cornwall carried passenger traffic until 1934 while, near Aberdare, two genuine Brunel timber viaducts of 1854 carried mineral traffic until 1939 and were not demolished until 1947.

The Brunel-designed timber viaducts are, of course, featured in this book. It should, however, be pointed out that while photographs of some of the lesser-known structures are included, the illustrations of the better-known viaducts are, on the whole, of the masonry replacements. That course has been adopted to avoid undue duplication as, of late, Brunel's civil engineering exploits have been subjected to considerable exposure in magazine articles.

As for other methods of constructing railway bridges and viaducts, lattice girder structures started to become popular in the 1850s. It is believed that the first two wrought iron lattice girder railway viaducts to be constructed in Britain were those at Darcy Lever and Burnden on the Bolton–Bury line in Lancashire, which opened in 1848. They were renewed in 1880/81. Crumlin Viaduct in South Wales was the first truly great lattice girder viaduct and, from the date of its unveiling in 1857 until the time of its demolition in 1967, it retained the title of Britain's tallest railway viaduct. Numerous lattice girder bridges and viaducts are still in regular use today.

Concrete viaducts made their début in Britain around the turn of the century, the McAlpine-designed structures on the Mallaig extension of the West Highland Railway (opened 1901) setting the trend. Pre-stressed concrete was first used in 1947, when the Adam Viaduct near Wigan was rebuilt, but many of the replacement (and completely new) structures built since then have been of conventional steel girder construction, albeit with welding eventually taking the place of riveting.

Having devoted a few brief paragraphs to the story of bridge engineering, it should be pointed out that this book is primarily intended to cover the railway history of the relevant bridges and viaducts and is *not* meant to be an engineering appraisal. This author readily admits that he has trouble differentiating between a Warren Triangular Girder and a lavatory brush. The text discusses the engineering aspects in very simple terms, concentrating more on other topics such as the social aspects and, to a limited extent, the engineers who were responsible for creating some of the most conspicuous components of Britain's railway infrastructure.

On a semi-technical note, the official differentiation between a bridge and a viaduct is that the latter has four or more spans, but that guideline throws up certain anomalies. For example, the 121-span structure across the Mawddach Estuary in North Wales is usually referred to as Barmouth *Bridge* and, similarly, the world-famous Tay Bridge has rather more than four spans.

It is estimated that, despite the line closures of the last 40 years or so, the present-day BR network still incorporates some 64,000 bridges of all shapes and sizes. It is, of course, impossible to give details of more than a very small proportion of those in a single book. The bridges and viaducts selected for inclusion in this book are, on the whole, those which have significant historical, architectural or visual interest or, in a few cases, unusual features.

Unfortunately, there are countless imposing structures for which space has been unavailable. In Scotland and the North of England, for example, the topography often necessitated the construction of huge viaducts, but while each structure had definite appeal in its own right, they were so numerous that the inclusion of more than a representative selection would, it is considered, become somewhat repetitive. Among the more interesting oddities which, sadly, have had to be ignored is the transporter bridge of Joseph Crosfield & Sons at Warrington - believed to be the only transporter bridge in Britain to carry railway vehicles.

The structures included in this book are listed chronologically. It is hoped that this will give an idea of how bridge building progressed over the years. In a few cases, bridges and viaducts were completed a year or more before the railway line across them was opened but, for the sake of stan-

Above:
Dare Viaduct, 1854: In this book, there are several references to the famous timber viaducts designed by Isambard Kingdom Brunel, particularly for railways in Devon and Cornwall. However, it is not always appreciated that Brunel was also active in South Wales, one of his achievements in that area being the engineering of the Vale of Neath Railway which, in true Brunel fashion, was built to the broad gauge and incorporated distinctive timber viaducts. The VoNR's colliery branch from Gelli Tarw to Dare Junction and Nantmelyn opened to traffic on 7 November 1854, and crossed two timber viaducts, Gamlyn and Dare.

Problems were soon encountered with the latter viaduct, heat expansion during the summer causing the rails on the curve to distort the structure by a few inches. The trouble was, however, cured by the fitting of expansion joints.

The Gelli Tarw–Dare Junction section closed to traffic from 1 September 1939, the two timber viaducts

having remained in use until the end. They therefore claimed the distinction of being the last two Brunel-designed timber viaducts to see active service. That fact is often overlooked as it is frequently reported that College Wood Viaduct on the Falmouth branch in Cornwall was, until its replacement in 1934, the last Brunel-style timber viaduct to remain in use. To set the record straight, College Wood Viaduct was the last of its type to carry a *passenger* line. So there! The two Welsh viaducts were finally demolished in 1947, this picture of Dare Viaduct being taken in 1893, by which time the line across it had been converted to the standard gauge. *Welsh Industrial & Maritime Museum*

Right:
Crumlin Viaduct, 1857: Britain's tallest viaduct was at Crumlin, in South Wales. Standing 200ft above the valley floor, it was of lattice girder construction and incorporated several novel features, more of which later on in this book. *British Railways*

10

Top:
The 'Armchair Bridge', 1877: For those who, like this author, have an interest in the obscure, the 'Armchair Bridge' must rate as one of Britain's more charismatic railway bridges. Situated ½ mile south of Watford Lodge, between Rugby and Long Buckby, it is officially known as 'Bridge No 69', but the nickname was coined by railwaymen and positively stuck. An alternative nickname was the 'Pulpit Bridge', local legend telling how clergymen used to preach to estate workers from the bridge. The bridge was erected by the LNWR to a design approved by the local landowner, Lord Henley, and although there was no road underneath, it provided access between different parts of His Lordship's estate. The bridge originally had some ornamental work in cast iron, but that deteriorated beyond repair and was removed in 1934. On the outside of the 'armchairs', the Henley family's coat of arms was, for many years, finished in gilt paint. *Ian Allan Library*

Above:
Pinmore Viaduct, 1877: One of the many superb structures which, due to lack of space, has had to be excluded from the main section of this book is Pinmore Viaduct, between Girvan and Stranraer. Although the line across the viaduct did not open to passenger traffic until 5 October 1877, it is believed that freight traffic had been accommodated on some sections of the line since the previous October. Here, 'Black 5' No 44791 is seen crossing the viaduct on 12 February 1963 - it is on snowplough duties prior to the passage of a Stranraer–Glasgow train. *Derek Cross*

Right:
Bath Spa, line opened 1841: The railway approaches to many towns and cities were (and still are) by means of lengthy elevated sections. At Bath, the line on each side of the station is carried on a succession of arches. A Paddington–Bristol HST is seen here approaching the station from the east on 26 August 1991. The width of the old broad gauge track bed, which was engineered by Isambard Kingdom Brunel, is clearly evident. *Author*

dardisation, the dates used are those when the relevant structure first carried revenue-earning railway traffic.

It will be noticed that certain geographical areas have stronger representations in this book than others. For example, the Northeast of England is heavily featured, but as so many of Britain's pioneering railways (and, consequently, historic bridges and viaducts) were in that area, it is hard to ignore the weight of numbers. Furthermore, there are significant concentrations of bridges and viaducts during certain periods of time, for example the late 1840s. This is due largely to the prolific construction of railways which followed the first bout of 'railway mania' in the mid-1840s. A second, albeit less frenzied, attack of 'railway mania' occurred ten years

later and, when combined with the enthusiasm of the early railway promoters in and before the 1830s, the outcome was that, between 1830 and 1860, some 25,000 railway bridges were constructed in Britain.

As the years progressed, railway traffic increased and consequently many bridges and viaducts required substantial alteration or even complete rebuilding. In most cases in this book, the relevant text starts with the original structures and, unless otherwise stated, the dimensions given in the tables are those of the first bridges or viaducts at the site.

Fortunately for railway enthusiasts, historians and modellers, the mass closures of the 1960s did not necessarily result in the obliteration of all the bridges and viaducts on lines which met their

doom. British Railways often considered that the cost of routine maintenance for a disused structure was preferable to the expense and logistical difficulties of a major demolition job. One example was provided by the disused Cullen Viaduct in Scotland which, in the late 1980s, was found to have serious structural faults - the cost of repairs was estimated at some £35,000, but the bill for demolition would have been £40,000!

Cullen Viaduct is one of many structures to be given increased protection by being granted the status of listed buildings. In certain cases BR tried to sell off such liabilities: Bennerley Viaduct on the Nottinghamshire/Derbyshire border, for example, being offered to local councils for the princely sum of £1. The outcome of all this is that a surprising proportion of imposing (but defunct) structures can still be seen today. Their continuing existence provides a fitting monument to the engineers who designed them and the labourers who built them.

Whether your interest is the famous or the obscure, it is hoped that the selection of bridges and viaducts featured provides an entertaining cross-section. I apologise if your favourite structure has been omitted.

Above:
Glen Ogle Viaduct, 1870: The railway lines through the Highlands of Scotland are famed for their engineering works, and some of those lines are discussed later in this book. At the risk of offending fans of the Caledonian Railway, the Callander & Oban line has reluctantly been excluded, but a peace offering is proffered in the form of this picture of a 'Type 2' descending Glen Ogle on the approach to Lochearnhead on 15 April 1963. These days, the men working on major civil engineering schemes are usually accommodated in reasonably comfortable portakabins, and transport is normally available for social visits to the nearest town - it takes a lot to imagine the working conditions endured by the railway navvies of the mid-1800s in terrain such as this. The old Callander & Oban line was formally closed between Callander and Crianlarich in October 1965 after a severe landslide in Glen Ogle had blocked and damaged the line beyond economical repair. *K. M. Andrew*

Right:
Lockwood Viaduct, 1850: The sheer size of the structure is clearly evident in this spectacular picture of Class 40 No 40181 working an enthusiasts' special on 8 December 1984. *Bob Avery*

14

1825: Gaunless Bridge, West Auckland, County Durham

Designer: George Stephenson
Original owner: Stockton & Darlington Railway
Contractor: John & Isaac Burrell, Newcastle
Type: Arch and suspension
Materials: Cast and wrought iron
Total length: 17yd
Max height of rails: 15ft
Spans: 4
Tracks: 1

The Stockton & Darlington Railway was one of the earliest public railways in Britain and had several claims to fame, but one of its lesser-known contributions to British railway history was a bridge over the Gaunless stream near West Auckland. It was the world's first railway bridge to be made of iron.

The design of Gaunless Bridge is credited to George Stephenson (1781–1848) who was, of course, one of the pioneering railway engineers. Stephenson's first employment as a boy had involved keeping cattle off the Dewley Wagonway, for which he had been paid 2d (1p) per day, and by the time he was 17 he had progressed to the position of engineman at a colliery incline near Throckley Bridge. Before long, Stephenson had enrolled at night school to learn reading, writing and arithmetic which, he had considered, would enable a better understanding of engineering. His big break had come in 1811 when he had volunteered to redesign the pumping engine at Killingworth High Pit, where he then worked. Stephenson succeeded in rectifying the engine's design faults, and that achievement had made his name in the area. He was on his way.

In 1821 the fledgling S&DR had appointed Stephenson as its engineer at the princely salary of £660 per annum, and he submitted a design for the bridge over the Gaunless in 1822. Stephenson was, at that time, a partner in the firm of Messrs John & Isaac Burrell, who had ironworks at Orchard Street and South Street in Newcastle; unsurprisingly, the contract for the erection of the bridge was given to Burrells. It is known that Stephenson relinquished his partnership in the firm at the end of 1824, but it is unclear whether that was because of any potential conflict of interests.

Gaunless Bridge was actually completed in 1823, two years before the S&DR opened. However, violent storms swept the Northeast in October 1824 and the bridge was among the many works which were damaged. The subsequent rebuilding of the bridge involved adding a fourth span to the original three-span structure. The cosmetic appearance of the bridge was one of comparative frailty, an oft-repeated description likening it 'to a piece of cottage furniture - but for a rather large cottage'.

The design of Gaunless Bridge, however, showed an advanced grasp of engineering techniques as it combined the arch and suspension principles and, furthermore, it incorporated two types

Below:
Gaunless Bridge, 1825. The world's first iron-built railway bridge was replaced by a masonry bridge in 1901, but the original structure was saved and is now exhibited outside the National Railway Museum. *M. Hall*

of material: cast iron and wrought iron. Cast iron was an ideal medium for sections subjected only to compression (eg supporting piers), whereas wrought iron was more suited to sections subjected to tension or bending (eg those carrying the decking). The cost of wrought iron was, however, very high and so contemporary bridge builders who were working to tight budgets had to ensure that its use was kept to a minimum.

Each of the four spans of Gaunless Bridge consisted of a pair of wrought iron fish-belly-shaped girders with cross-links of iron cast around them and extended upwards to carry the timber decking. The girders were cleverly interlocked at each end by a cast iron boss. The bridge was supported by three piers, each comprising a pair of cast iron columns braced together and splayed outwards. The ingenious construction resulted in the load carried by the bridge being shared, the outward thrust of each arch being counteracted by the inward pull of the suspension element.

Gaunless Bridge was on the 25-mile line between Stockton and Phoenix Colliery (two miles to the northwest of West Auckland). The line opened to goods traffic on 27 September 1825, its western extremity consisting of four rope-worked inclines and a 1½-mile horse-worked level stretch between Etherley and Brusselton inclines. Gaunless Bridge was on the level section. The S&DR introduced its own public passenger services on the line in 1833, and much to the chagrin of many local landowners and the drivers of horse-drawn trains, locomotive traction was soon introduced. One objector protested about '...those great snorting, roaring and mighty monsters, vomiting fire in all directions, which the horse by no means recognises as relations of his'.

Although locomotive traction did not appear on the Gaunless Bridge line until the 1830s, the S&DR had, of course, used locomotives on certain sections of its line since opening day. The company's Act of Parliament had made provision for the conveyance of passengers by steam power, the very first railway company Act to do so:

'It shall and may be lawful for any person or persons permitted by them, from and after the passing of this Act, to make and erect such and so many loco-motive or movable engines as the said company of proprietors shall from time to time think proper and expedient, and to use and employ the same in and upon the said railways or tramroads or any of them, by the said recited Act, and by this Act directed or authorised to be made, for the purpose of facilitating the transport, conveyance and carriage of goods, merchandize and other articles and things upon and along the said roads, and for the conveyance of passengers upon and along the said roads.'

The somewhat elaborate wording of that clause stemmed, almost certainly, from the lack of any precedent.

Passenger services on the line via Gaunless Bridge continued only until October 1858, when a diversion via the so-called Tunnel branch (to the north of Shildon) offered an easier route to and from West Auckland. The line nevertheless remained in use for mineral traffic, and the North Eastern Railway (which had absorbed the historic S&DR in July 1863) replaced Gaunless Bridge with a masonry structure in 1901. Appropriately, the original bridge was carefully preserved, and it is now a prized exhibit at the National Railway Museum in York.

1825: Skerne Bridge, Darlington, County Durham

Designer: Ignatius Bonomi
Original owner: Stockton & Darlington Railway
Type: Arch
Material: Stone
Spans: 1
Tracks: 1 (later 2)

The historic Stockton & Darlington Railway was administered by a board of directors who seemed insistent on the supervision of even the smallest details. This did not always make life easy for the company's engineer, George Stephenson, who on at least one occasion was overruled by his directors. The occasion in question was when the bridging of the River Skerne, on the northern outskirts of Darlington, was being planned.

After Stephenson had prepared a design for the bridge, the S&DR's directors insisted that he should consult Ignatius Bonomi (1787–1870), the well-known Durham architect who, in 1819, had designed the road-bridge over the River Wear at Lambton Castle. Stephenson was not amused by the directors' apparent lack of confidence in his abilities and tried to ignore the edict in the hope that it would be forgotten, but a reminder followed and so Stephenson dutifully presented his plans for Bonomi's approval. Bonomi proposed some alterations, and that has often given rise to speculation whether the design of the Skerne Bridge should be credited to Stephenson or Bonomi.

Sadly, the S&DR's records cast little light on the 'Stephenson or Bonomi' debate. One of the few (and inconclusive) references is hidden in the sub-committee minutes of 11 June 1824, the subject of the proposed bridge eliciting the resolution: '...that the secretary do write to Mr Bonomi and request his professional assistance in executing the same'. It is known that, by this time, Stephenson had abandoned his plans for an iron bridge across the Skerne, partly because of the high price of iron at the time, and partly because of the reluctance of iron founders to tender for work of that kind.

The bridging of the Skerne was made by means of a distinctive Italianate-style stone arch, two narrow land arches being built into the extensive curving wing-walls. When the doubling of the line was undertaken in 1831/32, it was necessary to strengthen the existing bridge and add a 'new' section on its north side. The S&DR opened on 27 September 1825, and Skerne Bridge was later immortalised in Dobbins's famous painting of *Locomotion No1* hauling a train across it on opening day. That was, however, painted several years after the event and entirely from memory.

Skerne Bridge is the structure which currently graces the reverse of the Bank of England's £5 notes, but its present-day cosmetic appearance is somewhat different to that depicted on the fivers. For some time now, the bridge has been covered by unsightly gas pipes but, at the time of writing, British Gas has just announced plans to remove the piping to help restore the structure to its former glory. The bridge is located between Bank Top and North Road stations, and is used by trains on the Bishop Auckland/Weardale line.

1830: Sankey Viaduct, Earlestown, Merseyside

Designer: George Stephenson
Original owner: Liverpool & Manchester Railway
Type: Arch viaduct
Material: Stone
Total length: 200yd
Max height of rails: 70ft
Spans: 9
Tracks: 2

The Liverpool & Manchester Railway, one of Britain's pioneering railway companies, ceremonially opened the line between the communities of its title on 15 September 1830, but the event was marred by the tragic accident at Parkside in which The Rt Hon William Huskisson MP sustained fatal injuries after being knocked down by the L&MR's locomotive, *Rocket*.

Contemporary newspaper accounts reveal that the arrival of the first train at Crown Street station in Liverpool was greeted by a band playing 'See the Conquering Hero Comes'. This cannot go without comment as, throughout the 19th century, almost every railway opening seems to have had a

band playing that very same tune. One could question the versatility of the bands of the day or, perhaps, it could be asked why no other tune was deemed appropriate. Alternatively, one could just be thankful that a song called 'Congratulations' wasn't around at the time.

In August 1830, the month before the public opening of the line, George Stephenson had personally driven the L&MR's newest locomotive, *Northumbrian*, along the route. Presumably for purposes of publicity, Stephenson was accompanied on the footplate by the actress, Fanny Kemble, who afterwards wrote about the crossing of Sankey Viaduct:

'I stood up, and with my bonnet off drank the air before me. The wind, which was strong, or perhaps the force of our own thrusting against it, absolutely weighed my eyelids down. When I closed my eyes this sensation of flying was quite delightful, and strange beyond description; yet strange as it was, I had a perfect sense of security and not the slightest fear.'

Sankey Viaduct, near Warrington, was one of the most impressive features of the L&MR's line. It carried the railway above the community of Sankey Brook which, incidentally, was later renamed Earlestown after Sir Hardman Earle, the North of England railway magnate. The viaduct which was eventually built was, however, far different from that which had originally been proposed. After the L&MR's formation George Stephenson had been appointed to survey the route, but there had been considerable opposition from some board members to Stephenson's methods and, in 1825, he had been replaced by the engineers John and George Rennie, with Charles Blacker Vignoles in the role of Chief Surveyor. The following year, however, Stephenson had been reappointed at a salary of £800 per annum. The Rennies' surveys had resulted in plans for a 237yd-long viaduct over Sankey Brook, the structure being 60ft high and having seven arches of 50ft span with a further 60ft span over the canal. Stephenson disregarded the Rennies' idea and instead formulated a design for a brick-built structure of 20 arches. That, however, was rejected by the directors.

Stephenson's ultimate design was for a viaduct of nine semicircular arches, each of 50ft span, supported by square piers with distinctive splayed bases. The stone-built structure stood some 70ft high, and was the world's first large railway viaduct. During the construction of the viaduct, the Sankey Navigation Co secured a payment of £500 from the L&MR as compensation for encroaching on their property, with an additional £30 for each day that canal traffic was detained.

During its early life, Sankey Viaduct required a degree of attention. As early as 1831 there were fears that the northwest wing-wall and abutment were settling, but a thorough inspection found no real cause for concern. In 1833 coping was applied to the parapet walls - a finishing touch that had, for whatever reason, been overlooked for three years. There were reports in 1838 and 1842 that one of the piers seemed to be sinking, and after the second report an arch at the eastern end was shored up. Nevertheless, Sankey Viaduct has gone on to have a lengthy existence. Its original owner, the L&MR, eventually became part of the London & North Western Railway and, later, the LMSR. The line across the viaduct is still in regular use today, although the cosmetic appearance of the structure is now somewhat spoiled by the paraphernalia of overhead electrification.

1830: Haggerleases Bridge, Butterknowle, County Durham

Designers: Thomas Storey/William Burn
Original owner: Stockton & Darlington Railway
Contractor: James Wilson, Pontefract
Cost: £420
Type: Skew arch

Material: Masonry
Total length: 14yd
Max height of rails: 15ft
Spans: 1
Tracks: 1

The Stockton & Darlington Railway opened its 4¾-mile branch from St Helen Auckland to a terminus at Haggerleases Lane, near Butterknowle, in October 1830. The line followed the course of the River Gaunless and, although known originally as the Haggerleases branch, was redesignated the Butterknowle branch in October 1899, the terminus being renamed accordingly. Although the branch was intended mainly to serve collieries near Butterknowle, passenger services were also provided and the public timetables continued to include Haggerleases until August 1859.

Horse power was the order of the day until the opening of a new connecting line at Shildon in 1858 enabled locomotives to work through to Haggerleases for the first time. The easternmost section of the Haggerleases branch, incidentally, later formed part of the West Auckland–Barnard Castle route, which opened in 1863.

About a quarter of a mile from Haggerleases, the original S&DR branch crossed the River Gaunless on what is believed to have been only the second skew arch on any British railway, the first having been built by George Stephenson at Rainhill on the Liverpool & Manchester Railway. The crossing of the Gaunless at right angles would have required an arch with a modest span of 19ft, but the lie of the land all but ruled out a right-angled approach on both sides and so a skew arch was built at an angle of 27°, the resultant span being 42ft. It is believed that, before construction of the stone arch commenced, a full-size prototype was built from timber in an adjacent field; in view of the untried nature of the engineering techniques which were required, the suggestion of a 'dry run' is quite plausible.

Haggerleases Bridge was designed by Thomas Storey, but the plans had been prepared by William Burn, the clerk of the works at the suspension bridge over the River Tees (opened December 1830). The contract for the bridge's construction had originally been let to Thomas Worth and John Batie for £327, but after piling the foundations and laying the lower courses of masonry, they had given up the work. The contract was subsequently re-let to James Wilson for £420. Cynics were quick to suggest that the arch would collapse even before the railway opened to traffic, but the structure proved the Doubting Thomases very wrong indeed. It remained in use until 30 September 1963 when the section of the line to the west of Evenwood Colliery closed, and still stands today.

It appears that, in the mid-1800s, Haggerleases Bridge caused some confusion. The S&DR minutes referred to the structure as a 'swin bridge', the term 'swin' being used locally to describe a diagonal crossing. However, when London-based Ordnance surveyors took an interest in the bridge in the late 1850s, they took the terminology to mean 'swing bridge' and consequently labelled the structure accordingly. No doubt the North-eastern dialect also came up with a term for a mere Southerner who thought that a sturdy masonry arch could be swung open.

1830: Tees Suspension Bridge, Nr Stockton-on-Tees, Cleveland

Designer: Capt Samuel Brown
Original owner: Stockton & Darlington Railway
Type: Suspension
Cost: £2,200
Total length: 137yd
Max height of rails: 20ft above high-water
Spans: 1
Tracks: 1

The Stockton & Darlington Railway's extension to Middlesborough was authorised in May 1828, but encountered considerable opposition from the outset. One of the obstacles the S&DR had to overcome was that the Bishop of Durham demanded more than £5,000 for a plot of land only a little over six acres in size. At an official inquiry, however, it was revealed that 100,000 of the 110,000 tons of coal which had already passed over S&DR metals had, in fact, come from the Bishop's collieries. The hypocrisy (or possibly greed) was clearly taken into account when the inquiry fixed the sale price at a more realistic £2,000.

Another opponent of the S&DR's Middlesborough extension was the Tees Navigation Co, which was committed to a series of new works despite the competition offered by the railway. The S&DR's line to Middlesborough had to cross the River Tees (which, at that time, marked the border between County Durham and Yorkshire) without causing even a temporary obstruction of the river which, of course, would have incurred the wrath of the Navigation Co.

Preliminary plans were made by one of the S&DR's engineering staff, James Dixon, for a cast iron bridge which could be constructed by prefabricating the girders on pontoons, floating them into position, and raising them hydraulically. Although this ingenious method was later used to great effect by such celebrated engineers as George Stephenson and Isambard Kingdom Brunel, it was not used at Stockton. Similarly, Timothy Hackworth's design for a wrought iron plate girder bridge was rejected partly because it was an untried technique. Instead, the S&DR appointed Capt Samuel Brown RN to design and build a suspension bridge. Chain suspension bridges were far from new, the use of iron in their construction having been developed by Capt Brown (1776–1852), who was responsible for the design of the once-famous Chain Pier at Brighton.

The suspension bridge across the Tees was completed in December 1830, its main span being 281ft long and 16ft wide with the decking supported by 110 perpendicular rods hung from a total of 12 chains, six on each side. The immediate priority was to subject the bridge to extensive tests. The S&DR had been led to believe that the bridge would be capable of carrying weights of up to 150 tons when the first test, in which a weight of 18 tons 1cwt was placed on the centre of bridge, resulted in an alarming deflection of over 9¼ins. A subsequent test involved an 8 ton locomotive hauling a 28-wagon train of some 37 tons across the bridge, and this produced a deflection of 5¾ins. In a later test with a 66½ton train, the masonry of both towers was damaged and two of the cast iron retaining plates on the east side of the bridge split. A partial solution to the problem was eventually found by connecting the wagons by means of chains and couplings which kept them 27ft apart, but timber piles were used to shore up the bridge as a form of insurance policy.

The Middlesborough branch was ceremonially opened on 27 December 1830, the inaugural train being hauled by Hackworth-designed wooden-wheeled 0-4-0 *Globe* which had been built specially for hauling 'express' passenger trains. *En route*, the train was stopped so that the official party could inspect the suspension bridge. The bridge might have looked impressive enough to the VIPs but the S&DR knew that, in view of the structure's inability to accept heavy loads, it was a great disappointment. The suspension bridge was replaced as early as 1841, the new structure being designed by Robert Stephenson and having five cast iron girders (three river spans of 89ft each and two land spans of 31ft each) supported by masonry piers. Each span comprised four girders as the two tracks were carried independently. That bridge was itself renewed in 1907, the piers and the foundations of the 1841 structure being reused.

Despite the short and far from auspicious life of Capt Brown's suspension bridge, it went down in the annals as one of only three suspension bridges in this country to carry a main-line railway. The second was Brunel's Wye Bridge at Chepstow, and the third was another Brunel structure, the Royal Albert Bridge at Saltash. Both of the others are featured later in this book.

1836: London (London Bridge Stn)–Greenwich

The London & Greenwich Railway opened its line as far as Deptford on 14 December 1836. The company's station, London Bridge, therefore became the first railway terminus in the metropolis, but few could have foreseen that it would eventually become the busiest. The L&GR opened its extension to Greenwich on 24 December 1838, thereby completing a remarkable stretch of railway.

For much of its length, the London Bridge–Greenwich line was carried on a continuous viaduct. The raised section, which stretched for all of 3¾ miles was, effectively, the longest railway viaduct in the country. The L&GR had opted for a

Below:
London & Greenwich Railway, 1836. This engraving is believed to show the railway crossing Corbett's Lane. Note the gas lamps on the viaduct and, in the distance, the masts of ships in the docks. *Ian Allan Library*

raised line to obviate the need for countless level crossings as, along its route, there were numerous streets through residential and industrial areas. The railway passed through Bermondsey and Rotherhithe, the former being described in an 1858 guide book as 'one of the most abominable slums in the environs of London', while the latter was noted for 'sending forth its clouds of sulphur and ammonia from the chimneys immediately below the level of the line, and presenting anything but an inviting prospect to the beholder.'

The L&GR's lengthy viaduct had 828 arches, the standard dimensions for most being 18ft span, 22ft high, and 25ft wide. The arches were built of grey brick, and a 4ft-high parapet wall was provided on each side of the top of the viaduct so that passengers did not feel too vulnerable while travelling at speed 22ft above ground level. The viaduct had a walkway on each side, one being used for access for maintenance and the other as a public toll-path. The viaduct was designed by Col G. T. Landmann, the L&GR's engineer, who later masterminded the construction of the Preston & Wyre Railway in Lancashire.

When the L&GR had been planning its route, it had anticipated that the revenue from suburban traffic would be inadequate. Consequently, the company had proposed to rent out the arches of the viaduct for use as homes, shops and warehouses. Although a few houses were built under arches at Deptford, the pervading dampness dispelled further thoughts of residential development. However, the arches proved popular as commercial premises, and are still widely used as such today.

The L&GR was leased by the South Eastern Railway in 1845. By then, two other companies were also using the route into London Bridge station, and the intensity of traffic was such that it became necessary to widen a section of the viaduct. This was undertaken in 1847, further widenings and remodellings taking place in 1866, 1879 and 1894, a total of eleven tracks ultimately being carried on the London end of the viaduct. It was a far cry from the early days of the L&GR.

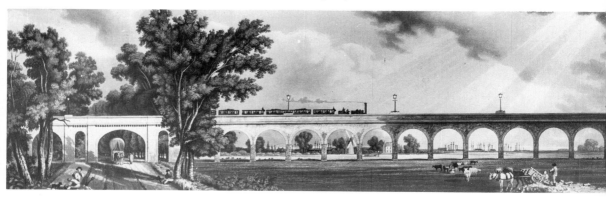

1837: Dutton Viaduct, Nr Weaverham, Cheshire

Designer: Joseph Locke
Original owner: Grand Junction Railway
Contractor: MacIntosh & Co
Cost: £50,000
Type: Arch viaduct
Material: Stone
Total length: 428yd
Max height of rails: 84ft
Spans: 20
Tracks: 2

The Grand Junction Railway was incorporated in 1833 principally to provide a connection between Birmingham and the Liverpool & Manchester Railway. The GJR grew rapidly, and absorbed the historic L&MR in 1845; the following year it joined forces with two other concerns to form the London & North Western Railway.

Before construction of the GJR's line commenced, the company announced its intention that George Stephenson would be responsible for engineering the northern part of the route, while his erstwhile pupil, Joseph Locke (1805–1860), looked after the southern part. Perhaps predictably, Stephenson was less than amused by that arrangement and soon resigned, Locke subsequently assuming charge of the entire route. It remains unclear just how much preliminary work had been undertaken by Stephenson prior to his resignation, and so it is difficult to apportion the credit for the design of the Dutton Viaduct, across the Weaver Valley to the north of Northwich. It has often been remarked that Dutton Viaduct has many Stephenson hallmarks, but its design is more usually credited to Joseph Locke who was in office during its construction.

During his apprenticeship at the locomotive works of Robert Stephenson & Co, Locke's potential had been noticed by Stephenson himself. Stephenson had subsequently involved Locke in the engineering of the Liverpool & Manchester Railway, and it had been the unfortunate Locke who had been driving the famous Liverpool & Manchester Railway locomotive *Rocket* when, in 1830, it had run over William Huskisson at Parkside on opening day. On the plus side, Locke had made a number of significant contributions to the work on the L&MR, but Stephenson had still regarded Locke as an apprentice and, consequently, saw no reason for paying him a penny for his efforts. Unsurprisingly, this had been one of the causes of a rift between Stephenson and Locke but, within a few years, the two men had again been able to work together. However, as already mentioned, the uneasy peace was broken by the Grand Junction Railway's appointment of Stephenson and Locke on an equal basis.

Returning to the more pertinent matter of Dutton Viaduct, it was regarded as Britain's first real railway viaduct - for various reasons, the London & Greenwich Railway's 3¾mile-long raised line (of 1836) was rarely looked on as a 'proper' viaduct. Dutton Viaduct was built from red Runcorn sandstone and had twenty spans, each 60ft wide, and broad-based piers. The structure consumed some 700,000cu ft of stone. The line across the viaduct opened to traffic on 4 July 1837. Interestingly, one of the competitors for its construction had been the famous engineer Thomas Brassey, but his tender had been some £5,000 more expensive than the lowest. Brassey's first railway viaduct was, in fact, at Penkridge, on the GJR's line between Wolverhampton and Stafford. Dutton Viaduct is, of course, still in use today but, in common with several other major bridges and viaducts, its visual appeal has suffered from the requirements of overhead electrification.

To the north of Dutton Viaduct, near Warrington, the GJR was carried over the River Mersey and the Mersey & Irwell Navigation canal (also known as the Old Quay Navigation) by means of the **Mersey Viaduct**. The structure was known locally as 'Twelve Arches' because of its total number of spans, the three largest spans being those over the river and the canal. Built of sandstone and measuring some 200yd long, the viaduct still stands today. However, it no longer carries the main line, a diversionary route via an embankment having been built and eventually used for crossing the Manchester Ship Canal, a new bridge having become operational in 1893.

1838: Wharncliffe Viaduct, Hanwell, Middlesex

Designer: Isambard Kingdom Brunel
Original owner: Great Western Railway
Contractors: Grissell & Peto
Cost: £55,000
Type: Arch
Materials: Brick; stone dressing
Total length: 300yd
Max height of rails: 65ft
Spans: 8
Tracks: 2 (later 4)

The first section of the Great Western Railway to open was that between Paddington and Maidenhead, public traffic commencing on Monday, 4 June 1838. The GWR's engineer was the legendary

Above:
Wharncliffe Viaduct, 1838 The first major Brunel-designed railway viaduct is still in use today. This is the south face of the viaduct, the structure having been widened on its north side in 1877 - note Lord Wharncliffe's coat of arms between the fourth and fifth arches. An unidentified 'Class 52' is seen with a Paddington–Swansea working on 15 February 1971. *J. H. Cooper-Smith*

Isambard Kingdom Brunel (1806–1859) who, of course, favoured a gauge of 7ft 0¼in instead of the 4ft 8½in commonly used elsewhere on Britain's embryo railway network. The controversial subject of gauge was not, however, the only reason for Brunel being constantly in the limelight; his feats in the field of railway engineering regularly ventured beyond the limits of contemporary experience, thereby ensuring his place in the engineering hall of fame.

Brunel was only 27 when, in 1833, he was appointed by the fledgling GWR as its Engineer. It appears that Brunel was subjected to a formal interview for the post, and an unconfirmed story relates that he was questioned about alternative routes for the railway between London and Bristol. The tale suggests that one of the interviewers implied to Brunel that even a man of the latter's capabilities would be unable to survey possible alternatives with adequate speed. According to the story, Brunel replied that surveys for alternative routes were unnecessary as the route which he proposed would not be the cheapest, but would certainly be the best. That answer, so the story goes, secured him the job.

Brunel was a renowned perfectionist who usually insisted on overseeing major projects himself, unlike his contemporary and rival, Robert Stephenson, who was happy to delegate. A consequence of Brunel's insistence on controlling everything himself was a working day which often spanned 20 hours, and it is arguable that the intensity of this partially self-induced workload contributed greatly to his death at the age of just 53.

On the Paddington–Maidenhead section of the GWR, the first construction contract to be let was for the Brunel-designed viaduct across the Brent Valley at Hanwell. The viaduct, which was just to the west of Hanwell station (opened December

1838), was completed in May 1837, construction having taken just fifteen months. The section of line across the viaduct was opened to traffic on 4 June 1838.

The viaduct had eight arches, each of 70ft span, and each pier was formed of two tapering pillars which, like some of Brunel's other work, were in the 'Egyptian' style. The GWR's Directors' Report of August 1837 noted: '...in acknowledgement of the zealous and indefatigable attention of Lord Wharncliffe, as Chairman of the Committee on the (GWR's) Act of Incorporation in the House of Lords it was, by his Lordship's permission, named the Wharncliffe Viaduct'. Lord Wharncliffe's coat of arms was carved in stone on the south side of the viaduct's middle pier. The viaduct itself proved to be a very sturdy structure, but the same could not initially be said for the embankments on the approach at either end, slippage being an infuriatingly regular occurrence in the early days.

As Britain's railway network expanded, Brunel's broad gauge came under increasing threat and, in 1861, third rails were laid between Paddington and Reading to permit mixed gauge operation. In 1877, Wharncliffe Viaduct was widened on its north side to enable the laying of quadruple tracks (two broad gauge and two standard gauge), the new brickwork and additional piers being in the style of the original structure. The extinction of the broad gauge in May 1892 resulted in the four-track standard gauge formation which has existed ever since. Since the widening of the viaduct in 1877, the structure has been subjected to little more than routine maintenance and, today, InterCity 125s hurtle across it at speeds which Brunel could never have imagined but of which he would certainly have approved.

A somewhat less successful Brunel-designed bridge was located just a quarter of a mile to the west of Wharncliffe Viaduct. To carry the railway across **Uxbridge Road**, Brunel designed a skew bridge which had its cast iron girders supported by two rows of eight pillars, the four pairs of pillars in the centre being of cast iron and the others of brick. At first, the spaces between the main and cross girders were filled by brick arches but, after the failure of a main girder in March 1839, timber planking was substituted in order to reduce the weight. The decking was also of timber and, in May 1847, the entire timber content of the structure was set alight, allegedly by a piece of burning coke dropped from a locomotive. The heat generated was such that most of the iron girders buckled or fractured.

As a temporary measure the tracks were shored up from the road, the replacement bridge being constructed in wrought iron. In a strangely punctuated missive to the GWR's directors in 1849, Brunel wrote:

Below:
Victoria Bridge, 1838: This magnificent structure still stands today, albeit in a 'mothballed' state. On 17 October 1981, it proved its worth as an alternative to the East Coast main line when, due to damage at Chester-le-Street, the 07.36 Plymouth–Edinburgh train was one of many to be diverted across the bridge. The locomotive in charge was Class 55 No 55004 *Queen's Own Highlander.* The Penshaw Monument can be seen above and behind the rear of the train. *Ian S. Carr*

'Cast-iron girder bridges are always giving trouble - from such cases as the Chester Bridge, and our Great Western road bridge at Hanwell, which since 1838 has always been under repair and has cost its first cost three times over, down to petty little ones, which either in frosty weather or from other causes are frequently failing. I never use cast iron if I can help it, but in some cases it is necessary and to meet these I have had girders cast of a particular mixture of iron carefully attended to, and I have taught them at the Bridgewater foundry to cast them with the flange downwards instead of sideways.'

1838: Victoria Bridge, Nr Penshaw, Tyne & Wear

Designer: Messrs Walker & Burges
Original owner: Durham Junction Railway
Contractor: John Gibb & Son, Aberdeen
Cost: £40,338
Type: Arch
Material: Stone
Total length: 270yd
Max height of rails: 135ft
Spans: 10
Tracks: 2

The Durham Junction Railway consisted of little more than a five-mile line between Washington (where a junction was made with the Stanhope & Tyne Railway) and a terminus at Rainton Meadows (closed in August 1844), but it was an important link in the chain of independent railways which eventually formed the York–Newcastle main line.

Despite being one of Britain's largely-forgotten railway companies the DJR left the magnificent legacy of the Victoria Bridge, which spans the River Wear between Penshaw and Washington. It is believed that the original intention was to build an

iron bridge but, instead, a stone structure was constructed. The bridge was built under the supervision of Thomas Harrison, who later became the Engineer of the North Eastern Railway, while the contractor was the grandfather of George Stegmann Gibb who later became the NER's Solicitor and, eventually, General Manager.

After a little over two years' work the last stone of the bridge was laid on 28 June 1838, the day of Queen Victoria's coronation and, predictably, the structure was christened the Victoria Bridge. The line across it opened to mineral traffic on 24 August 1838 and to passengers on 9 March 1840. The bridge had four main arches, those at each end being of 100ft span while the central pair were 144ft and 160ft; there were also three approach arches, each of 20ft span, at either end. On BR's present network, the only masonry arch with a longer span is that of Ballochmyle Viaduct in Scotland.

Walker's original design for the bridge at Penshaw had incorporated one large arch at each end instead of the three small arches, and that would have increased the total length of the structure by an estimated 45yd. Walker made no secret of his abhorrence of the alterations which had been made to his original plans, but the general consensus was that the finished product had a tremendous feel of solidity. An interesting feature of the bridge was its stone-flagged pedestrian causeway on each side. It was remarked that the cost of the bridge was, in proportion to its dimensions, less than any similar structure in the country. It is said to have been modelled on a Roman bridge at Alacantara in Spain which, coincidentally, has featured heavily in a 1993/94 tourist board advertising campaign.

The DJR was worked by the Stanhope & Tyne Railway, which was reincorporated in 1842 as the Pontop & South Shields Railway. The DJR was purchased in 1843 by the acquisitive George Hudson and was later amalgamated with his York,

Newcastle & Berwick Railway which, in 1854, became a founder member of the North Eastern Railway. The route across Victoria Bridge was, in effect, the first East Coast main line, but after those services were diverted via Durham in 1872, the bridge accommodated little more than local passenger and freight workings. The local passenger services were withdrawn in May 1964, but the 'Old ECML' via Victoria Bridge still remains open, albeit in a 'mothballed' state since 1991 and with only a single track.

1839: Scotswood Bridge, Newcastle-upon-Tyne, Tyne & Wear

Designer: John Blackmore
Original owner: Newcastle & Carlisle Railway
Type: Viaduct
Materials: Timber; stone
Total length: 235yd
Max height of rails: 35ft above low-water
Spans: 11
Tracks: 2

The Newcastle & Carlisle Railway opened the first section of its line to public goods traffic in 1834, and the first public passenger workings between Blaydon and Hexham took place on 3 March 1835.

Below:
Scotswood Bridge, replaced 1868: The original bridge, which dated back to 1839, was destroyed by fire in 1860. Its replacement fared somewhat better and remained in use until 1982. In this preservation era picture, 'K4' class 2-6-0 No 2005 (which never carried that number in service!) and 'Black 5' 4-6-0 No 4767 are seen double-heading a special working. *N.E.Stead*

The company extended its line to Redheugh, adjacent to Gateshead on the south bank of the River Tyne, on 1 March 1837, thereby leaving just two sections to be completed. One of those was the crossing of the Tyne into Newcastle itself.

Plans were considered for a bridge across the Tyne from Redheugh to The Spital at Newcastle, but the estimated cost put a damper on the scheme. Consequently, an idea which had first been proposed in 1825 by the engineer, William Chapman, was revived, this being for a crossing of the Tyne between Blaydon and Scotswood. One feature of the Scotswood route was an interesting bridge, designed by the N&CR's resident engineer, John Blackmore. It was built on the skew and comprised eleven trussed-rib spans of 60ft each; apart from the masonry abutments, it was constructed entirely of timber.

The N&CR's line into Newcastle via Scotswood Bridge was opened on 21 May 1839, but regular passenger services into the temporary terminus near the Shot Tower did not commence until 21 October. On 9 May 1860, during tests for the Board of Trade, Scotswood Bridge was destroyed by fire. It was replaced in 1868 by a five-span girder bridge, the N&CR having by then become part of the North Eastern Railway. The girder bridge remained in use until 1982 when Newcastle–Blaydon traffic was diverted via Dunston, but the redundant structure was left *in situ*.

Elsewhere on the route of the Newcastle & Carlisle Railway, there were other major viaducts, one of which was the 188yd-long **Wetheral Viaduct**, near the western end of the line. Built by W. S. Denton to the designs of the N&CR's Chief Engineer, Francis Giles, the viaduct carried the line 95ft above the River Eden on five arches, each of 80ft span; the foundation stone for Wetheral Viaduct was laid on 25 March 1830 and the work was finished on 12 August 1834. Not far away was the 160yd-long **Corby Viaduct** which had seven arches, each of 40ft span, and stood 70ft above the Drybeck Valley. Another structure of note was the skew bridge which crossed the **River Gelt** at an angle of 63°; it had three arches of 30ft span and was one of the largest skew bridges of the day. The Newcastle–Carlisle route via Dunston is, of course, still in use today.

1839: Willington Viaduct and Ouseburn Viaduct, Nr Newcastle-upon-Tyne, Tyne & Wear

Designer: John & Benjamin Green
Original owner: Newcastle & North Shields Railway
Type: Arch viaduct
Materials: Timber; stone
WILLINGTON VIADUCT: 349yd long; 82ft high; 7 timber spans (1 x 128ft, 4 x 120ft, 2 x 115ft)
OUSEBURN VIADUCT: 306yd long; 108ft high; 5 timber spans (3 x 116ft, 2 x 114ft)

The Newcastle & North Shields Railway opened the line between the communities of its title on 18 June 1839, and the railway later attracted the com-

ment that it 'presented as great an amount of skill in the construction of its works as any other line of equal length in the kingdom'. From an engineering point of view, the line's main features were undoubtedly the distinctive viaducts at Willington and Ouseburn, both of which were built to the designs of the architects John and Benjamin Green, two Newcastle-based brothers whose contribution to civil engineering in the Northeast should never be underestimated.

The spans of the two viaducts took the form of timber arches. However, Ouseburn Viaduct also had two stone arches on the approaches at each end, these being constructed not only to give length to the abutments but also to keep the embankments as far as possible from the steep sides of the ravine. When the foundations were being laid for the western pier it was necessary to fill up an old pit shaft immediately below the pier, another exhausted coal seam near the eastern pier also having to be filled with rubble. The piers and abutments of both viaducts were of stone, the railway company's directors having requested that the piers be strong enough to support the eventual replacement of the timber superstructures by those of more durable material.

The interest generated by these two viaducts centred largely on their use of laminated timber arches (on the Wiebeking system), one of the very first applications of such a technique in Britain. Each arch was formed of three parallel ribs, each 42in thick and 22in broad, which were tied together transversely by wrought iron bolts and diagonal braces. The braces comprised 14 layers of 3in planks, which measured between 20ft and 45ft in length and 11in in breadth, and were turned to the requisite form and pinned together by means of tree-nails and iron bolts. Each spandrel was divided by a strong principal extending from the crown of the rib in an oblique direction to one of the piers, the upper space being filled with vertical struts and the lower space with radiating struts.

The timber used was Baltic softwood, a popular 'engineering' timber which was readily available in large quantities. The timber was treated to a process called Kyanising, named after its originator, Dr John Kyan (1774–1850), which involved pickling the wood in bichloride of mercury. The treatment helped to preserve the wood and reduce its flammability and, although creosote became increasingly popular as a preservative after 1840, Kyanising did not fall out of favour for some time. Its use was perpetuated until at least the 1850s by, amongst others, Isambard Kingdom Brunel.

In 1869 the two viaducts had their timber arches replaced by ones of iron, the ironwork following a similar pattern to the original timberwork. Although both structures saw heavy usage, Ouseburn Viaduct became the higher-profile one as it carried the East Coast main line, and it was widened in 1885 to accommodate four tracks. Willington Viaduct has, in recent years, been given a new lease of life under the ownership of the Tyne & Wear Metro, more of which towards the end of this book.

Elsewhere on the N&NSR line, skew bridges similar in construction to the two viaducts were used to carry the railway over roads at Walker and Chirton. Another timber bridge was built over **Borough Road** at North Shields in readiness for the construction of a branch to the fish dock, but the branch never materialised. Nevertheless, the N&NSR and its successors remained responsible for maintaining the almost unused bridge and, since it was never subjected to the pounding from rail traffic, the structure survived virtually in its original form until 1937. As for the old N&NSR, it ultimately became part of the NER.

1839: Maidenhead Bridge, Maidenhead, Berkshire/ Buckinghamshire

Designer: Isambard Kingdom Brunel
Original owner: Great Western Railway
Contractor: Chadwick & Co
Type: Arch
Material: Brick
Total length: 253yd
Max height of rails: 39ft above water level
Spans: 2 main; 8 subsidiary
Tracks: 2 (later 4)

As we have already seen, the Great Western Railway proudly unveiled its line between Paddington and Maidenhead on 4 June 1838. On 1 July 1839, an extension to Twyford was opened, the bridging of the River Thames just to the west of the original station at Maidenhead being by means of another of Brunel's many masterpieces.

The design of Maidenhead Bridge attracted considerable controversy. At the chosen bridging point

Left:
Ouseburn Viaduct, rebuilt 1869: Ouseburn and Willington Viaducts were of similar design and, when rebuilt in 1869, the 'new' iron superstructures of both followed the lines of the original timber arches of 1839. On 9 September 1967, preserved 'K4' 2-6-0 No 62005 was photographed crossing Ouseburn Viaduct with the empty stock of a Newcastle–London special. *C. J. Mills*

the Thames was 100yds wide, but had a conveniently placed little island in the middle. Brunel chose to span the river with just two arches, each of 128ft span and with their common pier resting on the island, with a 21ft-span towpath arch and three 28ft-span floodwater arches on each side. The medium selected was brick.

The most significant feature of the bridge was that the two main arches had a rise of only 24ft 6in from the springing to the crown, thereby being, at the time, the 'flattest' brick arches in the world. Brunel's critics, of whom there were more than a few, predicted that, as the design of the bridge defied many tried and tested laws of engineering, it would inevitably collapse as soon as the centering was removed. Although Brunel knew that he had gone well beyond the bounds of contemporary knowledge, he had full confidence in his calculations. Both camps monitored the situation closely after the centering was eased and, much to the smug delight of the anti-Brunel faction, the eastern arch showed signs of settlement.

The settlement was, in fact, no more than a separation of about half an inch between the lowest three courses of bricks, and ran for just 12ft either side of the crown of the arch. Brunel's conclusion was that the centering had been removed before the cement had properly set and, furthermore, that the settlement was mainly superficial. The contractor readily accepted responsibility and, as the centering was still on site, the necessary remedial work was carried out promptly.

In October 1838, the centerings were eased for the second time, but were moved only by a matter of inches. To most observers, however, it appeared as if the centerings were still supporting the arch, and this resulted in the prophets of doom continuing their howls. The railway across the bridge opened to traffic in July 1839, but it was decided to leave the centerings standing for a second winter; it is, however, unclear whether that decision was Brunel's private joke, or whether he was acting on instructions from his directors. The Doubting Thomases, of course, still believed that the arch was actually supported by the centerings. On a stormy night in the autumn of 1839, the timber centerings were blown down and, when it was realised that trains had, in fact, been running across the unsupported arch for some months, a bout of the proverbial hat-eating ensued.

A glowing PR job for the bridge was given in the *Illustrated Guide to the GWR* of 1852:

'The Railway...quits the station on a highly elevated embankment, extending about a quarter of a mile to the bridge by which the Great Western crosses the Thames, a noble structure of two arches, made of brick, dressed with Yorkshire stone, and exhibiting, perhaps, the first example in this country of very flat elliptical arches in masonry, having 130 feet span. If the passenger will cast a hasty glance in passing, he will behold charming river-scenery bounded by woodlands and pleasant fields.'

The line across Maidenhead Bridge was originally broad gauge. It was converted for mixed gauge operation by October 1861, and the broad gauge rails were finally removed in May 1892. The wide track beds that had been necessitated by the broad gauge helped a great deal when single lines were doubled and double lines quadrupled, but many bridges and viaducts nevertheless had to be widened to accommodate the extra track or tracks. The widening of Maidenhead Bridge was undertaken between 1890 and 1893, the work taking some twelve months longer than the construction of the original bridge over fifty years earlier. The bridge was widened by skilfully adding a single track width on each side, the cosmetic finish being identical to that of the original and the 'joins' barely distinguishable. Maidenhead Bridge is, of course, still in use today, no significant alterations having been carried out to it since the widening of the early 1890s.

1840: Avon Bridge, Bath, Avon

Designer: Isambard Kingdom Brunel
Original owner: Great Western Railway
Type: Skew arch
Materials: Timber; masonry
Total length: 55yd
Spans: 2
Tracks: 2

The Bristol–Bath section of the Great Western Railway's main line opened to traffic on 31 August 1840. In the Bath area, the line was elevated for a considerable distance, Twerton Viaduct having 28 arches and the approach to the station being partly by means of a 73-arch viaduct. Even the station itself was built on arches. The most interesting engineering feature in Bath was, however, the twin-span skew bridge across the River Avon immediately to the west of the station.

Brunel had originally intended that the bridge should be built of iron, and some 500 tons of ironwork were ordered in May 1839. However, no contractor proved willing to take on the job and so, in view of the delays which had already dogged the construction of the Bristol–Bath line, Brunel considered that speed was of the essence and decided to build a timber bridge, the task being undertaken

Above:

Avon Bridge, second rebuilding 1959: The original Brunel-designed timber bridge immediately to the west of Bath station was replaced in 1878. The replacement bridge lasted until 1959, when a new structure was built. On 25 October 1959 Canton-based 'Hall' class 4-6-0 No 6932 *Burwarton Hall* was photographed coming slowly over the down line with the 10.10 Cardiff–Portsmouth train. The unidentified '2251' class 0-6-0 on the right is on an engineers' train which has possession of the up line. *Hugh Ballantyne*

by the GWR's own workforce. The shyness of contractors was, perhaps, surprising. It was known in engineering circles that Brunel would settle for nothing less than top-quality work, but for competent contractors that meant good rewards were available.

The definitive description of the skew bridge at Bath appeared in J. C. Bourne's guide to the Great Western Railway:

The angle at which the Bridge crosses the River is so considerable that, although the space from quay to quay is only 80 feet, the space traversed by the railway is 164 feet. The bridge is of two arches, each of 80 feet span. Each arch is composed of six ribs placed about 5 feet apart and springing from the abutment and a central pier of masonry. Each rib is constructed of five horizontal layers of Memel timber held together by bolts and iron straps. The end or butt of each rib is enclosed in a shoe or socket of cast iron, resting with the intervention of

a plate upon the springing stones, the shoes on the middle pier being common to the two ribs. The spandrels of the four external ribs are filled up with an ornamental framework of cast iron supporting the parapets. The interior ribs are connected by cross struts and ties. The cornice and parapet are both of timber; the latter is framed in open work of a lozenge pattern. The abutments are flanked by plain turreted piers, and the tow-path is carried on an iron gallery beneath the western arch.'

The timber bridge was replaced in 1878 by an iron girder structure which, in 1959, was replaced by the present-day bridge.

The city of Bath is famous for its Georgian architecture and for many years was a fashionable spa resort. Consequently, tourist brochures have never been slow to publicise Bath's attractions, the official GWR Guide of 1852, for example, providing this offering:

'The Great Western Railway enters Bath through a deep cutting close to Sydney Gardens, a favourite promenade and place of amusement in this gay city, which the Line, instead of injuring, contributes not a little to embellish. Beyond this the Line passes beneath several houses and a street, sweeping round to the Poulteney-road *(sic)* on an embankment, and over a beautiful stone viaduct bridge, forty feet above the Avon...'

Sadly, it appears that the GWR did not consider Brunel's skew bridge to be among the city's tourist attractions.

1841: Ouse Viaduct, Nr Balcombe, West Sussex

Designers: John Rastrick and David Mocatta
Original owner: London & Brighton Railway
Cost: £58,000
Type: Arch viaduct
Materials: Brick; stone
Total length: 492yd
Max height of rails: 92ft
Spans: 37
Tracks: 2

The London & Brighton Railway hired the eminent engineer, Sir John Rennie, to survey the route between the communities of its title. Several other proposals for a railway link between London and Brighton surfaced almost simultaneously, among them being one from Robert Stephenson. It was contended by a rival engineer, Nicholas Cundy, that Stephenson had 'stolen' his plans, Cundy's counsel accusing Stephenson of being like a gypsy '...who having purloined the child of another person, covers it with rags and dirt in order that he may pass it as his own, when he starts forward on his mendicant expedition'. Among the other proposals, one by John Vallance had by then died an inevitable death. It had suggested a tunnel extending the whole way between London and Brighton with the trains being worked by atmospheric pressure.

Despite the strength (and variety) of the opposition, Rennie's plans won the day. The engineer appointed to take charge of the construction of the line was John Urpeth Rastrick (1780–1856), one of the unsung names of pre-Victorian railway engineering. Rastrick hailed from Stourbridge and, as a partner of James Hazeldine of Bridgnorth, had in

1808 built Trevithick's *Catch Me Who Can*, only the third railway engine ever to have been constructed. Rastrick had built a superb cast iron bridge across the River Wye at Chepstow in 1816 and had later engineered the horse-worked Stratford & Moreton Tramway. In partnership with William Foster of Stourbridge, Rastrick had constructed three locomotives in 1828 for export to America while, the following year, he had been one of the three judges at the Rainhill trials. He then went on to engineer several other railways before being appointed by the London & Brighton.

Southwards from Norwood, the ruling gradient of the Brighton line was no greater than 1 in 264. This was achieved not only by the use of tunnels and extensive earthworks, but also a superb viaduct across the Ouse valley between Balcombe and Haywards Heath. The viaduct had 37 brick arches, each of 30ft span, which varied in height from 47ft at the southern end to 96ft in the centre; the piers were not solid, but were pierced by arches and inverts. The design of the viaduct itself is correctly attributed to Rastrick, but the ornamentation which made it such an attractive structure was designed by the L&BR's architect, David Mocatta. The embellishments included balustrades of Caen stone and, at each end, four classical-style pavilions.

The construction of the London–Brighton line progressed rapidly, over 6,200 men and almost 1,000 horses being employed by July 1840. It is believed that the Ouse Viaduct was completed in 1840, but the section of the railway between Norwood and Haywards Heath did not open to traffic until 12 July 1841. Trains started working to and from Brighton on 21 September.

The London & Brighton Railway became part of the newly-formed London, Brighton & South Coast Railway in 1846. The Brighton route became inten-

Left:
Ouse Viaduct, opened to traffic 1841: The sheer elegance of the Ouse Viaduct, near Balcombe, was still clearly evident some 120 years after the structure was built. *Brian Haresnape*

1842: Stockport Viaduct, Stockport, Gtr Manchester

sively used but, when quadrupling was debated in the early 20th century, it was considered that the cost of widening the Ouse Viaduct would be prohibitive. The widening of Balcombe Tunnel was also rejected on financial grounds, and so the quadrupling of 1910 reached only as far as the northern end of the tunnel.

Ouse Viaduct is still in everyday use. Throughout its long life it has been subjected to little more than routine maintenance, although during the 1960s there were fears that vibration was having a detrimental effect on the viaduct and so the rails across it were welded. The viaduct is now claimed to be the highest brick-built structure on the Southern Region.

The Manchester & Birmingham Railway reached the southern end of the uncompleted Stockport Viaduct in June 1840, the last 'stone' of the viaduct being laid six months later. However, the company then decided to channel its resources into the southern section of its line and, consequently, it was 10 May 1842 before the viaduct was brought into use. Stockport Viaduct was designed by George Buck and, with a length of 595yd and a height of 111ft above the bed of the River Mersey, it positively dominated the locality. Its presence was further emphasised in 1889 when it was widened on the west (down) side to accommodate four tracks. A temporary station was opened at the southern end of the viaduct in February 1843, Edgeley station later being built on the same site. The superb structure was treated to an intensive wash and brush-up in 1989 and on 24 November of that year (the centenary of its widening) it was illuminated on the town side. The impressive night-time illumination has been retained to this day.

Below:
Stockport Viaduct, opened to traffic 1842: A Manchester-bound local is seen crossing the superb viaduct on 20 May 1957. *T. Lewis*

1842: Etherow Viaduct, Nr Mottram, Greater Manchester

Designer: Joseph Locke
Original owner: Sheffield, Ashton-under-Lyne
   & Manchester Railway
Contractor: Smith & Hattersley
Cost: £20,000
Type: Arch viaduct
Materials: Timber; stone
Total length: 169yd
Max height of rails: 136ft
Spans: 3
Tracks: 2

The Sheffield, Ashton-under-Lyne & Manchester Railway opened its cross-Pennine route in a somewhat piecemeal manner - the first section was opened to traffic in November 1841 but the line was not completed throughout until December 1845. The SA&MR's route required considerable engineering works including two particularly noteworthy viaducts, the first to accommodate revenue-earning traffic being at Etherow, to the east of Manchester near Mottram. The line across Etherow Viaduct opened on 24 December 1842 to complete the section between Manchester and a station called Glossop (later renamed Dinting).

The original engineer of the SA&MR was Charles Blacker Vignoles (1793–1875). When making plans for the line, Vignoles bore in mind the viaducts with curved timber arches which had been built by the Green brothers in 1839 for the Newcastle & North Shields Railway, and he seemed set to demonstrate that imitation was the sincerest form of flattery by designing similar structures for the SA&MR. However, Vignoles resigned from his post in 1839 and was succeeded by Joseph Locke, one of Robert Stephenson's former pupils, who had by then made something of a name for himself with the engineering of the Grand Junction and the London & Southampton Railways. The idea for timber viaducts in the style of the Green brothers was perpetuated by Locke, but in the light of Vignoles' preliminary plans, it might be considered misleading to give Locke all of the credit for their design. Furthermore, another contender for a share of the credit was Alfred Jee, the SA&MR's Resident Engineer, who is known to have drawn up the plans for the viaducts.

The contract for the construction of Etherow Viaduct was awarded to Messrs Henry & Co of Chester, who had submitted a tender of £25,000. The contract was made subject to the satisfactory outcome of negotiations with the lessees of the land on which the four stone piers were to rest, but even protracted negotiations failed to reach an acceptable conclusion. The railway company therefore had little option but to agree to a viaduct with fewer supporting piers, cancel Henry & Co's contract, and invite new tenders for the work. Messrs Smith & Hattersley secured the contract with a tender of £20,000 - £5,000 less than the original contract awarded to Henry & Co. The viaduct was completed remarkably quickly, the foundation stone being laid in March 1842 and the structure being opened to traffic just nine months later. The

Below:
Etherow Viaduct, 1842: This picture of the viaduct was painted in 1846 and shows the structure in its original condition. The larger viaduct at Dinting Vale was of similar construction. *British Railways*

'revised' design resulted in a viaduct which had three arches, each of 125ft span, some 186,000 tons of stone from the nearby Tintwistle Quarries and 41,000cu ft of timber being used in its construction.

The SA&MR opened its extension from Glossop (Dinting) to Woodhead to public traffic on 8 August 1844, and this section incorporated a similar but larger viaduct at **Dinting Vale**. It had five main timber arches each of 125ft span and a total of 11 approach arches, each of 50ft span and built of brick; 386,179cu ft of locally extracted ashlar were absorbed by its large piers, wings, outside spandrels and parapets while the upper sections required 40,477cu ft of Memel pine which was preserved by being treated with a solution of copper sulphate. Of the two viaducts, that at Dinting Vale adhered most closely to the structures built near Newcastle by the Green Brothers.

The principal details for **Dinting Vale Viaduct** were:

Contractor: Buxton & Clarke
Cost: £32,250
Total length: 484yd
Max height of rails: 125ft
Spans: 16
Tracks: 2

By the late 1850s the timbers of both viaducts were found to have deteriorated badly and, in 1859, the reporting engineer, William Fairbairn of Manchester, declared them unsafe. He recommended that the timber spans should be replaced by wrought iron plate girders, and his tender of £28,700 for the reconstruction of both viaducts was accepted by the railway company. Fairbairn certainly pulled out all the stops. The work on both structures commenced in November 1859 and the rebuilding of Etherow

Viaduct was completed before the end of the year; the work on Dinting Vale Viaduct took only until the following spring. The speed of the work was even more remarkable considering that there was no real interruption to traffic, the new girders being prefabricated alongside the tracks on the approach embankments and moved into position by means of bogies which ran on the original timbers.

By the time of the rebuilding of the viaducts, however, the SA&MR was no more. In 1847 the company had amalgamated with three newly authorised railways to form the Manchester, Sheffield & Lincolnshire Railway, the title of which was changed in 1897 to the Great Central Railway. Over the years the cross-Pennine route became increasingly well used by heavy trains and, perhaps predictably, the two viaducts suffered. Eventually, it was realised that they needed major attention.

By 1918 the GCR had at last decided how to go about strengthening the two viaducts. Etherow Viaduct had, in fact, been strengthened in 1894 by additional girders, but in 1917 it had been proposed that a new viaduct be built alongside, the new structure accommodating the fast lines and the original structure carrying the slow lines. That proposal was, however, rejected. Instead, the original viaduct was strengthened by means of three additional piers, Dinting Vale Viaduct receiving similar treat-

Below:
Dinting Vale Viaduct, rebuilt 1860 and 1919: The massive brick pillars which were added to the viaduct in 1919 might have been the most cost-effective method of strengthening, but they did little for the viaduct's aesthetic appearance. Here, a three-car electric set is seen crossing the viaduct in August 1979. *Paul W. Roynon*

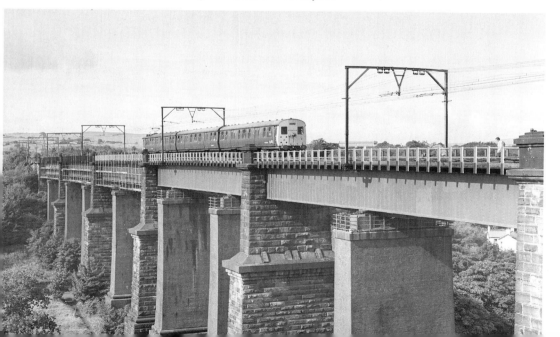

ment, albeit with seven extra piers. The work on both viaducts was completed in 1919.

The new brick piers did little for the appearances of the structures. This was particularly true of Dinting Vale Viaduct as the new piers had to be spaced irregularly in order to avoid the road and the stream in the valley below. Perhaps the final blow to the cosmetic appearance of the once-smart viaducts was the addition of overhead wires for electric workings. Those with a more fatalistic attitude might, however, merely express gratitude that the two viaducts are still in everyday use.

Returning briefly to the early days of the SA&MR, the nine-arch **Ashton Viaduct** on the Stalybridge branch partly collapsed during construction on 19 April 1845. Seventeen workmen fell to their deaths but, as the arches which gave way were above the River Tame (which marked the border between Lancashire and Cheshire), some of the men were considered to have died in Lancashire and others in Cheshire. Consequently, separate inquests were held in two different counties for men who had previously been working alongside each other. The collapse was blamed on uneven distribution of ballast and, although the SA&MR paid £47 4s 6½d (£47.23p) for the men's funerals, the company deducted that amount from the next payment to the contractors. Later, however, the railway company opened a fund for the widows and orphans of those who had been killed.

1843: Etherley Viaduct, Nr Witton Park, County Durham

The Stockton & Darlington Railway's branch to Crook opened on 8 November 1843, some of the upper sections of the line being worked by gravity instead of by locomotives. The railway crossed the River Wear just to the north of Witton Park by means of a handsome viaduct, but although the structure had no major architectural or historical claims to fame it was highly distinctive in that it passed over not only the river, but also a road bridge. A branch to Frosterley opened in August 1847, and it joined the Crook branch a little to the north of Witton Park. The Frosterley line was later extended to Stanhope and Wearhead, and the section as far as Eastgate, where a large cement works was established in the 1960s, still survives.

Below:
Etherley Viaduct, 1843: The viaduct crosses the minor road between Witton Park and High Grange, and also the River Wear. On 18 May 1993 Class 31 No 31547 was photographed returning from Eastgate to Doncaster with inspection saloon DM 395280. *Ian S.Carr*

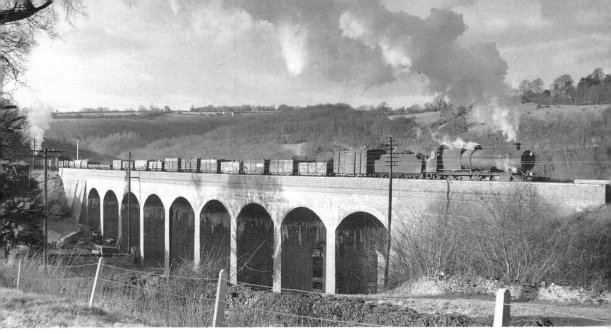

**Frampton Mansell Viaduct, original timber viaduct
built 1845:** Although the timber viaducts on the Stroud
Valley line have long since gone, their replacements
still provide fine settings for eye-catching pictures. In
this photograph, taken in March 1953, a '28XX' class
2-8-0 hauls a mixed freight across the viaduct. The
assistance at the rear by one of the Brimscombe
bankers is evident. *Ian Allan Library*

1845:
Swindon–Gloucester,
Wiltshire/Gloucestershire

(nine principal structures listed below)
Designer: Isambard Kingdom Brunel
Original owner: Great Western Railway
Material: Timber

Miles	Name	Description
5½	Frampton	12 x 30 ft spans
7	Slip	22 x 30ft spans; named after a nearby landslip
8	St Mary's	1 x 75ft skew span over canal
8½	Bourne	1 x 67ft skew span over canal; 16 others ranging from 18ft to 30ft
10	Capel's	18 x 30ft spans
11	Canal	1 x 51ft skew span over canal; 1 x 22ft; 1 x 28ft; 1 x 30ft
11	Watt's	8 x 30ft spans; 4 stone arches
11½	Stratford	1 x 40ft span; 7 x 30ft
12	Cainscross	4 x 32ft spans

Distances shown are those from Kemble (as quoted by MacDermot & Clinker)

Construction of the broad gauge line between
Swindon and Gloucester was started by the Cheltenham & Great Western Union Railway, but the
route remained uncompleted when the company
sold out to the Great Western Railway in 1843. It
was therefore left to the new proprietors to complete the line, and the grand opening took place on
12 May 1845.

The line passed through the Stroud Valley which
was described briefly but poetically in the GWR
Guide for 1852.

'The valley, in fact, assumes the character of a
mountain-gorge, with a brawling stream in the bottom, which partially forms the motive-power of the
numerous cloth and fulling mills of this well known
district...The Railway, during the whole of its
progress through this singularly beautiful scenery,
lies for the most part on a steep incline.'

The line necessitated considerable earthworks, the
boring of a 2,212yd tunnel at Sapperton, and the
building of nine sizeable viaducts. The viaducts

were all built of timber because of the requirement for fast and economical construction, but as early as 1859 a programme was instigated to replace the timbers by more durable materials.

The Stroud Valley line was converted to the standard gauge in May 1872. A little over 30 years later, in October 1903, the line was in the headlines when it became the testing ground for the GWR's steam railmotors. The railmotors were huge successes, particularly when additional halts were opened, and their use quickly spread throughout much of the GWR network. Of their activities in the Stroud area, the *Railway & Travel Monthly* of January 1914 opined:

'It would be difficult for anyone not conversant with the locality to appreciate the boon to the district that the introduction of a railmotor service has provided. Previously, the only means of transport between Stroud, Brimscombe and Chalford for the workers in the mills and factories in the valley was an antiquated horse 'bus, the stations being too far and the stopping trains too infrequent to tap this valuable source of traffic.'

The locomotive-worked auto-trains, which were the successors of the railmotors, worked the Stroud Valley line until November 1964.

The gradients through the Stroud Valley included some stiff climbs, the steepest being 1 in 57. Banking engines were often employed and outstationed at the small engine shed at Brimscombe, 2-6-2Ts being the usual steeds although, during World War 2, 2-8-0Ts and 2-8-2Ts were used. Right until the end of the steam era a heavily-loaded train, banked at the rear, passing across elegant viaducts in the

scenic valley was a common and very pleasing sight.

The Stroud Valley line remains in use today as part of the Paddington–Gloucester route. The diesel services may be clean, comfortable and fast, but they lack the charisma of the 'Cheltenham Flyer', which used the route after its introduction in July 1923. The 'Flyer' was, at the time, the fastest scheduled steam-hauled working in the world although, as has regularly been pointed out by one of the line's historians, Mr Mike West of Dursley, none of its flying actually took place in the Cotswolds.

1846: Arun Bridge, Ford, West Sussex

Designer: John Rastrick
Original owner: Brighton & Chichester Railway
Contractor: John Butt
Type: Telescopic
Materials: Timber
Total length: 41yd (exc approaches)
Spans: 1
Tracks: 1

In the 11th century the River Arun in Sussex was navigable as far as Pulborough, some 12 miles inland, and by the railway era sailing ships loaded with coal still worked as far up-river as Arundel. When the Brighton & Chichester Railway constructed its line, inland craft still had priority over railway traffic and so it was out of the question that the bridge needed to carry the line over the River

Arun near Ford should hinder shipping movements. Consequently, the bridging of the Arun required some ingenious thinking and the local engineer, John Butt, came up with the idea of incorporating a swinging span which, in preparation for being swung, could be raised by flooding the hollow central pier. Butt's proposal was, however, rejected by Parliament.

The design which won the day was by John Rastrick, a name not unfamiliar to railway company hierarchies in the Southeast of England. It was for a bridge containing two moveable sections, the first moving laterally thereby making room for the second (the middle section) to run back over the rails on wheels. The contract for the construction of Rastrick's bridge was given to John Butt, the creator of the earlier design which had been rejected. The bridge was built of Baltic timber and its total length was 273ft. Arun Bridge was opened to traffic on 8 June 1846, the company which owned the bridge, the Brighton & Chichester Railway, becoming part of the newly-formed London, Brighton & South Coast Railway on 27 July 1846.

A contemporary description of the bridge appeared in *Our Iron Roads*, written with a commendable proliferation of commas by the Rev F.S.Williams and published in 1852:

'There is a kind of bridge on the South Coast Railway which is worthy of notice. It is over the Arun, below Arundel, and is the first of its kind. At this point the Company was bound to leave a clear waterway of sixty feet for the passage of shipping, and this had to be accommodated by a contrivance called a telescope bridge. The rails, for a length of 144 feet, are laid upon a massive timber platform, strengthened with iron, and trussed by means of rods extending from its extremities to the top of a strong framework of timber rising 34 feet above the level of the roadway in the middle of the platform, the framework being ornamented so as to appear like an arch. Beneath this central framework and one half of the platform are mounted 12 wheels,

upon which the whole structure may be moved backwards and forwards so as to be either clear of the river or to project its unsupported half across it, to form a bridge for the passage of trains. To provide for moving this platform, when it is necessary to open the waterway, a second portion of the railway, 63ft long, is laid upon a moveable platform, which may be pushed aside laterally, while the end of the larger platform is pushed longitudinally into its place. Two men and a boy are able to open this bridge in about five minutes, the operation being performed by toothed wheels and racks, wrought by winches.'

On 27 November 1851 Arun Bridge was the scene of an accident in which a westbound passenger train hauled by Sharp Brothers 2-2-2 No 81 ran through signals and collided with an eastbound goods train. The passenger engine was derailed and went over the embankment, the fireman receiving fatal injuries. The driver immediately saw the consequences of his negligence and tried to commit suicide on the spot by cutting his throat; after being thwarted by the guard, the driver then threw himself in the river. The guard came to the rescue once again and saved the driver, but it is questionable whether the driver would have been particularly grateful as he was later convicted of manslaughter. The driver's extreme reaction to the accident has never been fully explained but it has been suggested that, like most LB&SCR drivers, he had a deep fear of incurring the wrath of the company's Locomotive Superintendent, John Craven.

The original Arun Bridge did not enjoy a very long life. However, that was not due to any defects in the structure but because of the need to provide a double-track crossing of the River Arun. The approaches on either side of the original bridge were doubled in 1857 and, in 1862, work was put in hand for new lines immediately on the east side of the River Arun, one of the lines going to Littlehampton and the other to Arundel and Pulborough. The 'new' bridge opened in 1862 and continued the tradition of providing something a little different for the crossing of the river.

Whereas the old bridge had been referred to as Arun Bridge, the new one was known as Ford Bridge, the station near its western end having had its name changed from 'Arundel' to 'Ford' in May 1850. As with the original bridge, the replacement had to incorporate a moveable section to allow sailing ships access to Arundel, and so the idea of a telescopic bridge was perpetuated, albeit to a completely different design.

The new bridge had two fixed girders, the western one of 70ft and the eastern one of 30ft, and both had intermediate piers. The moveable central girder was 90ft long. The procedure for opening the bridge was for the supports on the (fixed) western

Left:

Ford Bridge, rebuilt 1862: The 'telescopic' section of the bridge is below the locomotive's tender and the leading coach. Although this picture is undated, it is suspected that it was taken not long before the structure was replaced by a fixed bridge in 1938. The locomotive at the head of the westbound train is ex-L&SWR 'L12' class 4-4-0 No 416, which was one of ten class members to be transferred to the Eastern Section of the Southern Railway in the mid-1920s. Five of the ten were based at Battersea where, during the summer months, their duties often included excursion workings along the Sussex coast. *Lens of Sutton/Courtesy Brian Stephenson*

pier to be retracted so that the 'nose' of the moveable section dipped slightly and the 'tail' rose accordingly. This enabled the moveable section to be winched backwards over the tracks on the eastern section of the bridge. It was possible to open the bridge in eight minutes but, with the assistance of gravity, closing took only five minutes. Nevertheless, an opening of the bridge usually held up railway traffic for anything up to 40 minutes due to the additional tasks of detaching and subsequently reconnecting not only the fishplates, but also the signal and track circuit wires, and gas and water pipes at each end of the bridge.

To summarise, details of the new bridge were:

Designer: Robert Jacomb-Hood
Original owner: London, Brighton & South
Coast Railway
Contractor: Henry Grissell, Regent's Canal
Ironworks, London
Type: Telescopic
Materials: Wrought and cast iron
Total length: 66yd
Spans: 5
Tracks: 2

The new bridge came into operation in 1862. It was built on the north side of the original structure, the latter being retained until the new one was finished. Over the years the bridge proved costly to maintain, among the bills being that for substantial strengthening work in 1898. The LB&SCR and, later, the Southern Railway became increasingly frustrated by the legal obligation to maintain a 'moveable' bridge which, as the years progressed, was required to be moved less and less. The decline in river traffic to Arundel was such that, between 22 September 1919 and 4 May 1928, no bridge movements were required at all. It has been remarked that the signalling arrangements for trains at the bridge were probably simpler than those for shipping, the instructions for the latter being:

'On a vessel approaching the bridge, the Bridgeman will hoist on the flagstaff at the east end of the bridge a white flag to denote that the vessel is seen. If the bridge can be safely opened, a black ball will be hoisted. When the bridge is actually open, a red flag will be hoisted and kept flying until the bridge is about to be closed again for the passing of trains.'

In 1936, when the electrification of the South Coast line was being planned, the Southern Railway at last obtained powers to replace the old bridge with a fixed span. This was completed in July 1938, the last recorded opening of Jacomb-Hood's distinctive telescopic bridge having been on 5 April 1936.

1846: London Road Viaduct, Brighton, East Sussex

Construction of the magnificent London Road Viaduct at Brighton was certainly swift. The ceremonial laying of the first stone took place in May 1845, and the last arch was completed in March 1846. Less than three months later, on 8 June, the Brighton–Lewes line, which crossed the viaduct, opened for business.

The viaduct was designed by John Rastrick. From the western end, it comprised nine semicircular arches, each of 30ft span, then a 50ft-span elliptical arch which was 67ft above the London road and, finally, 17 more arches, again of 30ft-span. The structure consumed some 10 million bricks. The viaduct was on a continuous curve and so, in order to keep the sides of the arches parallel, all the piers were tapered with their northern ends being wider than their southern ends. London Road Viaduct had certain similarities to another famous Rastrick-designed structure, Balcombe Viaduct (on the London–Brighton line), one being that its piers were pierced with arches and inverts, another being that it was finished off with a stone balustrade. During World War 2 the viaduct received a direct hit, and the newer brick work on the repaired section was clearly evident for many years until weathering took its course.

1846: Dee Bridge, Chester, Cheshire

Designer: Robert Stephenson
Original owner: Chester & Holyhead Railway
Type: Girder
Materials: Wrought and cast iron; masonry
Total length: 109yd
Max height of rails: 36ft
Spans: 3
Tracks: 2 (eventually 4)

The Chester & Holyhead Railway, which connected the two communities of its title, soldiered on as an independent company until being formally taken over by the London & North Western Railway on 1 January 1859. The C&HR had, however, been worked by the LNWR from the outset.

The first section of the C&HR's line to open was the 1¼-mile stretch between Chester and Saltney Junction, which was unveiled on 4 November 1846 for use by trains of the Shrewsbury & Chester Railway. On the western outskirts of Chester, a bridge of wrought and cast iron carried the railway over

Above:
London Road Viaduct, 1846: An electric multiple-unit, presumably on a Brighton–Lewes working, crosses the viaduct in the 1950s. The largest arch crosses the London Road. *Ian Allan Library*

Below:
Dee Bridge, rebuilt 1847, quadrupled 1904: The two tracks on the right are those laid by the GWR in 1904 and are now the only two which remain in use. In this undated picture, '4300' class 2-6-0 No 5330 is seen in charge of a local working. *Ian Allan Library*

the River Dee, and the collapse of the bridge after only a little over six months of use was one of the very few blots on the otherwise illustrious career of its designer, Robert Stephenson.

Robert Stephenson (1803–1859) had followed his father's footsteps in the world of engineering, although some of Stephenson Jnr's early ventures were concerned with the surveying and sinking of mines in this country and in South America. Robert Stephenson returned to England in 1827 and, in 1830, he and his father were appointed to survey a route for the London & Birmingham Railway. In practice, it was Robert who undertook the more difficult duties, and he was subsequently hired as the L&BR's Engineer-in-Chief at a starting salary of £1,500 per annum. His work for the L&BR earned him a glowing reputation and did much to secure his future.

At Chester, the C&HR's bridge crossed the river at an angle of 48° and consisted of three cast iron girder spans, each of 98ft and trussed together by wrought iron bars, and supported by stone piers. On 24 May 1847, 5in of ballast were laid on the bridge and when the next train (an evening working to Ruabon) crossed, the westernmost girder on the down line fractured under the weight. The locomotive crossed safely, albeit with a completely derailed tender, but the carriages all fell into the river some 36ft below. Four of the 35 passengers on the train and the fireman died.

During the inquiry into the accident there was a strong feeling that a scapegoat was being sought, and some felt that Stephenson would carry the can. Somewhat alarmingly for Stephenson, the inquiry took the form of a hearing in a coroner's court, complete with a jury who could have had little knowledge of engineering technicalities. Nevertheless, the eventual culprit was cited to be, not Stephenson, but the fractured girder which, according to the jurors, was '…made of a strength insufficient to bear the pressure of quick trains passing over it '. Criticism was also made of the fact that the truss rods had not been properly tensioned and, furthermore, it had been revealed during the inquiry that one of the beams of the bridge had fractured the month previously. The whole incident gave rise to grave doubts about the suitability of cast iron in the construction of railway bridges.

The remains of the Dee bridge were supported by piles while renewal work was implemented. The work included the installation of an additional row of castings above the original ones, the new ones being shaped to fit the originals. During the work, passengers were conveyed by horse-bus. A single line across the bridge was reopened to traffic on 26 July 1847, the Board of Trade passing the structure for double-line working on 23 April 1848. Prior to the full reopening, tests with heavy trains had revealed a deflection of less than ¼in.

In 1870/71 the bridge was completely rebuilt in brick and wrought iron, the iron being supplied and the work undertaken by Messrs W.S.Woodall of Dudley. The bridge was widened from two tracks to four in 1904 but reverted to double-track status in the early 1980s, the 1904 'addition' being the section that was retained.

1848: Conway Tubular Bridge, Conwy, Gwynedd

Designer: Robert Stephenson
Original owner: Chester & Holyhead Railway
Type: Tubular
Materials: Wrought iron; masonry
Total length: 134yd
Max height of rails: 18ft
Span: 1
Tracks: 2

The Chester & Holyhead Railway's line between Chester and Bangor was opened to passenger traffic on 1 May 1848 and to freight on 1 June. The C&HR had intended to be a self-sufficient concern and, consequently, had ordered its own locomotives, but a working agreement was reached with the London & North Western Railway and the order for the engines was therefore transferred. In the best traditions of 'worked' companies the C&HR eventually sold out, the date of its formal acquisition by the L&NWR being 1 January 1859.

The Chester–Bangor line incorporated two tubular bridges: the Britannia Bridge across the Menai Straits near Bangor, and a smaller version across the river at Conwy (or as it was spelt at the time, Conway), both being designed by the C&HR's engineer, Robert Stephenson. The foundation stones for both bridges were laid in the spring of 1846, and the Conway Bridge became a sort of guinea pig for the construction of its big brother at Bangor. The Conway Bridge required only a single span of 400ft and, furthermore, as the River Conwy was not used by large vessels, the necessary clearance above the high-water mark was relatively insignificant.

The basic design of the Conway Bridge was, however, similar to that of the Britannia Bridge, a separate hollow 'tube' being used to carry each of the tracks between the masonry abutments. The tubes, which weighed 1,300 tons each, were prefabricated on the shore and floated into position by means of pontoons. When in position under the abutments, the tubes were raised by hydraulic presses, the apparatus used being that invented by Joseph Bramah and patented in March 1796. The official description of the presses did not exactly smack of snappy copywriting: 'Certain new methods of producing and applying a more considerable degree of power to all kinds of mechanical apparatus and other machinery requiring motion and force, than by any means at present practised for that purpose.'

The first tube was fixed on 16 April 1848 and a special train passed through just two days later. The obligatory Board of Trade inspection took place later that month, public services commencing on 1 May. The second tube was floated on 12 October, raised on 30 October, and opened to traffic early in November. When the first tube was in position, it was tested with a weight of 300 tons of iron, and the deflection was found to be 3in at the centre; the second tube was tested with almost 236 tons of ballast which caused a deflection of 1½in. In service, however, the passage of an ordinary train was reputed to cause a deflection of only ⅛in.

Much has been said elsewhere about the aesthetics of Conway Bridge and the manner in which the massive crenellated portals at the entrances to the bridge blend with the ruined medieval castle. During the mid-1800s, however, such considerations were not always common as many engineers tended to make their statements by ostentation rather than subtlety. Perhaps the design of the Conway Bridge and the larger Britannia Bridge were treated to special attention as, in close proximity to both, were roads carried by Thomas Telford suspension bridges.

A colleague once suggested that the design of the structure might also have an air of environmental awareness, that school of thought having been prompted during one of his many visits to the bridge. On the occasion in question, a father and his young son were standing within earshot. The lad asked his father why the bridge had a roof, and the parental reply was that it was 'to stop the smoke from the trains coming out and making a nasty mess'. Presumably, the father's method of building pollution-free railways would have been to enclose every last yard of them in tunnels.

The only significant alteration to which Conway Bridge has been subjected throughout its long life is the fitting of a pair of cast iron supporting columns. These were added in 1899 and nominally reduced the length of the main span from 400ft to 310ft.

Below
Conway Tubular Bridge, 1848: In this wide view, one of the two sets of additional piers (added in 1899) can be seen near the foot of the far tower. The train is the 10.15 Euston–Bangor, and the locomotive is Class 40 No 310. *Philip D. Hawkins*

1848: Crimple Viaduct, Nr Harrogate, North Yorkshire

On 10 August 1847 the York & North Midland Railway opened its Church Fenton–Harrogate branch as far as Spofforth. The Spofforth–Harrogate section was not ready for opening until 20 July 1848, the delay being due to the work involved on an 825yd tunnel and also the superb Crimple Viaduct. The viaduct had 31 arches, each of 50ft span, and crossed the valley through which the Leeds–Thirsk line passed. It was built of brick, with stone facings on stone piers, and was 624yd long and 110ft high. In August 1862 a connection was at last opened between that line and the Church Fenton–Harrogate branch so that trains from Leeds could enter Harrogate by means of Crimple Viaduct rather than the circuitous route via Starbeck. Crimple Viaduct is still in use today but, perhaps ironically, only by Leeds–Harrogate–York trains. The line which necessitated the building of the viaduct in the first place, the Church Fenton–Harrogate branch, was closed in January 1964.

Below:
Crimple Viaduct, 1848: Gresley 'A1' 4-6-2 No 2579 (later 'A3' No 60080) *Dick Turpin* crosses Crimple Viaduct with the 'Queen of Scots' Pullman. *Ian Allan Library*

1848: Totnes–Plymouth, Devon

(five viaducts, listed below)

Designer: Isambard Kingdom Brunel
Original owner: South Devon Railway
Contractors: Boulton & Watt; Rennie & Co; Maudslay & Field
Type: Timber viaducts
Tracks: 1 (later 2)

Like all obedient GWR-backed companies the SDR was a broad gauge concern, and it had opened as far as Totnes on 20 July 1847. The SDR was engineered by Brunel with the intention of using atmospheric traction, but innumerable problems were encountered and so, despite the smoothness and cleanliness of the atmospheric trains, that form of traction was completely dispensed with as from 10 September 1848. The 'atmospheric caper', as it had become known to its many critics, cost the SDR £426,368.

Miles	Name	Length	Max Height	No. of Spans
36¾	Glaze	163yd	81ft	7
38½	Bittaford	117yd	63ft	5 (plus masonry aproach arch)
40¾	Ivybridge*	252yd	109ft	11
43	Blachford	293yd	97ft	13
43½	Slade	273yd	100ft	12

Mileages are those from Exeter (St David's) station; *Also known as Erme Viaduct.

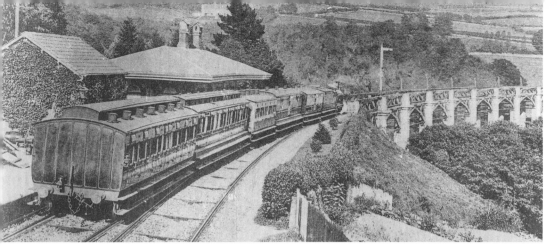

Above:

Ivybridge Viaduct, 1848: The original Brunel timber viaduct can be clearly seen just beyond Ivybridge station. Note the broad gauge rails, the singling of the tracks on the approach to the viaduct, and the wonderful assortment of rolling stock. The viaduct was replaced by a double-track masonry structure in 1893, the year after the broad gauge had been rendered extinct. *Lens of Sutton*

The SDR opened its extension from Totnes to Plymouth (Laira Green) on 5 May 1848, that section having five major Brunel viaducts (listed above). All five were of a similar design with timber superstructures on masonry piers, the two towers of each pier being linked by wrought iron ties at intervals of some 18ft. However, the viaducts had been built to take the weight of the atmospheric trains, which had very light 'locomotives', and when it was decided to use conventional steam locomotives all five viaducts had their original superstructures substantially strengthened by timber beams. In 1861, the timber beams were replaced by wrought iron girders seated on the masonry piers.

There were three other structures of note on the SDR's Totnes–Plymouth section. From the Totnes end, the first was **Rattery Viaduct**, which comprised six semicircular arches each of 25ft span and supported by pairs of pillars. The second was **Brent Bridge**, the largest of the four spans being 40ft, and the third was the well-known **'Cocked Hat' Bridge**, a timber-built skew bridge with a 102ft span over the main Exeter–Plymouth (later A38) road between Wrangaton and Bittaford. The last-named structure took its nickname from the distinctive shape of its timber balustrades.

The South Devon Railway was formally absorbed by the GWR in January 1876, and the controversial broad gauge was rendered extinct in May 1892. Almost immediately work was put in hand to double the remaining single-track sections between Exeter and Plymouth, and the five Brunel

Left:

Slade Viaduct, rebuilt 1893: In common with the four other Brunel-designed single-track timber viaducts between Totnes and Plymouth, Slade Viaduct was replaced by a double-track masonry structure in 1893. Here, No 7813 *Freshford Manor* is seen piloting No 4083 *Abbotsbury Castle* with a Manchester (London Road)–Penzance train on 8 April 1953. *R. E. Vincent*

Below:

Chirk Viaduct, 1848:
The viaduct was built alongside Telford's famous aqueduct carrying the Llangollen Canal. Although the sight of two such structures in close proximity is now considered quite spectacular, it was originally considered by some that the 'new' railway viaduct detracted from the aqueduct. The 'preservation special' seen on the viaduct operated on 22 September 1979, and was hauled by ex-GWR 'Hall' class 4-6-0 No 4930 *Hagley Hall* and ex-LMSR 'Black 5' No 5000. *Peter J.C.Skelton*

timber viaducts were replaced by new double-track masonry viaducts alongside the original structures, the piers of the old viaducts being left to stand. The new masonry viaducts were all brought into use in 1893.

Brunel's timber viaducts on the SDR were rather sturdier than their appearances suggested. The basic design was perpetuated by Brunel for viaducts elsewhere, particularly for those on the West Cornwall Railway (opened 1852) and the Cornwall Railway (opened 1859), and some of the Cornish structures went on to gain celebrity status.

1848: Dee Viaduct and Chirk Viaduct, Shrewsbury–Chester line

The Shrewsbury & Chester Railway opened its line on 14 October 1848. Along the route were two particularly impressive viaducts, both designed by the S&CR's engineer, Henry Robertson, and constructed by Thomas Brassey. The more northerly of the pair was Dee Viaduct which crossed the South Shropshire Plain south of Cefn station. Built of stone, it had 19 arches, was 510yd long, and stood 148ft high; at the time of its opening, it was said to be the largest viaduct in the country. A little to the south was Chirk Viaduct (also known as Ceiriog Viaduct) which was 283yd long and, at its highest, 106ft above the valley floor. Originally, the structure had ten stone arches, each of 45ft span, and a 120ft-wide laminated timber span at either end, but the two timber spans were replaced by stone arches during 1858/59.

Chirk Viaduct was built alongside Telford's famous aqueduct which carried the Llangollen Canal. Prior to the opening of the railway the Board of Trade Inspector, Capt Wynne, expressed his opinion of the aesthetics of the two structures being in such close proximity: '...the more recent one completely degrades the other...the proper effect of each is lost, and the scenery which is very beautiful not improved'. Nevertheless, Chirk and Dee Viaducts came to be regarded as masterpieces in their own right, and are still in use today.

Left:
Dee Viaduct, 1848: The steam-hauled special of 22 September 1979 was photographed crossing the Dee Viaduct on its return working towards Hereford. The Dee Viaduct and the nearby Chirk Viaduct are fitting monuments to their designer, the unsung Henry Robertson, and their builder, the better-known Thomas Brassey. *Peter J.C.Skelton*

1848: Ballochmyle Viaduct, Nr Mauchline, Ayrshire

Designer: John Miller
Original owner: Glasgow, Paisley, Kilmarnock & Ayr Railway
Contractors: Ross & Mitchell
Type: Arch
Material: Stone
Total length: 210yd
Max height of rails: 169ft
Spans: 7
Tracks: 2

The Glasgow to Carlisle route via Kilmarnock was built by two separate companies. The northern section was constructed by the Glasgow, Paisley, Kilmarnock & Ayr Railway, and the southern section by the Glasgow, Dumfries & Carlisle Railway. The completion of the line took just over eleven years, piecemeal openings being the order of the day, and when the last section was opened on 28 October 1850 the two companies amalgamated to form the Glasgow & South Western Railway.

One of the most celebrated features of the new line was Ballochmyle Viaduct, which crossed the River Ayr between Mauchline and Auchinleck. Work on the viaduct had been started by the GPK&AR in September 1846 and had been completed in March 1848, the section of line across the viaduct being opened to traffic on 9 August 1848. The viaduct had three 50ft-span arches at each end, and a 181ft-span central arch which formed a complete semicircle. The arch ring was built of hard stone brought from Dundee, but the red sandstone used for the rest of the viaduct was quarried near the site. The ceremony to mark the laying of the foundation stone had been something of a Masonic show of strength, the guests having received ceremonial plaques on which the names of the 'Officers of Mother Kilwinning Lodge' had appeared above the names of the railway company's directors. The plaques had also noted that the year, according to the Masonic calendar, was 5846.

Ballochmyle Viaduct was a triumph of design for John Miller of the Edinburgh-based civil engineering firm of Granger & Miller. Miller had been appointed on the strength of his CV, which included the design and construction of the viaducts on the Edinburgh & Glasgow Railway. It was said that the carpentry work involved in the timber supports and centering for Ballochmyle Viaduct was itself something of a masterpiece. The greatest tribute to the design of the viaduct is that, without having had any major structural alterations, it is still in everyday use.

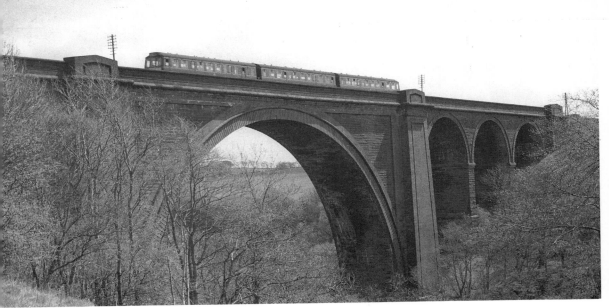

Significantly, Ballochmyle is now the highest railway bridge in Britain and also boasts what is believed to be the world's largest masonry arch. A larger arch was built by the Austrian State Railways at the end of the 1890s, but that structure was destroyed during World War 1. Furthermore, Ballochmyle Viaduct still carries its main-line traffic without weight or speed restrictions and, of course, the weights and speeds of the 1990s could never have been envisaged by John Miller back in the 1840s.

1849: Tay Bridge, Perth, Perthshire

For almost two years after its opening on 24 May 1847, the Perth & Dundee Railway remained unconnected to the two other railways which had subsequently reached Perth. The P&DR had opted for a terminus at Barnhill, on the east side of the River Tay and somewhat removed from the city centre, whereas the Scottish Central, which had opened to Perth on 23 May 1848, had stuck resolutely to the west side of the Tay which, after all, was far more convenient for the travelling public.

The main reason for the separatist goings-on was the expense of bridging the River Tay. A viaduct across the Tay had, in fact, been approved as early as 1845, but it had been 1847 before tenders for its construction had been invited. The viaduct was opened on 1 March 1849 and the old terminus on the east bank at Barnhill closed simultaneously.

The viaduct was constructed almost entirely of timber, but incorporated a 51ft-wide cast iron swinging span as, at that time, ships bringing in coal, limestone, fish and other merchandise required access to quays up-river. Before long the timbers and the foundations of the viaduct started to cause considerable problems, some of which were blamed on the structure's 15-chain curvature. Consequently, plans to replace the viaduct were put in hand as early as 1862, contracts being let for the construction of a new viaduct later that year. The new structure cost £27,000 to build and was designed by the engineers of the Caledonian Railway. It was opened in 1863.

The new viaduct was built on a slightly easier curve of 17 chains, and comprised six iron girder spans to the east of Moncriffe Island, ten stone arches on the island itself, and seven more girder spans to the west of the island. There was also a steel girder span crossing Tay Street, to the south of which were another six stone spans.

As with its predecessor, the new viaduct carried only a single track and, furthermore, its main section incorporated a swinging span (the span nearest to the Tay Street bank of the river). As the railway traffic increased, the Scottish Central Railway (which absorbed the Perth & Dundee in 1863) and its successor, the Caledonian Railway, tried repeatedly to secure priority for rail traffic. It appears,

Above:
Tay Bridge (Perth), rebuilt 1863: The first railway bridge across the River Tay at Perth was a timber structure, completed in 1849. It was replaced in 1863, and this vintage picture shows an unidentified Caledonian 0-4-2 crossing the swing section of the new girder bridge. The stone arches in the distance carry the line across Moncriffe Island. *Bucknall Collection/Ian Allan Library*

however, that shipping officially maintained priority, although the last recorded opening of the bridge was in the 1880s for the SS *Star of Gowrie*, the one and only steamship to pass through the viaduct; the mechanism and capstans nevertheless remained on the viaduct until comparatively recently. The structure is, of course, still in use today.

1849: High Level Bridge, Newcastle-upon-Tyne, Tyne & Wear

Designer: Robert Stephenson
Original owner: High Level Bridge Co
Contractors: Hawkes, Crawshay & Co, Newcastle (ironwork); Rush & Lawton (masonry)
Cost: £243,096, plus £113,067 for approach viaducts
Type: Tied arch
Materials: Cast iron; wrought iron; stone
Total length: 446yd
Max height of rails: 112ft above high-water
Spans: 6 (excluding approach viaducts)
Tracks: 3

The crossing of the River Tyne between Newcastle and Gateshead by means of a high level bridge was first mooted in 1825. That plan, however, came to nothing, and a similar fate befell an alternative scheme proposed by John and Benjamin Green in 1839. The Green brothers had another stab in 1841, this time for a railway bridge between Castle Garth in Newcastle and Greenesfield in Gateshead, to provide a connection between the Brandling Junction Railway and the Newcastle & North Shields Railway. Their plans were given serious consideration as, at the time, the Newcastle & Darlington Railway was edging towards Newcastle from the south and, in the eyes of many, it was only a matter of time before a line would be constructed northwards from Newcastle to Berwick. The prospect of a through line between London and Edinburgh via Newcastle and Berwick was a heady one and, of course, it would have to cross the Tyne valley somehow.

The plans for an Anglo–Scottish line took a major step towards reality in 1845 when the Newcastle & Berwick Railway was formally incorporated. The company joined forces with the Newcastle & Darlington Junction Railway to form the High Level Bridge Co, the principal intention of which was to construct and maintain a high level railway bridge across the Tyne. A similar company had, in fact, been formed in 1836 to construct a high level suspension bridge for road traffic across the Tyne, but the company had not even progressed as far as cutting the first sod. The Green brothers' plans of 1841 for a laminated timber bridge were, however, dropped as it was considered that a more durable material would be required to cope with the intensity of the anticipated traffic.

Robert Stephenson was appointed to design the bridge across the Tyne, the working drawings being prepared by Thomas Harrison who later became the Chief Civil Engineer of the North Eastern Railway. The structure Stephenson designed was a double-deck bridge, the railway being carried above a road in a piggy-back fashion. The bridge was supported by five masonry piers which were some 50ft wide and 16ft thick and founded on timber piles, some of which were sunk as much as 40ft into the soft mud below the river bed. For the first time in British bridge building, the piles were sunk using Nasmyth's steam pile-driver which enabled, for example, the first pile to be driven to a depth of 32ft in just four minutes. The bridge had six spans, each 125ft in length, under which a 20ft-wide roadway with two footpaths was carried. In all, it consumed a total of 5,050 tons of iron.

For a potted description of the ingenious design of the bridge, a quote from the 1849 Report of the Commissioners of Railways seems to say it all:

'The ribs of the arches, arranged in pairs, each 125ft in span, rested on piers of a peculiarly light construction, wrought-iron tension chains or ties taking the lateral thrust. The square hollow pillars rising from the ribs supported a longitudinal trough girder which sustained the weight of the cross-bearers and upper roadway *(sic)*. From this girder was suspended the lower roadway by means of wrought-iron rods passing through the pillars which, being extended below the ribs, afforded additional stiffness to the roadway.'

To assist the flow of rail traffic, a temporary single-track timber bridge was built on one side, parts of the foundations being those which were being built for the permanent structure. The timber bridge opened on 29 August 1848, but it did not carry regular traffic until 1 September. The permanent bridge opened to rail traffic on 15 August 1849, although the ceremonial opening by Queen Victoria was not undertaken until 28 September. Initially, only one track was available. The roadway underneath the railway was opened on 4 February 1850 and tolls were charged to road users, the maximum charges being 1d (½p) for pedestrians, 3d (1¼p) for a horse and wagon, and 10d (4p) for 20 head of cattle. The tolls were finally abolished in 1937, the last horse-buses having operated only six years earlier.

The bridge remained virtually in its original condition until 1893, when the cast iron cross girders carrying the rails were replaced by wrought iron girders. In 1906 the navigable width of the Tyne was increased by removing the outer row of coffer dam piles from the bridge's south pier, leaving the inner row of sheet piling to protect the foundations. However, in 1915 it was found that the concrete capping of the main piles had deteriorated considerably, but the need to maintain the maximum possible width of the river during the war years prevented remedial work from being undertaken until peace had been restored. A further bout of work followed in 1922, the timber crossgirders supporting the road deck being replaced by steel beams. This was done to enable trams to cross the bridge, a pair of tramway tracks being laid on timbers supported by the new beams.

From the outset the structure drew immense admiration from all quarters, the Rev Frederick Williams commenting in *Our Iron Roads* in 1852:

'The multiplicity of column-ribs, transverse and vertical braces, produces a combination of beautiful lines seldom seen'. The bridge has been heavily used throughout its long life and is regarded today as a classic example of Robert Stephenson's art.

1849: Folkestone Harbour Bridge, Folkestone, Kent

In 1843 the South Eastern Railway purchased the near-derelict harbour at Folkestone with the intention of turning it into a major cross-Channel port and, that same year, the railway company opened a branch to the harbour for freight traffic. In 1849 the branch was extended across the harbour by means of a centre-pivoting swing bridge which, on its completion two years earlier, had had the distinction of being the largest of its kind in the country. Passenger services to a new station on the south side of the harbour commenced in 1850.

The original swing bridge was replaced by a sturdier structure in 1893 and, during the weekend of

Below:
Folkestone Harbour Bridge, as rebuilt 1930: The third and final swing bridge at Folkestone Harbour was built by the Southern Railway. The South Eastern Railway's 'R' class 0-6-0Ts were first used on the sharply-graded harbour branch in 1892 and, by the late-1950s, it was usual to find up to seven of the class (by then rebuilt as 'R1s') at Folkestone Junction shed. They were replaced by WR 0-6-0PTs in 1959. *Ian Allan Library*

10/12 May 1930, the Southern Railway provided a new steel bridge to enable heavier locomotives to work through to the harbour station. However, the ferocious 1 in 30 gradient on the harbour branch was considered unsuitable even for the SR's best engines to work single-handed. Consequently, the tradition of using two, three or sometimes four tank engines to haul the boat trains between the harbour station and Folkestone Junction was perpetuated until the end of steam.

1850: Britannia Tubular Bridge, Nr Bangor, Gwynedd

Designer: Robert Stephenson
Original owner: Chester & Holyhead Railway
Cost: £600,000
Contractors: (Ironwork) Garforth & Co, Dukinfield; C.J.Mare, Blackwall (Masonry) Nowell, Hemingway & Pearson
Type: Tubular
Materials: Wrought iron; masonry
Total length: 600yd
Max height of rails: 120ft above high-water
Spans: 4
Tracks: 2

The Chester & Holyhead Railway opened its main line as far as Bangor on 1 May 1848. Across the Menai Straits, the section between the first station, (the tortuously named Llanfairpwllgwyngyllgogerychwyrndrobwllllantysiliogogogoch), and a

Above:
Britannia Tubular Bridge, 1850: On 15 March 1970, a little over two months before the Britannia Bridge was severely damaged by fire, a two-car Bangor–Holyhead local leaves the northern end of the bridge. The bridge was (and still is) one of the most famous in Britain, and the local scenery is spectacularly evident in this picture. It might, therefore, be considered a little ironic that railway passengers crossing the bridge these days would be unable to savour any of the views, that being due to the construction of a road above the railway line. *Ian Allan Library*

Right:
Britannia Bridge, rebuilt 1972: After the disastrous fire of 1970, the 'new' Britannia Bridge looked somewhat different. This picture of a Class 40 with a Holyhead-bound train was taken on 12 July 1974 and, since then, the bridge has been further altered by the construction of a road above the railway. *David A. Flitcroft*

temporary terminus at Holyhead opened on 1 August the same year. The missing link across the Menai Straits was not ready until March 1850.

The crossing of the Menai Straits was by means of a tubular bridge. A similar but far smaller structure had been opened in 1848 to carry the C&HR's line across the River Conwy, and provided invaluable experience during the construction of the Britannia Bridge over the Menai. The C&HR's engineer, Robert Stephenson, designed both bridges, the Britannia Bridge being the first in Britain to incorporate the flat beam principle for such a long span. From the outset Stephenson's plans had been dictated by the Admiralty's stipulations that, firstly, there should be no obstruction to shipping while the bridge was under construction and, secondly, the finished structure should have a headroom of at least 100ft above the high-water mark. Stephenson's answer was for the bridge to comprise a pair of hollow 'tubes', one for each track, suspended by chains. The chosen bridging point was to the west of Bangor where there was a small rocky island in mid-stream. The island was known as the Britannia Rock, and unwittingly provided the name for Stephenson's bridge.

During the preparatory design work Stephenson consulted William Fairbairn, a shipbuilder and engineer of Millwall, who conducted tests on model tubes in order to arrive at the optimum format. Fairbairn ultimately concluded that rectangular tubes would be the best, and that the use of suspension chains would be superfluous. Stephenson adopted Fairbairn's suggestion but, after the bridge had been completed, Fairbairn was somewhat miffed at not having received a significant share of the credit for its design. Fairbairn alleged that the idea of a self-supporting bridge had been his, but after a thorough investigation his claim was dismissed on the grounds that he had been employed as Stephenson's assistant. Perhaps predictably, another engineer whom Stephenson had consulted about the design, Eaton Hodgkinson, also chipped in with a claim for a share of the glory. That claim also failed. Stephenson publicly acknowledged the assistance of Fairbairn and Hodgkinson, but never wavered when it came to claiming the credit for the bridge's design.

The tubes for the bridge were prefabricated on the shore, floated into position on pontoons, and then raised with the building-up of the relevant piers. The nautical arrangements were taken care of by Capt Christopher Claxton RN, a colleague of none other than Isambard Kingdom Brunel. It is often thought that the rivalry between Brunel and Stephenson was bitter but the two men had immense respect for each other, that being demonstrated at Conwy when Brunel happily assisted Stephenson with the floating and fixing of the tubes. Nevertheless, Brunel failed to warrant a mention in an eye-witness account of the floating of the first tube, which was published in the *Illustrated London News*:

'Captain Claxton was easily distinguishable by his speaking-trumpet, and there were also men to hold the letters which indicated the different capstans, so that no mistake could occur as to which capstan should be worked; and flags, red, blue, or white, signalled what particular movement should be made with each. About half-past seven o'clock in the evening, the first perceptible motion, which indicated that the tide was lifting the mass, was observed, and, at Mr Stephenson's desire, the depth of water was ascertained, and the exact time noted. In a few minutes the motion was plainly visible, the tube being fairly moved forwards some inches. This moment was one of intense interest; the huge bulk gliding as gently and easily forwards as if she had been but a small boat. The spectators seemed spellbound; for no shouts or exclamations were heard, as all watched silently the silent course of the heavily freighted pontoons...It was impossible to see this imposing sight and not feel its singleness, if we may so speak. Anything so mighty of its kind had never been seen before; again it would assuredly be; but it was like the first voyage made by the first steam vessel - something till then unique.'

There were five towers to support the tubes, one at each end, one on each of the riverbanks, and a central one on Britannia Rock; the exteriors of all were built of limestone known as 'Anglesey Marble' extracted from Penmaen Quarries, and the interiors were of red sandstone quarried at Runcorn. The central tower was 221ft high, the riverbank towers 203ft high, and the abutment towers at each end 186ft high; the two spans across the water were 460ft each. When all the tubes were in position they were joined end to end by a pair of continuous beams, each 1,511ft in length. At either end of the Britannia Bridge, wing-walls extended along the abutments on both sides and terminated in massive pedestals, on which were mounted huge Egyptian-style stone lions. Each of the four lions weighed some 30 tons.

The construction of the bridge was not without its mishaps. The floating into position of the very first tube required three attempts while, later, an hydraulic press burst during the raising of a tube and, although the tube fell by less than 12in, it was enough to cause considerable damage to the masonry. During the construction of the bridge 19 men were killed in accidents, and they were commemorated by a monument in the churchyard on the Anglesey shore.

In his contemporary book *Tubular and other Iron Girder Bridges*, G.Drysdale Dempsey wrote:

'...the masonry of the central, or Britannia tower, was commenced in May, 1846...the first rivet for the tubes was put in on August 10, 1847. It is now expected that one line of railway will be completed through the bridge in March, 1850. If so, or even allowing two months later, four years only will have been occupied since the commencement of the tower; a period remarkably short, when all uncertainties and possible casualties belonging to so novel and extended a work are considered.'

Mr Drysdale Dempsey was not disappointed, as one of the two tubes was indeed completed early in 1850 and, on 5 March, Stephenson drove the first train across the bridge. Work on the second tube progressed rapidly and, on 19 October, the bridge was formally opened for double-line traffic. The structure was, at the time, the longest span bridge in the world - and the costliest. The owner of the bridge, the Chester & Holyhead Railway, was worked from the outset by the London & North Western Railway and formally taken over by that company on 1 January 1859.

As with many of the great railway bridges, the Britannia Tubular Bridge remained largely unaltered for most of its life. The most substantial alterations were, however, unanticipated. On 23 May 1970 a fire caused extensive damage to the bridge, the culprits being young trespassers who, allegedly, were looking for birds' eggs. The ferocity of the fire caused the central tubes to buckle irreparably, their roofing being all but destroyed. Rail services across the bridge had to be suspended and, as a temporary measure, passengers to and from Holyhead were conveyed by road between Bangor and Llanfair PG, wooden platforms having to be erected at the latter station as the old premises had been sold into private hands after their closure in February 1966. From Llanfair PG, a DMU shuttle service worked to and from Holyhead. Main-line boat services were transferred to Heysham while, for goods traffic, a temporary Freightliner terminal was established in June at Caernarfon, the line between Bangor and Caernarfon having to be resuscitated as it had closed to all traffic on 5 January of that year.

The abrupt severance of Anglesey's railways resulted in 13 main-line locomotives, six shunting engines and 72 carriages being marooned on the island. Apart from two of the main-line engines and four shunters, all the locomotives were shipped to Barrow between 13 and 22 June. Sixty-nine of the carriages also followed suit, the three captives being held in case of a DMU failure. The solitary DMU, a two-car set, was replaced in October 1970, the new arrival being winched carefully across Britannia Bridge minus its doorhandles.

As for the bridge itself, the co-ordination of the repair work was entrusted to Mr G. Woodhead, who had retired some time before from his position

as the LMR's Bridge and Structures Assistant. The 'new' bridge, a lattice steel arch structure, was designed by Husband & Co of Darlington and the work was carried out by the Cleveland Bridge & Engineering Co, also of Darlington. It was initially anticipated that the bridge would be reopened in July 1971, but an alleged shortage of steel resulted in the eventual reopening of the 'up' line taking place on 30 January 1972. The 'down' tube was not rebuilt. It was demolished by November 1973 and the running line was transferred to the new open-air deck. Demolition of the 'up' tube was completed by the following May.

That, however, was not the end of the story as, in October 1977, work started on the construction of a road deck above the railway, the road being ceremonially opened in July 1980 by HRH The Prince of Wales. Although the towers remain, the rebuilt structure is rather different from that which Robert Stephenson designed over 140 years ago. It has often been suggested that Stephenson would have been distinctly displeased by the fact that the new road virtually obscures the famous lions at either end of the bridge.

Having devoted a considerable amount of text to two Stephenson-designed tubular bridges, brief mention should also be made of a third such structure. The bridge in question is the little-known and long-departed **Brotherton Tubular Bridge**, which carried the Knottingley–Burton Salmon line of the York & North Midland Railway across the River Aire on what is now the West Yorkshire/North Yorkshire border.

The line across the Aire opened to freight traffic on, if not slightly before, 19 April 1850. It appears, however, that the bridge was not ready, a temporary wooden bridge being used instead. As far as can be determined, the first of the two tubes was passed for passenger traffic in July 1851 and the second was completed three months later. However, the Board of Trade Inspector was not satisfied with the restricted clearances, and the all-clear for passenger services through the second tube was not given until October 1852. Despite the sparsity of existing documentation, one thing that is clear is that the Y&NMR was somewhat persistent with its requests for a BoT inspection. A BoT missive to the railway company remarked that '...the repetitions of Inspecting by their Officers...were productive of inconvenience'.

The basic design of Brotherton Bridge was very similar to those of the Conway and Britannia Tubular Bridges. The usual method of a separate tube for each line was employed, each tube being 20ft 1in high and 12ft 10in wide. The bridge, which was 79yd long and 28ft above the river, rested on masonry piers. In 1854, the Y&NMR became one of the original constituents of the newly-created North Eastern Railway. The NER decided, in 1898, to replace the tubular bridge by a girder bridge which, in the opinion of the engineer, would cost £16,000, but the idea was shelved until 1900 and the cheapest tender received that year was for £17,700, from the Cleveland Bridge & Engineering Co. The new bridge was completed in 1902 and, during the mid-1920s, it was one of the structures which featured in the tests undertaken by the Bridge Stress Committee, more of which later on. The line across Brotherton Bridge is still used by freight trains today, although passenger services were dispensed with as long ago as 11 July 1947.

1850: Landore Viaduct, Swansea, West Glamorgan

Throughout this book, there are many examples of bridges and viaducts which were completely transformed by rebuilding. Rebuilding was, of course, essential in many cases where traffic loadings of later years far exceeded the original builder's wildest dreams, while other structures which had been built with extreme economy in mind provided no surprises when rebuilding became a priority. Among the last category was Landore Viaduct, a timber structure designed by Brunel for the broad gauge South Wales Railway. Landore Viaduct opened to traffic on 18 June 1850. It was 587yd long, had 37 spans ranging from 40ft to 100ft each, and carried the SWR's line over the River Tawe and the adjoining marshes.

In common with other timber viaducts it was later rebuilt, the new structure having a main wrought iron river span of 147ft and 21 wrought iron plate girder approach spans (2 on the Neath side and 19 on the Swansea side) which varied in length from 30ft to 74ft. During the course of rebuilding, several of the original spans at the Neath end were replaced by an extension of the approach embankment, the viaduct thereby being reduced to a length of 405yd.

A further rebuilding took place in 1978/79, during which the wrought iron girders and the timber decking were replaced by steelwork, the original stone piers being reused. The main river span escaped surgery, however, as it had been redecked and strengthened in 1960. The pier supporting the viaduct on the west side of the main Swansea–Neath road had comprised masonry beneath the westbound line and steelwork below the eastbound, but during the rebuilding work the steel supports were replaced by reinforced concrete. Each of the two tracks was dealt with separately so that single-line working could continue while work was in progress. The 'new' viaduct enabled the speed restriction over it to be raised from 20 to 40mph and, for the first time, was able to accommodate the heaviest freight vehicles.

Below:
Landore Viaduct, original timber viaduct opened 1850: When rebuilt in wrought iron, the viaduct had a total of 22 spans, the main one of 147ft carrying the railway across the River Tawe. The locomotive in this undated picture appears to be a 'Saint' class 4-6-0. *J.N.Westwood*

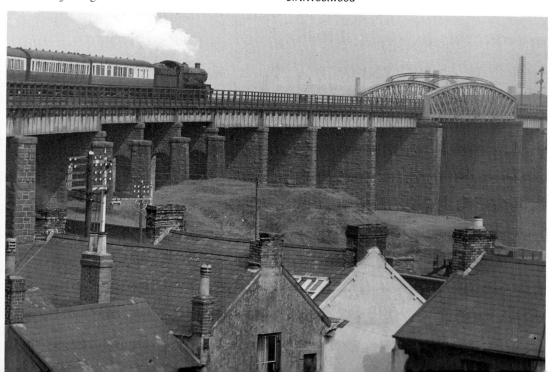

To the west of Swansea, the SWR's line to Carmarthen opened to traffic on 11 October 1852.
Along its route were two timber viaducts with
opening spans, one at Kidwelly, the other being
Loughor Viaduct which crossed the river of the
same name between Swansea and Llanelli. The first
Loughor Viaduct had 17 timber spans, each of
approximately 40ft, and a 30ft-long wrought iron
opening span. The opening span was, however,
replaced by a fixed section in the late 1800s as, by
then, the River Loughor had virtually ceased to be
used by shipping. The timber used in the construction of the viaduct was Memel pine, which was
reckoned to have a lifespan of at least 30 years.

Inevitably, the timbers gradually needed replacing, but by the turn of the century it had become
increasingly difficult to obtain new 'engineering'
timber of suitable quality. Consequently, iron plate
girders (and, later, steel girders) were used to
replace defective timbers on the superstructure.
However, the timber piles required less maintenance, let alone replacement, that being at least
partly due to the protection provided by barnacles
and the absence of the highly-destructive Toredo
shipworm. Nevertheless, additional timber piles
were driven in during 1981 when extensive maintenance work was carried out to the viaduct, the new
piles being jointed together with the old ones to
improve the stability of the structure. The new timber piles were of pitch pine, which has a much
shorter lifespan than that of the Memel pine originally used by Brunel. The continuing presence of
timber piles under Loughor Viaduct raises an interesting point as, short of discovering records of the
replacement of individual timbers, the chance that
the viaduct still has some of its original Brunel timbers cannot be completely ruled out.

Above:
Whalley Viaduct, 1850: Despite its size, Whalley
Viaduct is not widely known. The Gothic treatment of
the arch nearest Whalley Abbey can be clearly seen in
this picture; taken on 2 August 1968, it shows a double-
headed 'down' freight working. *C. T. Gifford*

1850: Whalley Viaduct, Whalley, Lancashire

The Blackburn, Clitheroe & West Yorkshire Railway (later part of the L&YR) extended its line as
far as Clitheroe on 22 June 1850. At Whalley, the
line was carried 70ft above the valley of the River
Calder by an imposing brick-built viaduct which
was all of 679yd in length - it comprised 48 arches
(20 of 40ft span and 28 of 30ft span), the arch nearest to Whalley Abbey being built in the Gothic
style to harmonise with the abbey. In October 1849,
while the viaduct was still under construction, two
arches collapsed, killing three workmen. Although
originally a single-track structure, it was widened in
1872 to accommodate a double track. The viaduct
is still in use today, but the double-track line across
it now carries little more than cement traffic from
Clitheroe, diverted and summer Saturday workings,
and Sunday specials for the Settle & Carlisle line.

Right:
Lockwood Viaduct, 1850: In this superb official
picture, the Huddersfield–Penistone line can be seen
disappearing into the distance while the Meltham
branch diverges to the right. *British Railways*

1850: Lockwood Viaduct, Nr Huddersfield, West Yorkshire

One part of the imposing 'double viaduct' at Lockwood was on the Huddersfield–Penistone line, which was ceremonially opened on 1 July 1850. The other part of the viaduct was built to accommodate the Meltham branch which, diverging from the main line at the northern end of the original viaduct, finally opened to goods traffic on 8 August 1868 and (after a closure of five months) to passengers on 5 July 1869. The Meltham branch was an early casualty of the competition offered by road transport, and it closed to passengers on 21 May 1949. The 'original' viaduct, which had 34 arches and carried the line 136ft above the River Holme, was one of the largest of its day. Its design is credited to the resident engineer, John Frazer, whose name was one of three to be inscribed on a plaque at the top of one of the piers.

Elsewhere on the line, there were three other major viaducts. One was **Paddock Wood Viaduct**, which had 15 arches and four iron spans, and carried the railway some 70ft above the River Colne. Another was the 112ft-high **Denby Dale Viaduct** which was originally built as a timber trestle structure because of a stonemasons' strike. The first timber structure at Denby Dale was somewhat flimsy and collapsed during a gale in January 1847, and the second lasted until May 1880 when it was finally replaced by a stone viaduct. The new viaduct, however, soon became destabilised by coal workings and extensive underpinning was carried out between 1881 and 1884, the old timber viaduct then being dismantled.

The other major structure on the line was **Penistone Viaduct**, which was 330yd long and carried the line at a maximum height of 98ft above the River Don. On 2 February 1916 its second and third arches collapsed, the cause subsequently being attributed to heavy rain which had damaged the foundations. At the moment of the collapse L&YR 2-4-2T No 661 was running round its train on the viaduct, and the locomotive plunged into the debris below; fortunately, the crew had managed to reach safety in the nick of time. The engine's chimney was saved and was put to use as a flowerpot at Brockholes station. The viaduct was rebuilt, and reopened the following August.

1850: Royal Border Bridge, Berwick-upon-Tweed, Northumberland

Designer: Robert Stephenson
Original owner: York, Newcastle & Berwick Railway
Contractor: McKay & Blastock
Cost: £120,000
Type: Arch
Materials: Stone and brick
Total length: 720yd
Max height of rails: 120ft
Spans: 28
Tracks: 2

On 22 June 1846 the North British Railway opened its line between Edinburgh and Berwick-upon-Tweed to public traffic and, on 1 July 1847, the Newcastle & Berwick Railway reached Tweedmouth, on the south bank of the River Tweed. In August 1847 the N&BR amalgamated with the York & Newcastle Railway to form the York, Newcastle & Berwick Railway, the new concern taking

over the responsibility of completing the 'missing link' between Berwick and Tweedmouth. That link took the form of the Royal Border Bridge across the Tweed.

The York, Newcastle & Berwick Railway, which owned the Royal Border Bridge, was one of the original constituents of the North Eastern Railway, founded on 31 July 1854. The newly-formed NER had, at that time, 703 route miles which made it the largest railway company in the country. At the Grouping, the NER and the North British Railway both became part of the LNER.

Until the bridge's completion in 1850, through passengers were ferried between Berwick and Tweedmouth stations by horse-drawn bus. Because of the somewhat tedious interruption to the journey, it might be thought that a new means of communication between the Scottish and English capital cities would have been regarded as a great novelty but, in 1849, the number of passengers wishing to travel from Edinburgh to London by train was only 5,792. By contrast, the steamships from Leith and Granton to London carried 11,584 passengers during the same year.

Even before the bridge was opened, the North British Railway promoted 'Excursions to England'.

One advertisement which appeared in *The Scotsman* on 18 August 1849 proclaimed the delights of a forthcoming excursion from Edinburgh to Berwick and Newcastle:

'A special train will leave the North Bridge Station (renamed Waverley in 1866) at Seven o'clock, on the Morning of Wednesday 22d August, Calling to take up Passengers at PORTOBELLO, INVERESK, LONGNIDDRY (for Haddington), and DUNBAR, reaching Berwick about Nine o'clock. The Train will wait here for a few minutes to take in Passengers from BERWICK to NEWCASTLE, arriving in Newcastle about half-past Eleven.

'The Parties who have arranged this trip to England announce it with perfect confidence, on account of the complete nature of the Travelling arrangements, and because the district of country through which the Party will pass is famed for its varied and picturesque scenery. Each Passenger, on Purchasing his Ticket, will be furnished with a Card, which will inform them of all that is to be seen in Newcastle.'

For that trip, the return fares between Edinburgh and Newcastle were 15s 0d (75p) first-class, 12s 0d (60p) second-class, and 9s 0d (45p) third-class. It cannot go unremarked that the PR omitted to mention the break of journey at Berwick due to the uncompleted bridge.

The foundation stone for the bridge across the Tweed at Berwick had been laid on 15 May 1847 (three months before the old Newcastle & Berwick Railway had become part of the YN&BR), and the last arch was keyed in on 26 March 1850. Each of the 28 arches had a span of 61ft 6in and, during the

Below:
Royal Border Bridge, 1850: This is one of Britain's best-known railway landmarks but, despite the bridge's title, it does *not* cross any border. In this early post-Nationalisation picture, 'A3' 4-6-2 No 60043 *Brown Jack* crosses the bridge with the 4.18pm Newcastle–Glasgow service. *E. R. Wethersett/Ian Allan Library*

construction of the bridge, the workforce reached a peak of over 2,700 men. At the time of its completion the bridge was the largest of its type in Britain. It was opened to freight traffic on 20 July, but the ceremonial opening of the bridge to passenger traffic did not take place until 29 August when Queen Victoria interrupted her journey from Castle Howard to Edinburgh in order to officiate. With the Queen's permission the structure was formally entitled the Royal Border Bridge, although that title was, and still is, a little misleading.

The bridge's title implies that the border between England and Scotland is at Berwick, but although that was once the case, the border has, since 1482, been to the north of Berwick with the town, therefore, being very firmly on the English side. The actual border itself is, in the words of Elizabeth Doley of Berwick Museum 'a very ordinary stone wall dividing two fields'. Meandering off into something which has nothing whatsoever to do with railway matters, Berwick's pre-1482 history was punctuated by frequent changes of 'ownership' between England and Scotland. Since then the town has retained many special privileges, but in more recent times its status has sometimes been overlooked. One such occasion was in 1856 when the Paris Peace Treaty was signed to bring an end to the Crimean War. State documents of that time generally referred separately to Berwick, but the Paris treaty contained no reference to the town and, therefore, Berwick was still technically at war with Russia. That, however, was resolved in 1966 during an official Soviet visit to the town. The Mayor of Berwick presented the Soviet delegation with a specially-prepared document, and delivered it with the words 'Now the Russians can sleep safely in their beds'.

Returning to the subject of the Royal Border Bridge, it is generally assumed that its title was merely a public relations exercise. The logical alternatives for a title, the Tweed Bridge or Berwick Bridge, had, in fact, both been used locally for a road bridge which had been built across the river in 1634.

As with several other bridges in this book, the Royal Border Bridge has been treated to little more than routine maintenance throughout its long life, but is still in everyday use by trains which could never have featured in its designer's wildest dreams. The East Coast main line has, in the last 20 years, been treated to a degree of investment and, therefore, the future of the bridge looks as safe as anything can be at present.

1850: Welwyn Viaduct, Welwyn, Hertfordshire

The Great Northern Railway reached London on 7 August 1850, trains using a temporary terminus at Maiden Lane until October 1852 when King's Cross Station was completed. At Welwyn, some 20 miles out from Maiden Lane, the line crossed the valley of the Mimram by means of an imposing viaduct. The structure, which was designed by William Cubitt and built by Thomas Brassey, was built of brick and had 40 arches; it was 519yd long and had a maximum height of 89ft. As the GNR's traffic increased, it became necessary to quadruple the main line. This was started in 1867, but it was considered that the cost of widening Welwyn Viaduct would be prohibitive and, instead, an

Left:
Welwyn Viaduct, 1850: The scale of many bridges and viaducts can be appreciated only from ground level, and Welwyn Viaduct is one for which that holds very true. These days inspection and maintenance work is carried out with strict awareness of safety, that being in marked contrast to some practices of earlier times. This inspection of Welwyn Viaduct took place on Sunday, 22 January 1967. *D. Percival*

avoiding line was eventually built via Cuffley. As intended, Welwyn Viaduct retained its double-track status.

1851: Knaresborough Viaduct, Knaresborough, North Yorkshire

The line from York opened to Haypark Lane (½ mile east of Knaresborough) on 30 October 1848, but the extension into Knaresborough, which made an end-on connection with a branch from Harrogate, could not be opened until 1 October 1851. The delay was because the viaduct across the River Nidd at Knaresborough had had to be almost entirely rebuilt, the original structure having collapsed on 11 March 1848 when nearing completion. The viaduct had no significant claims to fame regarding its historical or engineering aspects, but its visual appeal was indisputable. Today, it is still one of Britain's most photogenic railway viaducts.

Below:
Knaresborough Viaduct, 1851: Arguably one of the most eye-catching — and most photographed — viaducts in the country, Knaresborough Viaduct blends in magnificently with the environment. Despite views such as this there are, almost unbelievably, many Southerners who still believe that every last square inch of Yorkshire is heavily industrialised. The unusual duty undertaken by 'Jubilee' 4-6-0 No 45562 *Alberta* on 31 May 1967 was that of hauling the empty stock of the Royal Train from Nidd Bridge (near Harrogate) to York. *Maurice S. Burns*

Right:
Chacewater Viaduct, rebuilt 1888: The original viaduct at Chacewater was one of the many Brunel-designed timber structures, photographs of which appear elsewhere in this book. On 16 May 1959 an ex-GWR 'Grange' class 4-6-0 approaches the replacement viaduct of 1888 with the 6.07pm Plymouth–Penzance relief. *M.Mensing*

1852: Truro–Penzance, Cornwall

(nine viaducts, listed opposite)
Designer: Isambard Kingdom Brunel
Original owner: West Cornwall Railway
Type: Timber viaducts
Tracks: 1 (doubled 1893-1930)

The 25¼-mile long main line of the West Cornwall Railway connected Truro and Penzance. The Redruth–Penzance section was opened on 11 March 1852, and the Truro–Redruth section on 25 August the same year. On 16 April 1855, the WCR diverted trains into its new terminus at Newham but the opening of a connection with the Cornwall Railway on 11 May 1859 enabled WCR trains to use the latter's new station.

Below right:
Hayle Viaduct, rebuilt 1886: The iron girder superstructure replaced the original timber section of Hayle Viaduct, but the existing piers were reused. On 26 July 1975, Class 47 No 47061 crosses the 'new' viaduct with the 9.35am Penzance–Wolverhampton train. *Brian Morrison*

Miles	Name	Length	Max Height	No. of Spans	Date Replaced	Replaced by
½	Penwithers	124yd	54ft	8	1887	New masonry viaduct (7 spans)
4	Chacewater	99yd	52ft	7	1888	New masonry viaduct (5 spans)
4½	Blackwater	132yd	68ft	9	1888	New masonry viaduct (7 spans)
8½	Redruth	163yd	61ft	10	1888	Masonry viaduct
14	Penponds	291yd*	45ft	33	1900*	New masonry viaduct*
16¼	Angarrack	266yd	100ft	16	1885	New masonry viaduct (11 spans)
17	Guildford	128yd	56ft	8	1886	New masonry viaduct (6 spans)
18	Hayle	277yd	34ft	37	1886	Iron girders
25½	Penzance	347yd	12ft	51	1871†	Timber†

* 60yd of Penponds Viaduct replaced by embankment in 1864.
† Second timber viaduct replaced in 1921 by stone embankment.

NB: 1) The mileages are those from the present-day Truro station, which was not opened until August 1863.

2) The dimensions are those substantiated by MacDermot and Clinker in their definitive history of the GWR.

3) The use of the word 'new' in the final column denotes a replacement built alongside the original structure, instead of on the same alignment.

Both the West Cornwall Railway and the Cornwall Railway became justifiably famed for their Brunel-designed timber viaducts, those of the former company taking the seniority award. Originally, though, the WCR's engineer was Capt W.S.Moorsom, who came in for considerable criticism from many of his peers. The engineer and writer, Francis Conder, described a 'Captain Transom' (a thinly veiled Capt Moorsom) as 'a man too full of contradictions to be dismissed in a line' and 'perhaps difficult to be judged with fairness'.

Those opinions of Moorsom were based largely on the fact that the man had obtained responsible engineering positions with at least two major companies despite his blatant lack of adequate experience. It was considered that Moorsom had landed the posts due to a combination of bluff and a naïvety on the part of his employers; furthermore, rather than hire experienced assistants or listen to the advice of those who really knew what they were doing, he had insisted on going it alone.

One example of Moorsom's questionable desire to ignore advice was seen during his period in charge of the construction of the Birmingham & Gloucester Railway. Rather than heed the recommendations of George Stephenson and Brunel for a circuitous but gently graded line, Moorsom insisted on a direct route which included the 1 in 38 haul up the Lickey Incline. As the history books show, the Lickey caused problems right until the end of the steam era. Perhaps the most damning comment about Moorsom was that he had taken into Parliament more railway Bills than almost any other engineer, and had lost all but one of them. His only success, it was argued, had been due solely to the exertions of the contractor who had been engaged to build the line.

Perhaps fortunately, Moorsom's appointment as the West Cornwall Railway's Chief Engineer was not long-lived. The circumstances surrounding his replacement by Brunel are vague, but it is known that Moorsom was appointed to the WCR's board in 1847, thereby leaving the way clear for Brunel to utilise his wealth of expertise and experience. With a view to future connections with railways on the 'English' side of the River Tamar, Brunel favoured building the WCR to the broad gauge. In the best tradition of localised early-Victorian railway companies, however, the WCR soon found itself desperately short of funds and so, partly in order to reduce expenditure, it was decided to build a standard gauge line instead.

The terrain crossed by the WCR was hardly the flattest known to mankind, and so considerable engineering works were required. The construction of several viaducts was unavoidable, but Brunel reduced costs considerably by designing inexpensive but deceptively sturdy timber structures. It is believed that Brunel's initial intention was to standardise the design so that only a limited range of replacement components would be required, but two different styles were nevertheless evolved for the WCR. Furthermore, the individual requirements of each viaduct often necessitated slight deviations from the standard, and that all but nullified the attempts at overall standardisation.

The viaducts at Penponds, Hayle and Penzance had piers at 21ft intervals, each pier comprising a pair of legs secured to a cross-member set in the ground. The six other WCR viaducts, which were built across deeper valleys, had piers at 50ft intervals with centre struts as well as the two outer struts. Additional bracing was provided by a 'fan' of timbers from the piers to the underside of the decking. The timber used was American white pine, contradictorily known in this country as 'yellow pine', which was preserved by Kyanising.

As the loadings of trains increased, some of the WCR's viaducts required strengthening. For example, Penponds Viaduct had a central leg added to each of its piers in 1861 while, in 1864/65, Angarrack Viaduct had the lower sections of its piers replaced by masonry. Despite their appearance of frailty, all but one of the WCR's nine viaducts survived largely in their original form until at least the mid-1880s. The exception was Penzance Viaduct, 60yd of which was destroyed in a gale in 1852, a repeat performance in 1867 resulting in the loss of over half. The replacement sections, however, adhered to the original design format.

In 1864 the Cornwall Railway (which had opened its Plymouth–Truro line in May 1859) put pressure on the WCR to lay a third rail on the Redruth–Penzance line to permit broad gauge workings, and this was grudgingly completed in November 1866. The cost of adapting the bridges and viaducts along the line was £16,157. The WCR was formally taken over by the GWR on 31 January 1876, and the mixed gauge rails remained *in situ* until the total extinction of the broad gauge on the long weekend of 20/23 May 1892. By then, all the original viaducts except those at Penponds and Penzance had been replaced. The former was replaced by a new masonry structure in 1900, while Penzance Viaduct, which had been partially rebuilt of necessity on two occasions, was finally replaced in 1921 by a granite-faced embankment. At the western end of the embankment there were two arches built of Staffordshire brindle bricks, and an 18ft-span girder bridge which gave pedestrian access to the beach. It should be noted that, as detailed in the accompanying table, the replacement masonry viaducts on the line had a different number of spans to the original timber sources.

It is arguable that the original design of Penzance Viaduct had contributed to the structure's erratic existence. The floor of the first viaduct had been close-decked, and this closed off the obvious escape route for the sometimes vast amounts of water and shingle which were hurled on to the structure by heavy seas. That flaw had been remedied during the rebuilding which had followed the structure's partial collapse during a storm in 1867, but construction of the replacement viaduct was still beset by the problems of poor foundations. During the rebuilding, it had been possible to replace no more than nine of the timber piles by masonry piers, the rest of the viaduct being built over what was believed to be a submerged forest which, of course, provided no firm base.

Apart from the design faults of Penzance Viaduct, the comparatively lengthy lives of the elegant structures elsewhere on the WCR's line spoke volumes for Brunel's capabilities. The widespread respect for Bruneliana has, however, often resulted in the replacement masonry viaducts between Truro and Penzance being overlooked, and that is somewhat unjust. The seven masonry viaducts are magnificent structures in their own right and, unlike many others elsewhere in Britain, are still in everyday use.

1852: Yarm Viaduct, Yarm, Cleveland

Yarm Viaduct, on the line between Northallerton and Stockton, was planned by the Leeds & Thirsk Railway and was virtually completed in 1849. However, the line did not open to public traffic until 2 June 1852, by which time the L&TR had become part of the Leeds Northern Railway. The viaduct, which was designed by Thomas Grainger, carried the railway across the River Tees and above the old town of Yarm. It had 42 arches, 40 of which were each 40ft wide, the other two being 67ft wide. The larger pair were 65ft high.

1852: Wye Bridge, Chepstow, Gwent/Gloucestershire

Designer: Isambard Kingdom Brunel
Original Owner: South Wales Railway
Contractors: Finch & Willey, Liverpool
Cost: (estimated) £65,420
Type: Suspension and beam
Materials: Wrought iron; cast iron; stone
Total length: 200yd
Max height of rails: 57ft above high-water
Spans: 4
Tracks: 2

The broad gauge South Wales Railway opened its line between Chepstow (West) and Swansea in June 1850; the line from Chepstow (East) to Grange Court, where a connection was made with the Great Western Railway, opened in September 1851. The missing link at Chepstow, a one-mile section which included the crossing of the River Wye, was not opened until 19 July 1852.

The crossing of the Wye at Chepstow effectively involved not one bridge but two in tandem. This was necessitated mainly by the contrasting nature of the two riverbanks, but also by the need to retain

Below:
Yarm Viaduct, 1852: The latter-day description of Yarm Viaduct as an 'architectural dog's-dinner' is somewhat appropriate. Arguably, the only two arches which appear to be in reasonable condition are those over the River Tees (underneath the two Class 37s). This picture was taken in February 1976 and, apparently, the viaduct is still in a similar condition today. *Rodney Wildsmith*

Above:
Wye Bridge, 1852: The suspension section of Brunel's Wye Bridge at Chepstow continued in use for 110 years, during which time it remained largely unaltered. Rebuilding was, however, undertaken in 1962, this picture of August 1960 showing the original structure in its final form. *British Railways*

at least a 50ft clearance above the high-water mark. On the south bank of the Wye, the land rose only a little above the high-water mark and was composed of clay and loose shingle. Therefore, three conventional plate girder spans, each 100ft long and approached by a high embankment, were considered satisfactory for the southern part of the river crossing.

The north bank of the river was a very different matter as it lay beneath a steep limestone cliff, the top of which was 120ft above the bed of the river, and the bedrock beneath the river-bed was all of 84ft below the high-water mark. A pair of parallel plate girder bridges, each of 300ft span, was used for the crossing of the northern part of the river, the chosen method of support being suspension chains. The Wye Bridge therefore became only the second main-line railway suspension bridge to be built in Britain; the first, the Tees Suspension Bridge of 1830, had already been replaced.

The northern end of the suspension section was built on a ledge 20ft below the cliff-top. The 'mid-stream' end (which joined the plate girder section end-on) was supported by cast iron cylinders which were subsequently filled with concrete to force them down on to the rock beneath the river-bed. The suspension method used for supporting the section was somewhat unconventional as, instead of the chains being carried back from the towers and anchored into the ground, they were fixed to the tops of the towers. The inward pull of the chains was counteracted by fitting an 8ft diameter wrought iron tube between each pair of towers, thereby literally propping the ends apart. When completed, the entire structure incorporated just over 2,340 tons of cast and wrought iron.

The suspension truss carrying the 'down' line opened to public traffic on 19 July 1852, the truss carrying the 'up' line not being ready until 18 April 1853. In the opinion of many, the Wye Bridge was not one of Brunel's most attractive works. Nevertheless, a stab at aesthetic appeal had been incorporated in the design, the tower at the 'mid-stream' end having been made of cast iron flanged plates but finished as an exact replica of the stone tower at the landward end. Similarly, the decorative scroll work at the top of each tower looked very similar, but that at the top of the iron tower was, in fact, made of zinc sheeting on a light timber framework.

Such trivialities were overlooked by the *Illustrated London News*, which reported on the opening of the Wye Bridge in the issue of 24 July 1852:

'Hitherto an unfortunate break occurred at Chepstow, where passengers had to be conveyed about two miles over a rough country from station to station. On Monday this hiatus was abolished by the opening of the stupendous iron bridge over the river Wye for public traffic; and we may now anticipate that the rich minerals of South Wales - its coals of every available description for steaming and household purposes - will be found in all the midland and London markets.'

One great irony in that report was that the South Wales Railway and its parent, the GWR, had little interest in the potentially lucrative coal traffic. The South Wales line had been built mainly with the intention of providing access to new steamer ports in West Wales where Irish and transatlantic passenger traffic could be developed. Nevertheless, the same magazine made the very valid point that:

'....two years ago, the journey from London to Swansea, partly by railway and partly by coach, crossing by a ferry-boat the dangerous passage of the Severn at Beachley, occupied fifteen hours. The express trains are now timed to perform the same distance (216 miles) with ease and comfort in five hours'.

The SWR, incidentally, was formally absorbed by the GWR in January 1862, and converted to the standard gauge in May 1872.

The Wye Bridge remained virtually unaltered for almost a century, the first significant modifications being carried out in 1948 when the three conventional girders at the southern end were replaced by mild steel riveted plate girders. During the 1950s, the Western Region became increasingly frustrated at the speed limit imposed on trains crossing the bridge but, as suspension bridges were not suitable for fast trains, little could be done apart from completely rebuilding the suspension section.

An end to the operation department's frustrations came in 1962 when the Wye Bridge was almost completely rebuilt. For the 'new' Wye Bridge, the distinctive suspension section was replaced by welded and bolted steel trusses which supported the decking from underneath. This reduced the clearance below the bridge to just 17ft above the highwater mark, but that was unimportant as, by then, the activities of merchant shipping at Chepstow did little to occupy the compilers of 'Lloyd's List'. It was fortunate that Brunel had provided separate suspension sections for each of the two tracks, as this enabled the rebuilding to be undertaken one track at a time. Single-line working during the rebuilding might have been an inconvenience, but it was a far lesser evil than having to close the bridge completely.

The work was undertaken by the Fairfield Shipbuilding & Engineering Co of Chepstow. That firm had started life well over a century earlier as Messrs Finch & Willey - the very company which had constructed the original Brunel bridge. The rebuilding was completed in November 1962, and all that remained of the old Brunel structure were the piers. The 'new' Wye Bridge has been described as resembling a mediocre effort with a Meccano set but, at the risk of offending the members of the Isambard Kingdom Brunel fan club, the original bridge was, similarly, not without its critics.

1852: Lambley Viaduct, Nr Lambley, Northumberland

The lead workings around Alston, in what was then south-east Cumberland, prompted the Newcastle & Carlisle Railway to construct a branch from Haltwhistle to Alston and Nenthead. The section as far as Alston was finally opened throughout on 17 November 1852, but powers for the Nenthead extension were subsequently allowed to lapse because of the problems of crossing extremely difficult terrain. That was not to say that the construction of the Alston section was easy, as although the branch followed the valley of the South Tyne for all of its length, it still needed heavy earthworks and gradients of up to 1 in 56. Furthermore, a total of nine viaducts was required.

Below:
Lambley Viaduct, 1852: Ex-LNER 'G5' class 0-4-4T No 67241 leaves Lambley station, the viaduct being clearly visible in the background. *N. E. Stead*

All nine viaducts on the single-track branch were built of stone, three carrying the line over the South Tyne itself, and the others crossing Glendue, Thinhope, Knar, Thornhope, Whitley and Gilderdale Burns. The best-known was undoubtedly Lambley Viaduct, which carried the line 110ft above the South Tyne on nine semicircular arches, each of 58ft span. The structure was the final part of the branch to be finished, the rest of the route having been ready for 11 months prior to the viaduct's completion.

The Alston branch closed to public traffic on 3 May 1976, but its viaducts were left to stand. A preservation organisation, the South Tynedale Railway, is now based at Alston station. Incidentally, the town of Alston itself had two particular claims to fame, the first being that it was the highest market town in England (almost 1,000ft above sea level) - a claim contested by Buxton in Derbyshire - the second being that it was the only town in the country without street names.

1857: Durham Viaduct, Durham, County Durham

After considerable delays, the Leamside–Durham–Bishop Auckland branch finally opened to traffic on 1 April 1857. The line had several large viaducts, the best known of which is undoubtedly the stone-built 11-arch structure crossing what was then the New North Road at Durham. Among the other significant structures on the line were **Brasside Viaduct** (9 arches, 130ft high), and **Newton Cap Viaduct** (11 arches, 100ft high), both of which crossed the River Wear at different points and were built of stone. In common with Durham Viaduct, the arches on those two were built to a standard 60ft width. Durham Viaduct is now the best known of those on the Leamside–Bishop Auckland line, the reason being that, from January 1872, the route across it became part of the East Coast main line. Of the other viaducts on the line Newton Cap is, at the time of writing, in the process of being converted for road use.

1857: Crumlin Viaduct, Crumlin, Gwent

Designer: T.W.Kennard
Original owner: Newport, Abergavenny & Hereford Railway
Contractor: T.W.Kennard
Cost: £62,000
Type: Lattice girder
Materials: Wrought iron; cast iron
Total length: 553yd
Max height of rails: 200ft
Spans: 10
Tracks: 2 (singled 1927)

Of all the celebrated railway viaducts in South Wales the most famous was, arguably, at Crumlin. Built to carry the Taff Vale Extension of the Newport, Abergavenny & Hereford Railway across the Ebbw Valley, the viaduct appears to have caused as much trouble for the demolition contractors in the 1960s as it had done for the builders in the 1850s.

Below:
Durham Viaduct, 1857: The 'Queen of Scots' Pullman is hauled across Durham Viaduct by 'A3' class 4-6-2 No 2580 (later BR No 60081) *Shotover*. The viaduct was treated to major restoration work in 1985, by which time the face of East Coast motive power was, of course, somewhat different. *H.C.Casserley*

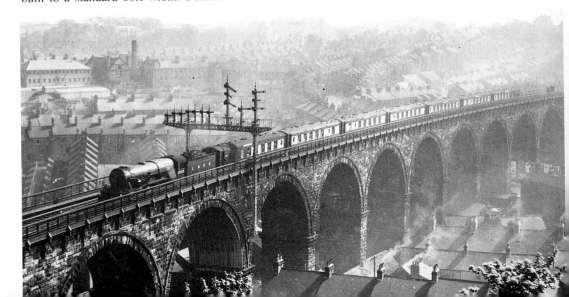

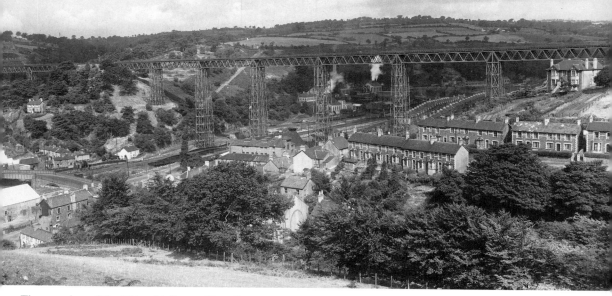

Above:
Crumlin Viaduct, 1857: Britain's tallest-ever railway viaduct was a much-photographed structure, but few pictures were taken to show both sections of the viaduct. The railway passing along the valley floor is the GWR's Newport-Aberbeeg line, part of Crumlin (Low Level) station just being visible on the extreme left of the picture. *British Railways*

The crossing of the Ebbw Valley at Crumlin presented the NA&HR with a problem. The logical choice of structure, a masonry viaduct, was ruled out as, at that time, it was considered too expensive to build one strong enough to withstand the buffeting of winds. It remains unconfirmed whether a Brunel-style timber viaduct was considered as an alternative, but the plan which won the day was for a lattice beam structure, based on the Warren Triangular Girder principle. Warren's partner, T.W.Kennard, was sensibly appointed to design and construct the viaduct. Crumlin Viaduct marked the first large-scale use of the Warren principle, the theory of which was that no individual girder would be subjected to bending or shearing, but only to tension or compression. It has often been suggested that the principle demonstrated an advanced grasp of stress distribution.

Work on the viaduct started in the autumn of 1853, the first piece of ironwork being ceremonially laid in position on 8 December by Lady Isabella Fitzmaurice, the wife of the NA&HR's Chairman. At this stage, it should be pointed out that Crumlin Viaduct was, in fact, not one structure but two, a 50ft-wide outcrop of rock separating the pair. The larger structure had six piers, the smaller having two, and each of the eight piers was formed from fourteen circular cast iron columns braced together with horizontal and diagonal wrought iron ties. Each pier was 13ft 6in on the square at the base, and most were built on masonry footings sunk 14ft into the ground, but where firm rock presented a ready-made base, the rock was merely dressed and the piers bolted to it.

The castings were made at Kennard's foundry in Falkirk, and the wrought iron supplied by the Blaenavon Iron Company, but the girders between the piers were prefabricated in a purpose-built workshop established by Kennard at Crumlin. The accuracy of the prefabrications and the simplicity of the wrought iron pin connections were such that it took a gang of men only two days to assemble an entire girder, and just one more day to hoist it into its final position. When the viaduct was completed in May 1857 it was thoroughly tested with heavy loads by the Board of Trade Inspector and, after gaining approval, was opened to traffic on 1 June. The NA&HR had, in fact, reached Crumlin Junction in September 1855, but even with the completion of the viaduct, the remainder of the line westwards to Quaker's Yard was not opened until January 1858. The NA&HR was absorbed by the West Midlands Railway in July 1860, the latter company being absorbed by the GWR in August 1863.

According to the NA&HR the viaduct was the highest in the world, but the Aqueduct of Spoletto in Italy and the Portage timber viaduct in America actually knocked Crumlin Viaduct into third place. Nevertheless, it was a remarkable structure which, throughout its long life, not only retained the status of Britain's highest railway viaduct, but also remained substantially unaltered, The *Illustrated London News* of 29 August 1857 reported:

'...in a scientific point of view, this wonderful structure is more remarkable as a combination of lightness and economy of material, than it is for boldness of design and beauty of execution...it is within two feet of the height of the London Monument...the ordinary expansion and contraction in summer, between midday and midnight, does not exceed ¼ inch... notwithstanding the magnitude of the undertaking, it was said to have been the cheapest structure of its kind'.

Crumlin Viaduct originally incorporated 2,390 tons of iron, but a further 160 tons was added in 1868 when the timber decking was replaced by iron plates. The only other significant alteration to which the viaduct was subjected was the singling of the track across it in 1927. The new track was laid along the centre of the viaduct to enable heavier loads to cross and, when necessary, the use of double-heading. The Working Instructions for 1960 stated that, except in cases of emergency, the only engines in the 'Red' classification allowed across the viaduct were 'Grange' class 4-6-0s, '56xx' and '66xx' class 0-6-2Ts, and '15xx', '34xx', '84xx' and '94xx' class 0-6-0PTs. Of the 'Blue' classified engines only '9F' 2-10-0s were permitted, although class members Nos 92163-67 were forbidden because of their heavier weights. The 8mph speed limit across the viaduct nevertheless remained in force until the very end.

The working life of Crumlin Viaduct ended on 15 June 1964 when the line across it was officially closed, the last through trains between Pontypool Road and Neath having run two days earlier. Fittingly, Crumlin Viaduct was scheduled for preservation, but nobody seemed to inform the authorities as the structure received no maintenance and began to deteriorate rapidly. However, the viaduct found fame in the summer of 1965 when Universal Films used it as the location for a chase sequence in the film *Arabesque*, in which those well-known railway enthusiasts, Gregory Peck and Sophia Loren, rode horses across the viaduct while Alan Badel tried to exterminate them by shooting from a helicopter. Apparently, most of the locals were dispatched on a picnic (paid for by the film company) during filming so that the scene would be suitably devoid of uninvited extras.

Shortly after the viaduct's moment of cinematic glory, dismantling was ordered. That, however, proved a difficult task as five different companies, one of them brought in from Germany, failed in their objective. The task was eventually completed in 1967 by Messrs Birds & Co who built a temporary bailey bridge which could be moved along as each section of the viaduct was demolished. When this writer last visited the site in 1989, the abutments of the viaduct high up on each side of the valley were still clearly visible, but it was nevertheless hard to visualise the spectacular structure that had positively dominated the scene only a few years earlier.

1858: Hownes Gill Viaduct, Nr Consett, County Durham

Designer: Thomas Bouch
Original owner: Stockton & Darlington Railway
Contractor: John Anderson
Cost: £15,756
Type: Arch viaduct
Material: Firebrick
Total length: 243yd
Max height of rails: 150ft
Spans: 12
Tracks: 1

The railway line between Stanhope and Annfield Plain was opened by the Stanhope & Tyne Railway on 15 May 1834. The line had several inclines which were worked by stationary engines, and this uneconomical aspect of operation was one of the causes of the company's financial demise in 1841. The Stanhope–Annfield line later became the property of the Stockton & Darlington Railway, but the problem of the troublesome inclines was not tackled for a few years. The major obstacle on the line was at Hownes Gill, where a pair of wagon lifts was used to cross the 800ft-wide, 160ft-deep steep-sided ravine. Although proposals had been made in 1836 and 1844 for a viaduct across Hownes Gill, the plans had not come to fruition.

The wagon lifts were a positive hindrance to speedy operation. When a train reached the side of the valley, it was necessary to detach the wagons, turn them sideways, and fix them on to a cradle on which they were lowered to the floor of the valley. At the other side of the valley floor the procedure was repeated, in reverse, to raise the wagons before they could continue their journey over slightly easier ground. Even though the inclines were worked by engines, an average of only 12 wagons per hour could be worked across Hownes Gill.

Despite their drawbacks, the wagon lifts were considered to be masterpieces of engineering. They are believed to have been designed by Robert Stephenson, and certainly drew considerable attention in engineering circles. They were described in 1843 by James Clephan, the editor of the *Gateshead Courier* as: '...one of the most wonderful railway rarities in existence'. An interesting observation made by William Tomlinson in his definitive history of the North Eastern Railway was that: 'It is somewhat curious that the same device which was used in 1843 in northwest Durham for conveying the waggons in a horizontal position across a ravine should have been adopted in Central Africa in 1901'. Tomlinson's reference was to the Kikuyu inclines on the Uganda Railway.

Above:

Above:
Hownes Gill Viaduct, 1858: This very early view could possibly have been taken relatively soon after the opening of the viaduct. If all is what it seems, the locomotive appears to be one of the Stockton & Darlington's Hackworth-designed 0-6-0 mineral engines.
Bucknall Collection/Ian Allan Library

By 1853 the inclines at Hownes Gill had been improved so that three wagons could be taken across at a time but, in view of the ever-increasing traffic, this was still considered unsatisfactory. In 1855 plans were approved for constructing a new line to avoid Hownes Gill completely but, the following year, it was at last decided to construct a viaduct on the original alignment. The design was by Thomas Bouch and, with an apparent degree of foresight about slender Bouch-designed structures, the railway company's directors decided to consult Robert Stephenson about the design. Stephenson considered that the design was basically sound, but nevertheless suggested that the central piers be strengthened by means of inverts, primarily to spread the load over a wider area of ground. Furthermore, Stephenson observed that the design left little leeway for inferior materials or workmanship which, in view of the fall of Bouch's Tay Bridge in 1879, was more than a little uncanny.

Work on Bouch's viaduct at Hownes Gill commenced in 1856. The viaduct had 12 semicircular arches and was built of firebricks which were made at Pease's Wear Firebrick Co at Crook. The bricks cost £1 11s 2d (£1.56p) per 1,000 on site, and a total of some 2,655,000 were used; an alternative tender for common bricks had been submitted and would have saved some £2,000, but they were known to be of an inconsistent quality.

The first train passed over the viaduct on 1 July 1858, only 17 months after the laying of the first brick. Traffic continued for over a century, the last remnants of the once busy line west of Consett closing completely on 1 May 1969. Until 1965, 'Q6' class 0-8-0s had been the usual steeds for the thrice-weekly freight trains. Fittingly, Hownes Gill Viaduct was designated as being of special architectural and historical interest, and was subsequently converted for use as a footpath. It now forms part of the Waskerley Way Railway Walk.

1858: Nairn–Keith, Nairnshire/Morayshire/Banffshire

(principal structures listed overleaf)
Designer: Joseph Mitchell
Original owner: Inverness & Aberdeen Junction Railway

During the early 1850s the preference in Inverness was for a direct railway line to Perth and the south, but the proposal for a route which had been surveyed by the civil engineer Joseph Mitchell failed to gain Parliamentary approval. The only logical alternative was for a line which connected with the Great North of Scotland Railway's Aberdeen–Keith line, thereby providing a route to the south via Aberdeen.

The link between Inverness and Keith was built in two parts and by two nominally different companies. The Inverness & Nairn Railway constructed the 15-mile section between the communities of its title, the line opening on 5 November 1855, while the 40-mile Nairn–Keith section was built by the Inverness & Aberdeen Junction Railway and opened throughout on 18 August 1858. The I&NR was formally absorbed by the I&AJR in May 1861,

Name	Length	Height*	Spans	Cost	Description
Nairn Viaduct	124yd	56ft	4 x 55ft	£8,620	Stone viaduct
Findhorn Viaduct	203yd	46ft	3 x 150ft	£21,430	Box girder viaduct; stone piers
Spey Bridge	220yd	74ft	1 x 230ft	£34,432	Box girder bridge; stone approach spans
			6 x 30ft		

* Heights are those above the river beds.

the latter company becoming a founder member of the Highland Railway on 29 June 1865.

The section between Nairn and Keith incorporated several fine bridges and viaducts across the main rivers, the design of the structures having to take into account the floodwater from the mountains which, particularly in spring, caused the rivers to swell enormously. On the bridges, a visual reminder of the high water levels attainable by typical Highland rivers was usually evident in the form of lofty cutwaters which sometimes extended right up to the underside of the decking.

The I&AJR's bridges and viaducts were designed by Joseph Mitchell (1803–1883), whose name became synonymous with the construction of Scottish railways but, unjustly, failed to achieve the same celebrity status south of the Border. Mitchell's father, John, had been Chief Inspector on the big Highland road building programme carried out by Thomas Telford in the early 1800s, and young Joseph had, after working as a stonemason on the construction of the Caledonian Canal, been a pupil of Telford's. After John Mitchell's death in 1824, 21-year-old Joseph had been appointed as Inspector of the Highland roads, and had gone on to become an extremely well-respected civil engineer.

The very first of Joseph Mitchell's several railway viaducts was the structure crossing the river at Nairn. It seems that the building of the viaduct kept the journalists on the *Nairnshire Telegraph* busy, reports on progress frequently occupying several column inches. For example, the issue for 13 August 1856 observed that:

'The contractor has already brought to the spot many hundred tons of ponderous blocks of stone, which Kingsteps Quarry supplies *ad libitum*, and a strong force of labourers have been at work for several weeks excavating the foundations of the landpier on the westward side of the river. All things having been got ready, the first stone of this important structure was laid yesterday at two o'clock, by Mr Dallas, Inspector of the Works. An excellent foundation has been obtained - the first blocks being laid on, or rather in, the living rock. This commencement of the work was unmarked by any public masonic ceremony or demonstration; but we believe success to the work was heartily pledged in champagne by the contractor, Mr Falshaw, Mr Dallas, the Messrs Squair, builders, to whom the erection of this magnificent structure has been entrusted, and other gentlemen present.'

The mention of a 'masonic ceremony' in the above account is not as unusual as it might seem as many railway companies, particularly in Scotland, turned ceremonial occasions into a display of masonic strength.

In another curiously punctuated piece of journalism, the *Nairnshire Telegraph* reported on 25 June 1858:

'This beautiful piece of work (the Nairn Viaduct) has now been divested of all appliances used in its construction, and acquired the finished and permanent form in which it will, in all probability, meet the gaze of many generations. There is decidedly nothing of a similar kind to compare with it in the north in elegance and workmanship, excellence of material, and symmetry; and perhaps no bridge in the south of Scotland can surpass it in these respects. Its four arches extend over about 250 feet and the height being in fine proportion to the span of each, which is between 50 and 60 feet, give a natural grace to the whole design, evidently without the least straining at effect on the part of the architect. In fact, an entire want of outward display forms its most pleasing feature. Rising as if by chance from off the piers, and in relief from the body of the building; the appearance of half columns of an octagonal shape terminating in a tastefully cut moulding meet the eye, while all the other portions finish in a line of flat stone, shewing, only a plain bead on the edge to recommend it to notice. Viewed from the turnpike bridge the structure has a very attractive appearance, which is in no small measure enhanced by a very picturesque intervening space. Reposing at its base on the left bank of the river - mid a multitude of grave stones and mouldering heaps of bygone generations, eminently suggestive of the future - is the Parish Church, with no pretensions to architectural ornament, but bearing with it many a hallowed recollection; while further down on the river side are sloping gardens, and several trees over-hanging its brink, which had cast their leaves on the water at least a century before the first steamer splashed in the adjacent bay, or the railway bridge was dreamed of...

Right:
Spey Bridge, 1858: Joseph Mitchell's stylish work was evidenced by the Spey Bridge near Orton. Again, high cutwaters are very noticeable. *Bucknall Collection/Ian Allan Library*

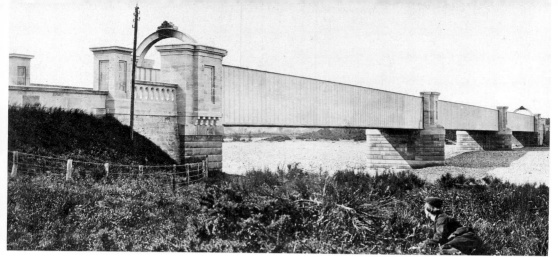

'...But the bridge is seen to by far the best advantage from the Grantown Road, near Househill, about a mile and a half distant from the town. It is there developed in full front, and its connection with the line at both ends observed, so that no finer sight is in the neighbourhood than that of the 'iron horse' spinning along as if in a breathless hurry.'

When commenting on the Nairn Viaduct in later years, Mitchell explained that the contractor had insisted that no special care needed to be taken about the foundations as, in his opinion, rock would be found just 3-4ft below the river-bed. During the construction work, however, rock had not been reached until the sinkings had reached a depth of 13-14ft. Mitchell's magnanimous comment about the contractor's erroneous opinion was that the episode showed that 'experienced persons may be misled even under the most convincing circumstances'.

After leaving Nairn, the railway continued eastwards and crossed the River Findhorn between Brodie and Forres by means of a low wrought iron

Above:
Findhorn Viaduct, 1858: Despite appearances, this is a box girder bridge and not a tubular structure. The high cutwaters on the piers are a reminder of the seasonal levels of the River Findhorn. Sadly, no enlightenment can be offered regarding the poacher/escaped convict/ photographer's assistant lurking in the foreground. *Bucknall Collection/Ian Allan Library*

viaduct, the box girder construction giving the appearance of a tubular bridge, albeit without a roof. It had originally been intended that the foundations for the bridge should be sunk to a depth of 6ft below the river-bed. However, during the construction of the east abutment, solid rock was found at a depth of 18ft and, as subsequent investigations revealed that the rock continued underneath the entire width of the river, the foundations were sunk on to the rock with the aid of coffer-dams.

Near Orton, the River Spey was crossed by means of another box girder bridge, although at the time the line opened, the bridge was in an unfin-

ished state. As a temporary measure, scaffolding was used to carry the rails across the river but, somewhat predictably, the Board of Trade refused to sanction its use by passenger trains. Consequently, carriages were hauled across the top of the scaffolding by ropes while passengers walked across the nearby road bridge and rejoined their train on the other bank of the river. It is believed that the permanent bridge over the Spey was not completed until 1860, but it claimed the distinction of having the longest single span of any open girder bridge in Scotland. In 1906 the bridge was replaced by a lattice girder structure.

When the HR's direct line between Perth and Inverness via Forres opened in 1863, the Inverness–Aberdeen route via Elgin and Keith lost much of its importance as part of a long-distance through route. Nevertheless, it remained well used as a 'localised' main line despite the HR's frequent scraps with the Great North of Scotland Railway, which owned the metals southeastwards from Keith to Aberdeen. The Nairn–Keith line eluded the widespread closures of the 1960s and is still in use today.

1859: Royal Albert Bridge, St Budeaux–Saltash, Devon/Cornwall

Designer: Isambard Kingdom Brunel
Original owner: Cornwall Railway
Contractors: C.J.Mare, Blackwall
Cost: £225,000
Type: Arch and suspension
Materials: Cast iron; wrought iron
Total length: 734yd
Max height of rails: 100ft above high-water
Spans: 19 (including approaches)
Tracks: 1

The Cornwall Railway's broad gauge main line between Plymouth and Truro was ceremonially opened on 4 May 1859. The line was initially worked by the contractors, Messrs Evans & Geach, but the South Devon Railway took over that responsibility on 1 July 1866. Both the CR and SDR were absorbed by the Great Western Railway on 31 January 1876, and their lines converted to the standard gauge on 20/23 May 1892.

When the Cornwall Railway was in the planning stage, the greatest of the many obstacles it faced was undoubtedly the crossing of the River Tamar to the west of Plymouth. The CR's engineer, Capt W. S. Moorsom, proposed a crossing of the Hamoaze (the lower reaches of the Tamar) between Devonport and Torpoint by means of a ferry or floating bridge, but that idea was one of many Moorsom schemes which failed to gain approval.

Below:
Royal Albert Bridge, 1859: A train from Plymouth approaches Saltash station, at the western end of the famous bridge. The section of line across the bridge was the only part of the main line not to have been doubled. The L&SWR's line to Plymouth can be seen in the distance between the piers of the first main span. *Ian Allan Library*

Moorsom was succeeded by Brunel who subsequently proposed a new alignment two miles to the north which crossed the Tamar between St Budeaux and Saltash. A significant advantage of Brunel's route was the avoidance of gradients as sharp as 1 in 45, as had featured in Moorsom's proposed route, but Brunel still had the problem of taking the railway across the river which, at Saltash, is 1,100ft wide and 70ft deep at high-water. Brunel's initial scheme was for a bridge comprising one span of 225ft and six of 105ft, with a clearance of 80ft above high-water. That proposal was rejected by the Admiralty as certain minimum clearances had to be observed, and so Brunel substituted a plan for a bridge consisting of two spans of 300ft and two of 200ft, a clear headway of 100ft being provided.

Although the new plan was accepted by the Admiralty, Brunel found himself faced with the prospect of having to build three piers in deep water. Arguably, he would have relished the challenge, but the Cornwall Railway's sparsely-filled coffers ruled out any time-consuming and potentially expensive experiments.

Brunel revised the plans once again, his new scheme for the bridge including only one pier in deep water and two spans each of 465ft (later reduced to 455ft). His previous plans for the crossing of the Tamar were for timber bridges, but the final one was for a wrought iron structure with the decking suspended from massive arched 'tubes'. Only two suspension bridges had previously been built in this country for main-line railway use, the first across the River Tees in 1830 and the second across the River Wye in 1852. The Tees Bridge, designed by Capt Samuel Brown, had proved such a flop that it had been replaced within ten years, but the Wye Bridge had been designed by Brunel and was altogether more successful. Significantly, though, the bridge across the Tamar was the last main-line railway suspension bridge to be built in Britain.

Preliminary work was put in hand in 1848. Initially, a wrought iron cylinder, 6ft in diameter and 85ft long, was sunk through 16ft of mud and clay on the river-bed to enable borings to be made to investigate the underlying rock. The contract for the bridge's construction was not let until January 1853, by which time Brunel had abandoned thoughts of accommodating a double line of track. He estimated that £100,000 could be saved by providing the Cornwall Railway with only a single-track line, although most of the route could be doubled at a future date and with relatively minimal expense. Doubling was indeed undertaken between 1860 and 1908, but the bridge at Saltash was designed for only a single track and was never to be widened.

The first stage in the construction of the bridge was the building of a large cylinder for the central pier. This was 37ft in diameter, 90ft high, and weighed some 300 tons; it became known, rather unimaginatively, as the 'Great Cylinder'. In the lower part of the cylinder there was a central diving bell compartment surrounded by a second annular compartment. The cylinder was floated out and sunk in position in June 1854, its lower edge having been profiled to fit the shape of the bedrock. Brunel's intention had been to pressurise the diving bell compartment, but the bedrock on which the cylinder rested proved to be badly fissured, and water entered faster than the extractor pumps could cope with. Brunel ingeniously decided to construct a further cylinder which could be installed inside the existing one and, with additional airlocks and pumps, an effective pressurised working area was provided.

Work then progressed slowly but surely, a masonry ring 35ft in diameter being constructed inside the 'Great Cylinder' to a height of 12ft above the high-water mark. When this was done, the cylinder was removed in halves and towed ashore. By this time, the contractor had become bankrupt but, with the most difficult part of the job completed, the Cornwall Railway considered that its own labour force could finish the task. The original contract, incidentally, was worth £162,000, some £63,000 *less* than the final bill.

The track bed was carried on two trusses, each 455ft long, 56ft high and weighing 1,060 tons, which were constructed on the Devon shore and floated into position on top of the partly-finished piers. Hydraulic lifts raised the trusses 3ft at a time and the piers were built up under them. Although the central pier was built up by means of octagonal cast iron columns, the landward piers were built from masonry and therefore it was necessary to allow time for the masonry to set. Consequently, the bridge grew at the agonisingly slow rate of only 6ft per week. The land piers carried a total of 17 approach spans, the entire ensemble being some 2,200ft in length. It has been alleged that some of the ironwork used in the construction had been prepared for the Clifton Suspension Bridge in Bristol, work on that structure having, at the time, been held in abeyance.

By February 1859 the work on the bridge across the Tamar was virtually complete, and the first train to cross the bridge was a special working on 11 April 1859. Sadly, though, Brunel's health was by then deteriorating, the stress of a lifetime's overwork having caught up with him, and he was convalescing in Cairo when the bridge at Saltash was ceremonially opened on 4 May 1859. The guest of honour at the opening was HRH The Prince Consort, who had agreed to give his name to the structure.

Since September 1857 Brunel had been preoccupied with work on the SS *Great Eastern* and so his Chief Assistant, Robert Brereton, had been more or less in charge of the construction of the bridge. When Brunel eventually managed to visit the bridge, his health had deteriorated to such a degree that his honorary trip was in an open truck, specially laid on to carry the couch to which he was confined. Brunel died on 15 September of the same year. He was buried at Kensal Green Cemetery which, as the GWR later pointed out, was 'on the borders of that railway with which his name will ever be most prominently associated'. The Royal Albert Bridge was, therefore, the very last of the great man's marvels to be completed in his lifetime. Soon after Brunel's death the directors of the Cornwall Railway had an inscription applied at each end of the bridge. It read, quite simply: I. K. BRUNEL, ENGINEER, 1859.

The all-round excellence of Brunel's design was evidenced by the fact that the Royal Albert Bridge needed nothing more than routine attention until 1903, when new steel cross girders supporting the decks of the trusses were installed. The plate girders of the approach spans were renewed in 1928 and wind bracing was added in 1930, but the first major replacements were not required until 1960, by which time the bridge was 101 years old. For the centenary of the bridge in 1959, a plaque in Brunel's memory was unveiled at Saltash station, just beyond the western end of the bridge. With the complete rebuilding of Brunel's suspension bridge across the River Wye at Chepstow in 1962, the Royal Albert Bridge became the only remaining railway-carrying suspension bridge in Britain.

Below:
Weston Mill Viaduct, rebuilt 1903: The original Brunel-designed timber viaduct of 1859 was replaced by this steel viaduct in 1903. An unidentified Class 47 is seen hauling the 5.45pm Plymouth–Penzance train on 23 June 1976. *Les Bertram*

1859: Plymouth–Truro, Devon/Cornwall

(34 viaducts, listed opposite)

Designer: Isambard Kingdom Brunel
Original owner: Cornwall Railway
Type: Timber and masonry viaducts
Tracks: 1 (doubled 1860-1908

As mentioned in the previous section, the broad gauge Cornwall Railway opened its 53½-mile main line between Plymouth and Truro on 4 May 1859. On replacing Capt W.S. Moorsom as the CR's Chief Engineer, Brunel inherited a difficult task as the terrain which the railway had to cross was very hilly, but the CR's poor financial health necessitated the keeping of expenditure to an absolute minimum. To help reduce costs, Brunel perpetuated the basic design for the inexpensive but sturdy timber viaducts which he had built for the South Devon Railway (1848) and the West Cornwall Railway (1852).

Brunel's Cornish viaducts came to be regarded as masterpieces, the combined length of the 34 structures on the Cornwall Railway's main line being virtually *four miles*. Many of the viaducts survived almost in their original form until the 1900s, one on the CR's Falmouth branch of 1863 lasting until 1934 to claim the disputed status of the last Brunel timber-built viaduct to remain in use on a passenger-carrying railway.

Although the theory behind the design of the CR's viaducts was similar to that used for the WCR, there was one major difference. Whereas the viaducts on the WCR incorporated timber piers, the standard pattern for the CR's viaducts included masonry piers with timber being used for the upper sections. Brunel intended that as great a degree of standardisation as possible should be applied to

Miles	Name	Length	Max Height	No. of Spans	Date Replaced	Replaced By
1¼	Stonehouse Pool	107yd	57ft	6	1908	Iron girders
1½	Keyham	144yd	90ft	7	1900	Steel girders
2	Weston Mill	400yd	46ft	30	1903	New steel viaduct
4¼	Combe by Saltash*	201yd	86ft	10	1894	New masonry viaduct
5½	Forder	202yd	67ft	17	1908	Line resited
6¼	Wivelscombe	66yd	25ft	5	1908	Line resited
8	Grove	38yd	29ft	3	1908	Line resited
8¼	Nottar	307yd	67ft	28	1908	Line resited
8¾	St Germans	315yd	106ft	17	1908	Line resited
13¾	Tresulga	175yd	93ft	9	1899	Masonry viaduct
14¼	Coldrennick	265yd	138ft	13	1897	Steel girders
15½	Treviddo	162yd	101ft	8	1897	New masonry viaduct
16¾	Cartuther	137yd	89ft	7	1882	New masonry viaduct
17	Bolitho	182yd	113ft	9	1882	Masonry viaduct
17½	Liskeard	240yd	150ft	12	1894	Steel girders
18¼	Moorswater	318yd	147ft	15	1881	New masonry viaduct
22	Westwood	124yd	88ft	6	1879	New masonry viaduct
22¼	St Pinnock	211yd	151ft	10	1880	Iron girders
22¼	Largin	189yd	130ft	9	1886	Iron girders
23	West Largin	105yd	75ft	6	1875	New masonry viaduct
23¼	Draw Wood	223yd	42ft	18	1875	Wall and embankment
23¾	Derrycombe	123yd	77ft	6	1881	New masonry viaduct
24¼	Clinnick	110yd	74ft	6	1879	New masonry viaduct
25¼	Penadlake	142yd	42ft	11	1877	New masonry viaduct
31¼	Milltown	167yd	75ft	8	1896	New masonry viaduct
39½	St Austell	240yd	115ft	11	1898	New masonry viaduct
40¼	Gover	230yd	95ft	11	1898	New masonry viaduct
44	Combe St Stephens*	246yd	70ft	12	1886	New masonry viaduct
44½	Fal	190yd	90ft	9	1884	New masonry viaduct
48	Probus	145yd	43ft	12	1871	Embankment
49¼	Tregarne	202yd	83ft	10	1902	New masonry viaduct
49¾	Tregagle	105yd	65ft	5	1902	New masonry viaduct
52¾	Truro	443yd	92ft	21	1904	New masonry viaduct
53¼	Carvedras	323yd	86ft	16	1904	New masonry viaduct

NB: 1) The mileages are those from Cornwall Junction, where the CR joined the SDR's line just to the north of Millbay station in Plymouth. 2) The dimensions are those substantiated by MacDermot and Clinker in their definitive history of the GWR. 3) The use of the word 'new' in the final column denotes that the replacement was built alongside the original structure, instead of on the same alignment. 4) Some of the replacement structures had a different numbr of spans to the original timber structures.

*Original spelling. Present-day spelling is *Coombe*.

permit an interchange of components as and when necessary but, in practice, the individual requirements of each viaduct often varied, and even the slightest variation from the basic design nullified most of the attempts at standardisation.

The piers of the CR's viaducts were spaced at intervals of approximately 66ft and built to a height of 35ft below rail level. Originally, Brunel had planned to space the piers at 40ft intervals, but the need for the utmost economy had dictated a revision of the plans. The tops of the piers were, in most cases, 22ft x 6ft, and each provided a base for a four-strut 'fan' of 2ft x 1ft timbers which sup-

ported the decking. The method of bracing the 'fans' often varied in detail from viaduct to viaduct. In common with the viaducts on the WCR, the Cornwall Railway's structures were built from 'yellow pine' which was preserved by Kyanising (see Willington and Ouseburn Viaducts, 1839).

Along the CR's main line there were 'non-standard' viaducts at Weston Mill, Coombe, Forder, Wivelscombe, Grove, Nottar and St Germans. The mud in the creeks crossed by those seven viaducts was sometimes up to 70ft deep, and this necessitated the use of timber, not only for the superstructures, but also for the piers. The last five of those

Above:
Moorswater Viaduct, rebuilt 1881: The Brunel timber viaduct of 1859 was replaced in 1881 by a new masonry viaduct built alongside the original structure. Some of the piers of the Brunel viaduct have been left to stand, and two are clearly visible on the nearside of the 'new' structure. The eastbound train of china clay wagons is hauled by Class 37 No 37142, the date being 8 July 1981. *Brian Morrison*

viaducts, however, became redundant on 22 March 1908 when a new alignment about ½mile to the north was opened.

The new alignment included three masonry viaducts. The first, Forder Viaduct, was 233yd long, stood 69ft above the high-water mark, and had nine arches; the foundations for the piers were sunk 30ft below the high-water level. The second structure, Nottar Viaduct, spanned the River Lynher by eight arches; it was 210yd long, 63ft high, and the average depth of its piers was 41ft below the high-water mark. The third was St Germans Viaduct, 326yd long, 99ft high, and with the piers of its 13 arches 58ft below the water.

It is a little uncertain who should take the credit for the design of the three viaducts on the new line as, in 1903, there had been several changes among the GWR's key personnel. The former Chief Engineer, James Inglis, had become the new General Manager and had appointed W.W.Grierson as the GWR's Chief Engineer while, simultaneously, W.Y.Armstrong had been appointed as the company's New Works Engineer (a post abolished in 1916 following Armstrong's resignation). Inglis, however, had retained the role of Consulting Engineer.

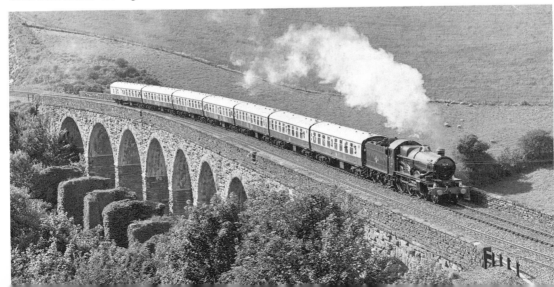

The original all-timber viaducts on the old Saltash–St Germans alignment looked somewhat more flimsy than their stone-and-timber counterparts, and any doubts the public might have had about the safety of those structures were not quelled by an incident at Grove Viaduct. On 6 May 1859, just two days after the public opening of the Cornwall Railway, 4-4-0ST *Elk* and the leading carriage of a three-coach train plummeted over the parapet of the viaduct and finished up almost 30ft below in the muddy banks of the River Lynher, killing the driver, fireman and guard. The ensuing report pointed out that the locomotive and carriage had actually been derailed on the approach to the viaduct and had been carried on to the viaduct purely by momentum, no criticism being made of the viaduct itself.

Brunel considered that the timber viaducts were not long-term propositions; his estimate was that, after ten years or so, maintenance would cost more than £10,000 per annum. The replacement of the viaducts was first considered by Peter Marjary, Brunel's former assistant, who in 1868 was appointed as the Cornwall Railway's Chief Engineer. Until his retirement in 1891, Marjary masterminded the replacement of several of the timber viaducts for the GWR, the programme being completed by his successors.

The conversion of the former Cornwall Railway line to the standard gauge in 1892 enabled the eventual doubling of the entire route between Plymouth and Truro except, of course, for the section across the Royal Albert Bridge. Even before 1892 Marjary's replacement viaducts had been constructed with gauge conversion and doubling in mind. Such was the inevitability of the demise of the broad gauge.

With the replacement of the timber viaduct at Stonehouse Pool by an iron girder structure in 1908, and the new alignment of the line between Forder and St Germans the same year, the last of the Brunel viaducts on the old Cornwall Railway main line were dispensed with. However, those on the ex-CR Falmouth branch (opened 1863) lasted rather longer. As for the replacement viaducts on the main line, only the one at Stonehouse Pool has gone. The closure of the Millbay line in Plymouth on 16 January 1964 brought about the redundancy of Stonehouse Pool Viaduct, and the superstructure was subsequently demolished.

1859: Magpie Viaduct, Nr Horrabridge, Devon

The South Devon Railway's Plymouth–Tavistock branch was engineered by Brunel and, in typical Brunel fashion, the six principal viaducts on the line comprised timber superstructures on stone piers. However, due to Brunel's preoccupation with other matters, including the building of the Royal Albert Bridge, and also his deteriorating health, much of the work was supervised by his assistant, Robert Brereton.

One of the structures on the Tavistock branch was Magpie Viaduct, which was 216yd long and 62ft high. In common with most other Brunel-designed part-timber viaducts, it was eventually

Above:
Grosvenor Bridge, original structure built 1860: The present-day form of Grosvenor Bridge is rather different to that of the original structure, a complete renewal having been undertaken between 1963 and 1967. On 18 March 1989, the 10.50am 'Gatwick Express' approaches Victoria station in the charge of Class 73/2 No 73204 *Stewarts Lane 1860–1985. Brian Morrison*

replaced; a new structure of Staffordshire brick was built alongside and brought into use on 8 June 1902. Another well-known structure on the same branch was **Bickleigh Viaduct**, 167yd long, 123ft high and comprising seven spans; it was replaced by a granite viaduct which was brought into use on 12 March 1893.

The Tavistock branch, which was later extended to Launceston, opened on 22 June 1859, and the section south of Lydford was converted from broad gauge to mixed gauge in May 1876 to give L&SWR trains access to Plymouth. The broad gauge rails were removed in May 1892. The Plymouth–Launceston branch was scheduled for closure on 29 December 1962 and the two final workings set out as planned. However, that month saw the start of one of the worst West Country winters for many years, and both trains became marooned in snowdrifts. The second of the pair finally emerged two days later, and so the official closure date of the line entered the record books as 31 December.

1860: Grosvenor Bridge, London

Designer: John Fowler
Original owner: Victoria Station & Pimlico Railway
Contractor: John Kelk (masonry); Bray & Waddington, Leeds (ironwork)
Cost: £84,000
Type: Girder
Materials: Wrought iron; brick; masonry
Total length: 233yd (plus approaches)
Height of rails: 25ft above high-water
Spans: 4 (plus approaches)
Tracks: 2 (later 7; now 5)

Prior to 1860 no railway line crossed the River Thames in the Inner London area but, between 1860 and 1866, five crossings were made. They were Grosvenor Bridge (then known as Victoria Bridge), opened in 1860, Battersea Bridge (West London Extension Railway), opened 1863, Hungerford Bridge and Blackfriars Bridge of 1864, and Cannon Street Bridge of 1866.

The first of those, Grosvenor Bridge as it later became known, was opened by the Victoria Station & Pimlico Railway, a company supported by the London, Brighton & South Coast and the London, Chatham & Dover Railways for the construction of a 73-chain extension from Stewarts Lane, on the south side of the Thames, to a new terminus on the site of the Grosvenor Canal Basin, on the north side of the river.

It was stipulated that the proposed railway bridge across the Thames should not impede shipping and so, in order to leave the necessary 22ft headroom above high-water, the approaches to the bridge had to be steeply graded to attain the necessary height. Furthermore, although the Thames was some 700ft wide at the proposed crossing point, the siting of river piers had to be carefully considered. It was decided to build a bridge of four spans supported by three piers, the two outer piers being in line with those of the suspension bridge 150yd downstream, with the middle pier in line with the centre of the suspension bridge. This necessitated each of the four spans being 175ft long.

The footings for the piers and abutments were of cement concrete, the upper sections being of brick faced with masonry. The four spans were each formed of six wrought iron arched girders, and the timber decking was supported by a series of cross members. Initially, a double track of mixed gauge rails was laid, one of the intended users of Victoria station being the GWR whose route from Paddington was via an extension of the West London Railway.

The bridge was constructed very quickly, the first stone being laid on 9 December 1859 and public traffic across the bridge into Victoria station commenced on 1 October 1860. London, Chatham & Dover Railway trains used the London, Brighton & South Coast Railway's facilities until its own were opened in August 1862.

With intense usage from three railway companies, the line across the bridge into the station soon required widening, and this was accomplished by the construction of a new bridge alongside the original one on the east (downstream) side. Work on the additional bridge started in February 1865 and was completed in August 1866. The 'new' bridge, which was designed by Sir Charles Fox, was capable of accommodating ten tracks but was laid only with seven, three of which were for use by the LB&SCR, two exclusively by the LC&DR, and the other two were laid with mixed gauge rails for use by either the LC&DR or the GWR. As traffic to and from Victoria station continued to increase, a third bridge became necessary. This was built in 1901.

Perhaps predictably, the trio of bridges did not have an indefinite lifespan. In 1958 it was decided that a complete renewal of the bridge was more cost-effective than the ever-increasing maintenance bills for the three older structures. Work started in May 1963 and was completed by the end of 1967, the task being hampered by the necessity to maintain a full train service throughout and also by the Port of London Authority's requirement that two navigation spans be kept open. The continuity of train services was accomplished by erecting the steelwork for one line over the whole length of the bridge, and moving adjacent tracks sideways, invaluable use being made of the space left by the long-since abandoned approach to Grosvenor Road station (closed 1911).

The new bridge used the existing piers, but they had to be underpinned to take the weight of ballasted track, the original tracks having been carried on flat steel decks. During the work, a 220ft-long service girder was positioned a few feet above rail level to support the old arches while they were being cut up for removal. The new arches were assembled in two parts at a site down-river, floated up to the site, and lifted into position by the service girder, a total of 44 arch girders being erected for the four river spans. The new Grosvenor Bridge is 303yd long and today it carries five tracks (two up, two down and one carriage road) and is used by over 1,300 trains every weekday.

1861: Castle Douglas–Stranraer, Kircudbrightshire/ Wigtownshire

(various structures, see below)

1 Loch Ken Viaduct; 2 Stroan Viaduct; 3 Wee Fleet Viaduct; 4 Big Fleet Viaduct; 5 Graddoch Viaduct; 6 Palnure Viaduct; 7 Cree Viaduct; 8 Bladnoch Viaduct; 9 Glenluce Viaduct
Original owner: Portpatrick Railway
Engineers: Messrs B & E Blair, Edinburgh
Contractors: 1 Thomas Nelson; 2/3/4 McNaughton & Waddell; 6/7 McDonald & Grieve; 8/9 James Falshaw

This region of Southwest Scotland is one of Britain's unpublicised gems. The scenery is truly magnificent, but the area is far from overrun with tourists and, even today, the locals still consider that more than three cars on the same stretch of road (even in summer) constitutes a traffic jam. The area attracted many early railway promoters, but their schemes were aimed neither to attract tourists nor to serve the scattered population. The target was Portpatrick, which offered theoretical potential as a terminal for ferries to and from Ireland. As things transpired, Portpatrick's heyday as an Irish ferry port was shortlived; maritime activities were subsequently concentrated on nearby Stranraer, and the direct rail route between Carlisle and Stranraer via Dumfries & Galloway saw many years of heavy usage.

The Dumfries-Stranraer route was built in two sections. The Castle Douglas & Dumfries Railway opened its line between the towns of its title on 7 November 1859 while, westwards from Castle Douglas, the line to Portpatrick was built by the appropriately-named Portpatrick Railway; it opened as far as Stranraer on 12 March 1861, the extension to Portpatrick itself not being unveiled to the public until 28 August 1862. The entire line between Dumfries and Stranraer was eventually worked as one unit by the Glasgow & South Western Railway.

Between Castle Douglas and Portpatrick, the terrain across which the railway was built presented considerable challenges and, predictably, some substantial engineering works were required. These included nine major viaducts, the first being **Loch**

Ken Viaduct which was built under a separate contract by Thomas Nelson at a cost of £12,289. The structure comprised three main bowstring girder spans supported by stone piers; at the bridging point the loch was some 300ft wide and 36ft deep, the two piers in deep water being constructed inside iron cylinders. On each side of the main viaduct, there were two small approach spans. During the construction of the viaduct, the 1 September 1859 issue of the *Dumfries Courier* contained a report on progress. It concluded: 'This promises to be not only a stupendous but a most elegant erection, and must prove an ornament to the beautiful scenery around the Boat of Rhone, where wood, mountain, water and classic ground unite to form a most interesting landscape'.

Above:
Glenluce Viaduct, 1861: A woodworkers' excursion hauled by 'Black 5' No 45158 crosses Glenluce Viaduct on 28 May 1964. No doubt the coaches will be of interest to rolling stock enthusiasts. *Derek Cross*

Continuing westwards, the Black Water of Dee was crossed by the four-arch **Stroan Viaduct**, the largest span of which was 50ft. Then came **Wee Fleet Viaduct** which carried the line 51ft above the Wee Water of Fleet on nine arches, and **Big Fleet Viaduct**, a 20-arch structure with a maximum height of 70ft above the Big Water of Fleet. The two Fleet viaducts were built of granite, some quarried locally and some obtained from the cuttings which had been excavated along the route.

Loch Ken Viaduct, 1861: A boat train from Stranraer is hauled across Loch Ken Viaduct by 'Black 5' No 44996 on 11 June 1963. *Derek Cross*

In the vicinity of Creetown, there was a low-level four-arch viaduct which carried the railway across Culcronchie Burn. There was also **Graddoch Viaduct**, which had eight sandstone arches, and **Palnure Viaduct**, a three-span girder bridge supported by sandstone piers. The wide, marshy estuary of the River Cree was crossed by **Cree Viaduct**, a girder structure supported by timber piers. During the construction of Cree Viaduct the combined effects of an exceptionally high tide and a proliferation of floating ice resulted in extensive damage to the piers, and although the timber was somehow recovered, the piers had to be completely rebuilt.

Near Newton Stewart, the construction of **Bladnoch Viaduct** presented problems as, during the excavations for the foundations, so much water kept bursting in that pumps had to be used non-stop. To the west, the Water of Luce was crossed by **Glenluce Viaduct**, an eight-arch stone structure 47ft high.

As previously mentioned, the Stranraer–Portpatrick section of the line did not open until August 1862. Its major engineering feature was **Lochans Viaduct** which carried the line across Piltanton Burn; the structure was built of whinstone rubble with 13 arches of brick, each of 36ft 9in span, and a maximum height of 73ft. During the construction of Lochans Viaduct two arches fell but, as the mishap occurred on a Saturday night after the workmen had finished, there were no casualties. A little while after that narrow escape, however, two teenage boys were killed when the timber staging collapsed while they were pulling a cart-load of stone across. It was concluded that heavy falls of rain had loosened the staging.

The Dumfries-Stranraer route, complete with its many bridges and fine viaducts, became known as the 'Port Road' and justifiably gained a firm following among passengers and enthusiasts. It often saw intensive usage, particularly during the war years when heavy trains worked to Stranraer and Cairnryan. Even during the final weeks of the line's life, troop trains were hauled to Stanraer by 'Clan' class Pacifics. The line closed on 14 June 1965, BR preferring to route Stranraer trains circuitously via Ayr. The Stranraer–Portpatrick section, incidentally, had been dispensed with as early as 6 February 1950. Between Castle Douglas and Stranraer, some sections of the old track bed were subsequently used for the widening of the A75 trunk road but substantial parts of the route, particularly those across uninhabited moorland, remain relatively untouched to this day.

1861: Waterside Viaduct, Nr Sedbergh, Cumbria

The line between Ingleton and Tebay opened to goods traffic on 24 August 1861 and to passengers on 16 September. Known over the years as the Lune Valley line, it had been promoted by the Lancaster & Carlisle Railway, but that company had been leased to the LNWR while the line had been under construction.

It was an extremely scenic route, and among its five viaducts was Waterside Viaduct (alternatively

Below:
Waterside Viaduct, 1861: The scenic Lune Valley line lost its passenger services in 1954, but goods workings continued until 1966. Here, Ivatt '4MT' No 43029 is seen crossing the delightful Waterside Viaduct with a Clapham–Tebay pick-up goods on 21 August 1964. *Derek Cross*

known as Firbank or the Lune Viaduct) which carried the railway over the River Lune near Sedbergh. The viaduct was 177yd long, had a maximum height of 100ft, and was on a skew angle of 38°. It comprised a 120ft-long cast iron arch flanked at each end by three arches built of Penrith stone. Its design has usually been credited to the L&CR's engineer, J. E. Errington, who in 1861 became Vice President of the Institution of Civil Engineers.

Elsewhere on the route, the 267yd-long **Ingleton Viaduct** carried the line 80ft above the River Greta on 11 arches, each of 57ft span. The viaduct was built of white sandstone, quarried at Bentham. In theory, the structure provided a link at Ingleton between the L&CR (LNWR) station and that of its arch-enemy, the Midland Railway, but in practice no through trains were run at first, and so passengers had to walk between the two stations.

Initially, the Lune Valley line had been planned as part of an Anglo–Scottish route but, partly due to the friction between the LNWR and the MR, it never developed as such. Its secondary status was effectively sealed in 1875 when the MR opened its nearby Settle–Carlisle line. The Lune Valley line closed to passengers on 1 February 1954 and to goods on 19 June 1966, the track being lifted at the end of 1967, but this author was pleasantly surprised to find Waterside and Ingleton Viaducts still intact when he last visited the area in the summer of 1991.

1861: Barnard Castle–Tebay, County Durham/Cumbria

(9 viaducts, listed below)

Designer: Thomas Bouch
Original owner: South Durham & Lancashire Union Railway
Tracks: 1 (most parts later doubled)

Below:
Tees Viaduct, 1861: Despite its apparent frailty, this 132ft-high viaduct lasted rather longer than some other Thomas Bouch structures. It also outlived the Stainmore line, as it was used by goods trains to and from Middleton-in-Teesdale until 1965. *J. W. Armstrong*

Viaduct	Length	Max Height	No. of Spans	Type	Contractors
Percy Beck	87yd	66ft	8	Stone	D.P.Appleby
Tees	244yd	132ft	7	Lattice girders; stone piers	D. P. Appleby (masonry); Kennaird & Co (ironwork)
Deepdale	247yd	161ft	11	Lattice girders; cast iron columns	D. P. Appleby (masonry) Gilkes Wilson (ironwork)
Mousegill	81yd	106ft	6	Stone	Chambers & Hilton
Belah	347yd	196ft	16	Lattice girders; cast iron columns	Gilkes Wilson
Aitygill	108yd	94ft	9	Stone	Chambers & Hilton
Merrygill	122yd	78ft	9	Stone	Chambers & Hilton
Pod Gill	155yd	84ft	11	Stone	Chambers & Hilton
Smardale	184yd	90ft	14	Stone	Wrigg & Co

The South Durham & Lancashire Union Railway opened its entire 34½-mile line between Barnard Castle and Tebay to mineral traffic on 4 July 1861, a public passenger service of two trains in each direction on weekdays commencing on 8 August. The line was worked from the outset by the Stockton & Darlington Railway and formally absorbed by that company in 1862, but became the property of the North Eastern Railway on 13 July 1863. The S&DR purchased two new Stephenson 4-4-0s for working the line. Named *Brougham* and *Lowther*, they were the first bogie tender engines to be used in Britain and survived to be taken into NER stock, but were cut up in 1888.

The first sod for the Barnard Castle–Tebay line was cut at Kirkby Stephen on 25 August 1857, but work progressed rapidly despite the challenging terrain which the line crossed. The magnificently bleak landscape, however, necessitated a climb to the 1,370ft summit at Stainmore and the construction of several fine viaducts. For the sake of speedy construction, the three longest viaducts on the line were built of iron, their designer being Thomas Bouch who, at the time, was flavour of the month although, in 1879, the fall of his Tay Bridge raised more than a few questions about his methods. Furthermore, it is of interest that the ironwork for Belah and Deepdale Viaducts was supplied and erected by Messrs Gilkes Wilson, the forerunner of the very firm which came in for a great deal of criticism for the way it had built the Tay Bridge.

The cost of the iron viaducts, as given in official records, was: Tees £25,119, Deepdale £20,687 and Belah £31,630. In his superb book *The Stainmore and Eden Valley Railways*, Peter Walton relates that two 'time capsules' were placed in Belah Viaduct at the time of its construction. Beneath the foundation stone laid in November 1857 was buried a bottle containing a florin and a paper giving details of the ceremony. Over a century later, when the viaduct was being dismantled, another docu-ment was found inside the central pier. It was headed: 'Beelah *(sic)* Viaduct on Tuesday the 6th September 1859. A document was deposited in the inside (from the top) of one of the centre columns of the Eighth Pier, to commemorate the hitherto successful efforts of the Workmen engaged in the erection'. The document went on to list the principal staff employed by the contractor, followed by a helping of somewhat unclassical poetry credited to one Charles Davis Brough. Belah Viaduct never lost its status as the highest in England, the claim for the tallest in Britain going to Crumlin Viaduct by a margin of just 4ft. Prior to the construction of Belah Viaduct, incidentally, the course of the river 196ft below had been altered to fit in with the erection of the piers.

During the building of the line the locals lived in trepidation of the railway navvies, whose antics throughout many parts of Britain had become quite infamous. The Chief Constable of Westmorland suggested providing four constables to keep an eye on the navvies, but required that the railway company foot the bill for the constables' wages. The SD&LUR baulked at such an outlay, but grudgingly agreed to pay for just one constable at a cost of £1 1s 0d (£1.5p) per week plus 1s 6d (7½p) per month 'boot allowance' and 1s 0d (5p) per month for lamp oil. Interestingly, the navvies were paid up to 3s 4d (16p) per day while masons received 5s 0d (25p) per day which, on the basis of a six-day week, produced bigger wage packets for the masons than those for the constable.

The line was initially built with a single track, but although the railway company was far-sighted enough to purchase adequate land for eventual doubling, three of the viaducts between Belah and Kirkby Stephen were, perversely, built wide enough for only a single line. When doubling of that section was undertaken in the 1890s, new viaducts were constructed alongside the originals and 'joined' to them to give the appearance of pur-

Left:
Belah Viaduct, 1861: England's tallest railway viaduct had a working life of just over a century. In its later years the Stainmore line, which crossed the viaduct, was regularly worked by Standard 2-6-0s, '2MT' No 78016 being seen at the head of an eastbound train of coke empties with classmate No 78018 providing assistance at the rear. *Cecil Ord Collection*

pose-built double-track structures, but the passing of trains on those three viaducts was never permitted. Ironically, Smardale Viaduct (between Kirkby Stephen and Tebay) had been built to accommodate a double track but never did so.

The Barnard Castle–Kirkby Stephen line became famed as one of Britain's most scenic secondary routes. However, that accolade didn't guarantee a profitable, let alone indefinite, existence and, like many other cross-country lines, it eventually saw many of its passengers defect to the roads. The Kirkby Stephen–Tebay section lost its scheduled passenger services on 1 December 1952, but passenger workings were retained on the Barnard Castle–Kirkby Stephen section. Freight traffic (and a number of excursion workings) nevertheless continued to operate over the entire route.

The complete repainting of Belah Viaduct in 1956 might have implied to some that BR valued the line as a long-term proposition, but that proved to be a naïve notion as closure of the line was announced just three years later. A reprieve was granted, but lasted only until 20 January 1962 when the final scheduled passenger workings ran between Barnard Castle and Kirkby Stephen. Demolition of the famous Belah Viaduct took place during the summer of 1963 but, as partial consolation to those who knew and loved the line and its engineering works, Tees Viaduct at Barnard Castle remained in use until 5 April 1965 for goods services on the branch to Middleton-in-Teesdale, passenger services on that branch having been dispensed with five months earlier.

This author last visited Barnard Castle on a cold and wet summer's day in 1988 and was delighted to find that the stone viaducts at Percy Beck, Aitygill, Merrygill, Pod Gill and Smardale were still standing. According to Peter Walton's excellent 'Stainmore' book, that same situation prevailed in 1992.

1862: Victoria Bridge, Nr Arley, Hereford & Worcester

Today, the name of the Severn Valley Railway is usually associated with the preservation movement. However, the original company of that name was a subsidiary of the West Midlands Railway which, in 1863, was taken over by the GWR. The 'original' SVR opened its line between Hartlebury and Shrewsbury on 1 February 1862, the line being carried across the River Severn near Arley by means of the Victoria Bridge.

The bridge was built of cast iron from the world-famous Coalbrookdale foundry and, at the time, was acknowledged as having the largest cast iron arch in Britain. The world's first cast iron bridge, incidentally, had been built across the Severn at Coalbrookdale in 1777. By the 1860s, however, cast iron was falling out of favour as a material for use in bridge components which would be subjected to bending or tension, and so Victoria Bridge demonstrated a very late use of the medium. After the collapse of a cast iron bridge at Norwood in London in the early 1890s, the Board of Trade effectively banned the use of cast iron for the construction of entire railway bridges.

Victoria Bridge, which was quoted as having a span of 200ft, was designed by John Fowler (1817–1898) and built by the Coalbrookdale Co. The route across the bridge is, of course, now part of a preserved line and the structure underwent major repairs in 1979/80 during which the timber joists were replaced by ones of steel. The listed status of the bridge was acknowledged, and some £22,000 of the £94,000 bill was met by a grant from the Department of the Environment.

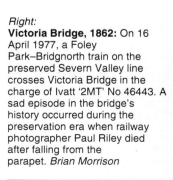

Right:
Victoria Bridge, 1862: On 16 April 1977, a Foley Park–Bridgnorth train on the preserved Severn Valley line crosses Victoria Bridge in the charge of Ivatt '2MT' No 46443. A sad episode in the bridge's history occurred during the preservation era when railway photographer Paul Riley died after falling from the parapet. *Brian Morrison*

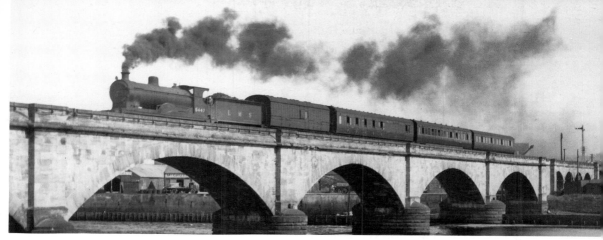

Above:

Ness Viaduct, 1862: One of Joseph Mitchell's finest works was the Ness Viaduct at Inverness. In this splendid picture, '3P' 4-4-0 No 54471 is seen crossing the viaduct with the 3pm Inverness–Tain local in August 1948. Note the 'LMS' inscription on the tender.
W. J. V. Anderson/Rail Archive Stephenson

Towards its northern end, the 'old' SVR was crossed by the Wellington–Much Wenlock line at Buildwas. After leaving Buildwas, the Wellington line crossed the Severn by means of the **Albert Edward Bridge** which was built to the same pattern as the Victoria Bridge. One of the few significant differences between the two structures was that, although both had been designed for a double-track line, the Albert Edward Bridge carried its two tracks on the outer pair of ribs while the Victoria Bridge was laid with only a single track, that being carried on the inner pair of ribs. The Albert Edward Bridge, which opened to traffic on 1 November 1864, is still in use by BR today, its traffic comprising diesel-hauled merry-go-round coal trains for Ironbridge Power Station.

1862: Inverness–Dingwall, Inverness-shire/Ross & Cromarty

(principal structures listed below)

Designer: Joseph Mitchell
Contractor: Deakin & Co
Original owner: Inverness & Ross-shire Railway

The completion of the Inverness & Nairn Railway in 1858 triggered thoughts of a line to the extreme north of Scotland, but the bridging of the Caledonian Canal at Inverness provided a daunting obstacle. In a bout of lateral thinking, one proposal for a railway link to the far north involved the establishment of a steamer service from Nairn to the north side of the Cromarty Firth, from which point one railway would be built to Tain and another to Invergordon with a possible extension to Dingwall. Eventually, though, an 'all-railway' route to the north was agreed upon, the Inverness–Dingwall section being promoted under the banner of the Inverness & Ross-shire Railway.

The line between Inverness and Dingwall was opened on 11 June 1862 and among the engineering works along the route were four particularly noteworthy bridges and viaducts. All were designed by Joseph Mitchell, the engineer who had been responsible for the construction of the Inverness & Nairn Railway. The first sod for the Dingwall line had been cut on 19 September 1860, and the completion time of under two years for a line which incorporated such engineering features as the Ness and Conon Viaducts was a tremendous tribute to Mitchell's engineering expertise and administrative capabilities.

After leaving Inverness station the first notable structure was the Ness Viaduct, which carried the line over the River Ness on five main spans and four approach arches. There were also two cast iron spans (one of 27ft and the other of 35ft) over roads. In his paper read to the members of the Highland Railway Literary Society *circa* 1910, a Mr M. Mackay opined:

Name	Length	Height*	Spans	Cost	Type
Ness Viaduct	223yd#	40ft	5 x 73ft	£13,410	Stone viaduct
			4 x 20ft		
Clachnaharry Bridge	42yd	—	1 x 252ft	£4,718	Swing bridge
Conon Viaduct	180yd	45ft	5 x 73ft	£11,391	Stone viaduct on skew

* Heights are those above the river-beds; # including two minor road-spans.

'The Ness Viaduct alone is proof, if such was needed, of the masterful style in which the construction was attacked and carried on. Nor did our plucky engineer for a moment overlook the economical side of such matters as we find that the splendid viaduct, which carries the line across the Ness, was built for £13,000 as against a cost of £30,000 for the Public Suspension Bridge which crosses the Ness below the Castle.'

The original structure proved remarkably sturdy, and for over a century was treated to little more than routine maintenance despite the sometimes intense usage of the line to the north, particularly during both world wars. Despite its distinguished life, however, the viaduct proved no match for the weather on the night of 6/7 February 1989, when it was washed away by floodwater. The replacement for the demolished viaduct was a functional but decidedly unlovely three-span girder bridge which, cosmetically and aesthetically, was as far removed from Mitchell's original viaduct as was possible. The new bridge was formally opened on 9 May 1990, Malcolm Rifkind (the Minister of Transport) being in the cab of the first DMU to make an official crossing.

Shortly after negotiating the Ness Viaduct, the line crossed the Caledonian Canal at Clachnaharry by means of a swing bridge, an opening bridge having been necessary to provide access to the canal for shipping. The bridge was built on an angle of 65°, and consisted of a pair of girders 126ft in length of which 78ft (from the centre) spanned the canal and the remaining 48ft formed the balance weight. The construction of the masonry foundations was made easier as, at the time they were laid, the canal was empty while undergoing repairs. In the early 1900s the bridge was strengthened, and this enabled the Highland Railway's legendary 'Jones Goods' 4-6-0s to work regularly to Wick. In later years the structure was painted white in order to reflect the heat of the sun and minimise the thermal expansion of the ironwork.

At Beauly, 10 miles to the west of Inverness, the railway crossed the river by means of a timber viaduct which, in 1909, was replaced by a plate girder structure. The 'new' structure was assembled alongside the original one and then rolled into position, the original timbers subsequently being removed. The other important engineering work on the line was the masonry viaduct over the River Conon, a little to the south of Dingwall. The viaduct was built on an angle of 45° to the river, and Mitchell later revealed that an iron bridge had originally been considered a more suitable structure for such an angle. However, Mitchell had calculated that, with good-quality stone being readily available from nearby quarries, the cost of an iron bridge and that of a stone structure would have been comparable. Furthermore, a stone viaduct had the great advantage of requiring less maintenance.

Northwards from Dingwall, the line was opened through to Bonar Bridge on 1 October 1864. The Inverness & Ross-shire Railway had, by then, been absorbed by the Inverness & Aberdeen Junction Railway which, in June 1865, became a founder member of the Highland Railway. Meanwhile the nominally independent Sutherland Railway was working on the section northwards from Bonar Bridge to Helmsdale, which finally opened throughout on 19 June 1871, while the Sutherland & Caithness Railway was incorporated to build the line between Helmsdale and Wick, which opened on 28 July 1874. Predictably, the SR and the S&CR were subsequently absorbed by the Highland Railway.

The construction of the route between Dingwall and Wick necessitated extensive engineering works and numerous bridges and viaducts. Arguably the

Below:
Oykel Viaduct, 1868: To the north of Inverness, the line to Wick was carried across the Kyle of Sutherland by the distinctive Oykel Viaduct. An unidentified Class 24 is seen crossing the viaduct on 11 April 1973 with a southbound train of ballast empties. *Peter W. Robinson*

Above:

Marple Viaduct, 1862: The Peak Forest Canal was (and still is) carried alongside Marple Viaduct by means of an impressive aqueduct. Here, 'Black 5' No 44688 is seen crossing the viaduct on 20 April 1966 with the 5.30pm Sheffield Midland to Manchester Central working. *John R. Hillier*

most distinctive viaduct on the line was **Oykel Viaduct**, which was opened to traffic on 13 April 1868 and carried the railway across the Kyle of Sutherland; it consisted of a 280ft lattice girder span and five approach arches built of stone, each with a 30ft span. The viaduct was strengthened with additional ironwork in 1912/13, and this at last permitted the HR's 'Castle' class 4-6-0s to work through to Wick. The first member of that class to visit Wick was No 143 (later LMSR No 14678) *Gordon Castle*, which made the trip on 23 May 1913.

Just beyond the northern end of the viaduct was Invershin station and, in 1871, a platform was opened at Culrain, near the southern end. The two stopping places were only 772yd apart but each served very different communities and, before the opening of Culrain platform, the only viable alternative means of communication between the two was via a road bridge between Ardgay and Bonar Bridge - a detour of around five miles. Predictably, the rail link between Culrain and Invershin proved popular and the platform at the former became a permanent fixture in the public timetables from 1873. Prior to 1917, a third-class single ticket between the two stations cost ½d (¼p), the lowest fare on the Highland Railway.

The Inverness–Wick route retained an air of individuality until well after the Grouping, and it was not until the late 1930s that the dull and dreary LMSR 'Black 5s' started to oust the charismatic (but admittedly ageing) ex-Highland Railway steeds from the line. In later years the line was one of the first in Britain to be dieselised, BR's prime

reason being to avoid the high cost of transporting locomotive coal to the farthest extremities of its network. The route's importance as a vital means of communication across difficult terrain ensured its future, and apart from the hiatus following the destruction of the Ness Viaduct in 1989 it has continued to serve the community well.

1862: Marple Viaduct, Marple, Gtr Manchester

The line between Hyde and Compstall opened on 5 August 1862. It followed the valley of the River Goyt for much of its length and, near Compstall, the railway was carried by a viaduct which was parallel to an aqueduct. The aqueduct had been built between 1796 and 1801 to carry the Peak Forest Canal over the River Goyt, and the two impressive structures in such close proximity made for a very pleasing sight. The railway line across Marple Viaduct is still in everyday use. The aqueduct, incidentally, was restored in the early 1960s at a cost of some £50,000 after having gained the status of a listed structure.

1862: Usk Bridge, Abergavenny, Gwent

The Abergavenny–Brynmawr section of what became known as the 'Heads of the Valleys' line opened on 29 September 1862; it opened with only a single track, but had been built for a double-track, doubling being undertaken in the mid-1870s. At Abergavenny, the railway bridge across the River Usk replaced an old tramroad bridge and, over the years, the seemingly fragile railway bridge accommodated some of the heaviest locomotives which the LNWR could offer. The line was closed to traffic on 6 January 1958, but a spur to Brecon Road goods depot in Abergavenny survived until 5 April 1971. On a visit to the site in 1988 the red sandstone abutments of the Wye Bridge were still clearly evident, and the names of the engineer of the line (John Gardner) and the contractor who had built the bridge (William McCormick), which had been carved on each abutment, were still discernible.

Below:

Usk Bridge, 1862: The 'Heads of the Valleys' line between Abergavenny and Merthyr was one of the more charismatic outposts of the LNWR empire. On 11 September 1952 'G2a' class 0-8-0 No 49226 was photographed crossing the Usk Bridge, having just left Abergavenny Junction with the evening freight for Brynmawr. *Philip M. Alexander*

1863: Monsal Dale Viaduct, Monsal Dale, Derbyshire

The laboriously-titled Manchester, Buxton, Matlock & Midlands Junction Railway opened its line between Ambergate and Rowsley in June 1849. The company's intention was to continue to Manchester, but it was the Midland Railway which ultimately completed the line.

Under MR auspices, the Rowsley–Buxton section opened to public traffic on 1 June 1863. For much of the way it passed through magnificent Derbyshire scenery, and one of the best-known of its many engineering works was Monsal Dale Viaduct. The five-span viaduct was 111yd long and stood some 75ft above the River Wye; the approach embankment was formed from spoil which had been excavated from Headstone Tunnel at the eastern end of the viaduct. It is believed that the viaduct was designed by F.Campion, the Resident Engineer during the early part of the line's construction.

Other structures of note along the route included four almost identical bridges, one of which was **Topley Pike Bridge**. Built of wrought iron girders, and with its piers founded on stone bases, its elegant arches were replaced in 1932 by straight steel girders.

1863: Craigellachie-Nethy Bridge, Morayshire/Banffshire/Inverness-shire

(three principal structures)

The Great North of Scotland Railway's expansion in the 1860s was largely undertaken by independent companies in which it had a significant shareholding. The Keith & Dufftown and the Strathspey Railways were two such concerns, developing the scenic route through Scotland's main whisky producing area initially to a terminus near Abernethy (renamed Nethy Bridge in 1867).

The Speyside line opened as far as Aberlour on 1 July 1863, Abernethy being reached ten days later. In August 1866 the line was extended to Boat of Garten. Simultaneously with the opening of the line to Aberlour, the Morayshire Railway unveiled its extension across the Spey at Craigellachie, this new line providing not only a connection with the Speyside line, but also an alternative route between Keith and Elgin.

The Craigellachie–Abernethy route incorporated three particularly noteworthy bridges, all of which crossed the River Spey. The first of these, **Craigellachie Bridge**, comprised a 200ft-long lattice girder span across the main channel of the river and three plate girder spans, each 57ft long, on the west (Morayshire) side. The masonry piers supporting the main span were founded to a depth of 14ft.

On the Strathspey section itself, **Carron Bridge** carried not only the railway, but also a minor road over the Spey. The bridge was a graceful cast iron structure. Built by MacKinnon & Co of Aberdeen, its main span was 150ft long and was formed of three substantial ribs, cast in seven segments; it was flanked on each side by a single ashlar arch. Six miles farther south, **Ballindalloch Viaduct** (as it was originally known) carried the line over the Spey once again. The 'viaduct' was, in fact, a lattice girder bridge similar to that at Craigellachie - it had a main span of 198ft and smaller arches at each end, the track being some 20ft above water level. The Great North's civil engineer at the time of the Strathspey line's construction was Alexander Gibb, but it is uncertain whether the design of the bridges should be credited to him or the respective builders.

The Strathspey line lost its passenger services on 18 October 1965, total closure taking effect on 4 November 1968. Craigellachie Bridge was subsequently dismantled, but the other two still stand to this day. Carron Bridge, which was the last cast iron bridge in Scotland to carry rail traffic, remains open to road traffic, while Ballindalloch 'Viaduct' now forms part of the 'Speyside Way' public footpath. The latter still bears at each end the large maker's plates proclaiming 'G.MacFarlane, Engineer, Dundee 1863'.

Above:
Penryn Viaduct, 1863: This official picture was taken on 6 November 1924, the year after the timber viaduct had been replaced by the adjacent embankment which carried the Truro–Falmouth branch on a new alignment. *British Railways*

1863: Truro–Falmouth, Cornwall

(eight viaducts, listed below)

Original owner: Cornwall Railway
Designer: Isambard Kingdom Brunel/R. P. Brereton
Type: Timber viaducts
Tracks: 1

The construction of the Cornwall Railway's 11¾-mile long broad gauge line between Truro and Falmouth started in 1853. However, the CR was not the most wealthy of companies and, in 1854, work ceased as the company's limited funds were channelled into the Plymouth–Truro section. Work on the Falmouth section recommenced in 1861 with the financial assistance of the GWR, the Bristol & Exeter and the South Devon Railways, and the line

eventually opened to passenger traffic on 24 August 1863. These days, the Truro–Falmouth line is usually referred to as a branch, but the CR originally regarded the entire Plymouth–Truro–Falmouth route as a continuous main line.

As with the Plymouth–Truro section, motive power for the Falmouth section was initially supplied by the contractors, Messrs Evans & Geach, the South Devon Railway taking over in July 1866. The ever-impecunious Cornwall Railway was formally absorbed by the GWR in 1876, and the Falmouth line was converted to the standard gauge in May 1892.

Miles	Name	Length	Height	Spans	Replaced	Replaced By
¾	Penwithers	271yd	90ft	13	1926	Embankment
3¼	Ringwell	122yd	70ft	6	1933	Embankment
3½	Carnon	252yd	96ft	12	1933	New masonry viaduct
5	Perran	113yd	56ft	6	1927	New masonry viaduct
6	Ponsanooth	215yd	139ft	10	1930	New masonry viaduct
6½	Pascoe	130yd	70ft	7	1923	New embankment
8	Penryn	114yd	83ft	6	1923	New embankment
8¼	College Wood	318yd	100ft	15	1934	New masonry viaduct

NB: 1) The mileages are from Truro station.

2) The dimensions are those substantiated by MacDermot and Clinker.

3) The use of the word 'new' in the final column denotes that the replacement was built alongside the original structure, instead of on the same alignment.

4) The replacement viaducts did not necessarily have the same number of spans as the original timber viaducts.

College Wood Viaduct, original viaduct of 1863 replaced in 1934: The last Brunel-inspired timber viaduct to carry a passenger line was rendered redundant in July 1934. College Wood Viaduct, on the Falmouth branch, was superseded by a masonry structure on a modified alignment. This picture of the old and the new was taken on 30 January 1934, just six months before the new viaduct was brought into use. *British Railways*

The engineer in charge of constructing the Falmouth line was Robert Brereton, who had succeeded Brunel after the latter's death in 1859. For the line, Brereton perpetuated the basic pattern of Brunel viaducts, the structures having masonry piers spaced either 58-59ft or 65-66ft apart, and all-timber superstructures with four-strut 'fans' to provide additional strengthening for the decking. The timber was, once again, Brunel's old favourite of 'yellow pine' which had been preserved by Kyanising. The viaducts on the Falmouth line were among the longest-lasting Brunel-style timber structures. Carnon and College Wood Viaducts were inspected in 1887 with a view to replacing their timber superstructures with wrought iron girders but, apart from minor decay in a few of the timbers, the viaducts were considered sound. Similarly, the inspection of the other branch viaducts in the same year revealed masonry replacements to be unnecessary.

The inspection and repair of the lofty timber viaducts involved considerable athleticism, not to mention pluck. Because of the height of the viaducts, ladders were no use and so the favoured method was described in the *GWR Magazine* of March 1921:

'...it has become the custom to use ropes, by means of which the men sling themselves. A bowline loop is made in the end of a 2½ inch rope, whilst the other end is placed over the viaduct handrail. Using this loop as a seat, the man lowers himself to the required point of inspection, having reached which, the loose end is made fast round his body, remaining in that position as long as is necessary. Upon completion of his task, the man would be hauled by his comrades to the top, to another point of inspection, or lowered to the ground.

'So expert are the older men in rope work that it is nothing unusual for one to swing himself sideways a distance of several feet whilst suspended in the air, returning to his old position in a similar manner when necessary. Needless to say, this expert efficiency is only obtained after considerable practice, and is not included in the curriculum of the viaduct gang recruits.'

On the Falmouth line, the replacement programme did not start until 1923 when Pascoe and Penryn Viaducts were superseded by embankments on new alignments. Penwithers and Ringwell Viaducts were similarly replaced in 1926 and 1933 respectively, albeit on the original alignments with the earth of the embankments enveloping the old masonry piers. The last viaduct on the Falmouth line to be replaced was College Wood, a new masonry viaduct being built on the down side of the original one. The new College Wood Viaduct came into use in July 1934, thereby rendering the 71-year-old part-timber structure redundant.

It has often been stated that the original College Wood Viaduct was the last Brunel timber viaduct to remain in regular use on a passenger-carrying line, but that claim to fame requires a little qualification.

Right
Ponsanooth Viaduct, 1930: The original part-timber viaduct was replaced in 1930, the piers of the old structure being left to stand - they are visible through the arches of the replacement viaduct. A diesel multiple-unit crosses the viaduct on a Falmouth–Truro working on 9 April 1977. *P. H. Wells*

The original route to Falmouth had, indeed, been surveyed by Brunel, but when construction work finally commenced, the line was built on an alternative alignment as specified by Brereton. The basic Brunel design was perpetuated by Brereton for College Wood Viaduct, but whether the credit for the viaduct should go to Brunel or Brereton remains a matter for debate. A further fly in the proverbial ointment is provided by the Brunel-designed Loughor Viaduct, on the South Wales main line, as the presence of some original timbers in its piers cannot be totally discounted.

Perhaps the final word on the distinctive Cornish timber viaducts should be taken from the *GWR Magazine* of March 1921:

'Imposing in appearance, cleverly designed, simply constructed to facilitate subsequent maintenance, comparatively cheap in original cost, the old Cornish viaducts have done their bit as silent units from the inception and throughout the subsequent growth of the Great Western system as we know it today.'

1863: Dunkeld–Forres, Perthshire/Inverness-shire/Morayshire

(various bridges and viaducts, principal ones listed below)

Designer: Joseph Mitchell
Original owner: Inverness & Perth Junction Railway

The Inverness & Perth Junction Railway provided something of an object lesson for other railway companies. While countless companies throughout Britain struggled to build lines across somewhat tame terrain, the I&PJR took less than two years to construct its 104-mile line through some of the more inhospitable parts of the Scottish Highlands. The line between Dunkeld (16 miles to the north of Perth) and Forres (25 miles to the east of Inverness) opened throughout on 9 September 1863. It was a remarkable achievement.

Name	Length	Height*	Spans	Cost	Description
Dalgusie	172yd	67ft	1 x 210ft 1 x 141ft	£20,395	Lattice girder; stone piers and abutments
Ballinling	117yd	36ft	2 x 122ft 2 x 35ft	£11,156	Lattice girder on cast iron piers
Logierait	140yd	49ft	2 x 137ft 2 x 41½ft	£13,772	Lattice girder on cast iron piers
Killiecrankie	169yd	54ft	10 x 35ft	£5,720	Stone viaduct
Blair Atholl	85yd	40ft	1 x 150ft	£6,500	Lattice girder; stone abutments
Calvine	91yd	55ft	1 x 80ft 2 x 40ft	£5,100	Stone viaduct
Dulnain	27yd	27ft	1 x 80ft	£3,298	Lattice girder; stone abutments
Dunphail	159yd	106ft	7 x 45ft	£10,231	Stone viaduct

* Heights are those above river-beds.

Killiecrankie Viaduct, 1863: A viaduct at the Pass of Killiecrankie was constructed in preference to extensive earthworks and substantial retaining walls. The resultant structure was, in true Joseph Mitchell fashion, extremely elegant, the mock turrets being added out of deference to the local Laird, the Duke of Atholl. As evidenced by this picture, the railway leaves the viaduct and immediately enters a tunnel, the entrance to which also has mock crenellations. *Ian Allan Library*

At Dunkeld, a connection was made with a line from Perth while, at Forres, the line linked up with the Inverness & Nairn Railway, thereby providing a new direct route between Perth and Inverness. The I&NR subsequently merged with the Inverness & Aberdeen Junction Railway which, in June 1865, joined forces with the Inverness & Perth Junction Railway to form the Highland Railway. One of Britain's most charismatic railway companies was born.

The Dunkeld–Forres line included a total of eight viaducts, 126 bridges over streams and 119 over roads but, somewhat surprisingly, only two tunnels. The engineer responsible for the works was Joseph Mitchell, the same gentleman who had engineered the impressive bridges and viaducts on the Inverness–Nairn–Forres–Keith line which had opened throughout in 1858.

Starting from the south, the first bridge of note was across the River Braan, a little to the north of Dunkeld. The bridge was built of stone and had a single span flanked by extensive wing-walls and was decorated with turrets complete with mock arrow slits. The pseudo-crenellations were a feature of many Scottish bridges and viaducts, as landowners whose holdings were crossed by railways often insisted on such embellishments. The power and influence of Scottish Lairds was not to be underestimated, the landowner in the case of the railway bridge across the Braan being the Duke of Atholl.

Continuing northwards, the River Tay was crossed at Dalgusie by means of a wrought iron lattice girder bridge supported by stone piers and having stone abutments. Similar lattice girder bridges crossed the River Tummel at Ballinling and the River Tay at Logierait, but these were supported by 8ft-diameter cylindrical piers of cast iron. The piers were weighted down by 3ft of concrete which was topped with masonry rubble filled with Portland cement. The provision of additional side spans was a precaution against floodwater.

The route through the Pass of Killiecrankie necessitated the construction of a 10-arch stone-built viaduct (with the obligatory mock turrets) which led directly into a tunnel 128yd long. Joseph Mitchell later wrote about the difficulties encountered with this section of the line:

Above:
Blair Atholl Bridge, 1863: Joseph Mitchell's bridge
across the River Tilt at Blair Atholl was yet another
stylish piece of design work from the much-underrated
engineer. The elaborate portals at each end of the
bridge are something of a giveaway that the land on
which the structure was built was owned by the Duke of
Atholl. *Bucknall Collection/Ian Allan Library*

'At the Pass of Killiecrankie the banks proved so
precipitous that the line had to be supported by
retaining walls to the extent of 690yd and an average height of 26ft, the extreme height of one being
55ft; and in order to carry the railway at the nar-
rowest point in the pass, where the precipice closes
in, as it were, on either side, and affords scarcely
any additional space beyond that occupied by the
channel of the river, instead of supporting the line
by breast-walls, it was deemed prudent to construct
a viaduct of ten arches 60ft above the river.'

Just to the south of Blair Atholl a wrought iron lattice girder bridge carried the railway over the River
Tilt. In deference to the Duke of Atholl, a stone
portal complete with mock fortifications was built
at each end of the bridge. As Joseph Mitchell tact-
fully pointed out at a later date, '...it has been made
somewhat more ornate than was otherwise necessary'. A little further north near Struan was the celebrated Calvine Viaduct which had three arches, a
central one of 80ft span flanked by two of 40ft
span, the central arch crossing not only the River
Garry but also a stone bridge which carried the
Rannoch road. Once again the viaduct was finished
off with decorative turrets. The unusual practice of
building a viaduct over and above an existing road
bridge had been necessary largely because the railway company had failed to suggest any alternative
crossing of the River Garry which had met with the
approval of the Duke of Atholl.

The line through Struan was doubled at the turn
of the century and the striking appearance of
Calvine Viaduct took a severe blow when a lattice
girder bridge was added to one side of the structure
to carry the additional line. Admittedly, the presence of the skew bridge carrying the road underneath the railway viaduct presented a difficult problem for the engineers when the doubling was
undertaken, but the way the task was tackled
resulted in a real case of 'beauty and the beast'.
Towards the northern end of the line, the River
Dulnain was crossed between Broomhill and
Grantown-on-Spey by means of a small but imposing lattice girder bridge. A little farther north, Dun-
phail Viaduct carried the railway across the deep
valley of the River Divie.

The strength (or alleged lack of it) of some of the
Highland Railway's bridges and viaducts resulted
in one of the better-known sagas of British locomotive history. In 1914 a batch of six new 'River'
class 4-6-0s was ordered from Hawthorn Leslie to
specifications laid down by the HR's Locomotive
Superintendent, Frederick Smith. When the first of
the 'Rivers' was delivered it was found to weigh
72ton 7cwt, some six tons more than had been originally intended. The HR's Chief Civil Engineer,
Alexander Newlands, refused to accept such a
heavy locomotive for regular work over the company's bridges, and pointed the proverbial finger of
accusation at Frederick Smith. Newlands and Smith
were not exactly the best of chums and, as the former had a closer relationship with the board than
the latter, the dispute became a sort of 'Newlands
versus Smith' contest. The outcome was that Smith
resigned and the two locomotives which had, by
then, been delivered were sold to the Caledonian
Railway.

Those who supported Smith had been heard to
comment that 'it was a poor civil engineer whose
bridges couldn't take a little extra axle weight',

although that comment was aimed at Newlands and not the designer of the bridges, Joseph Mitchell. In Mitchell's day, of course, locomotive and train weights were somewhat lighter, and his bridges were more than adequate for contemporary needs. It later came to light that the all-important hammer-blow of the 'Rivers' was, in fact, less than that of other HR locomotives. Smith was eventually vindicated, albeit rather too late in the day, as, from 1927, the 'Rivers' were put to work on former HR lines and acquitted themselves very well. Trials had been conducted beforehand, and the only significant upgrading of the permanent way which had been deemed necessary had been the strengthening of two or three culverts and a degree of overdue attention to the bridge at Dalgusie.

Over the years, the Perth–Inverness route became renowned as one of the most difficult in Britain to operate; severe gradients, harsh winter weather, a predominance of single-track and huge seasonal fluctuations in traffic all added to the problems. With the completion in 1898 of the cut-off route between Aviemore and Inverness, the Aviemore–Forres section of the original line was effectively relegated to secondary status. Perhaps predictably, that section was axed during the cuts of the post-Beeching era, the date of closure being 18 October 1965. Today the Perth–Inverness route is still a vital means of communication between Central Scotland and the north and it offers one of the most scenic main-line journeys anywhere on BR's network.

1864: Charing Cross Bridge, London

Designer: Sir John Hawkshaw
Original owner: Charing Cross Railway
Contractor: Cochrane & Co, Dudley
Cost: £180,000
Type: Lattice beam
Materials: Wrought iron; cast iron
Total length: 450yd (river section only)
Max height of rails: 31ft above high-water
Spans: 9
Tracks: 4 (later 6)

The second railway company to build a line across the River Thames in Inner London was the South Eastern Railway. A new and enthusiastic board, which had taken control of the SER in 1855, chose to combat their energetic and highly competitive rival, the London, Chatham & Dover Railway, by

Below:
Charing Cross Bridge, 1864: Although the bridge has significant historical value, it is neither the prettiest structure known to mankind, nor the easiest to photograph. This picture of Class 202 unit No 1014 arriving at Charing Cross with the 10.44am ex-Hastings was taken on 14 September 1977, two years before the bridge girders were renewed. *Brian Morrison*

extending the SER line from London Bridge station across the Thames to Charing Cross. The 1¼mile extension is reputed to have been the most expensive piece of railway building in history.

The new line was promoted under the banner of the Charing Cross Railway, and work began in February 1860. A total of 17 iron bridges and two iron viaducts were required, one of the viaducts being the 135yd long structure over Borough Market; as if those engineering features weren't enough, the railway company had to overcome ferocious opposition before acquiring possession of the necessary land.

On the immediate approach to the new terminus at Charing Cross, the railway bridge across the River Thames replaced a footbridge. The footbridge had been designed by Brunel and had opened to the public in May 1845; although known officially as the Hungerford & Lambeth Suspension Footbridge, it was more commonly referred to as Charing Cross Bridge. The railway company's Act of Incorporation had authorised: '...the appropriation, alteration, and adaptation to the objects of the undertaking of the Charing Cross Bridge, and either wholly or partly the discontinuance of its present use by the public as a passenger thoroughfare and the providing of a substitute thereof'. The suspension chains and ironwork of the old footbridge, which amounted to some 1,040 tons of materials, were sold for £5,000 and reused in the completion of the famous Clifton Suspension Bridge which carried a road across the Avon Gorge in Bristol. The Clifton bridge was also designed by Brunel but, at the time of his death in 1859, was unfinished.

Charing Cross station and the new railway bridge across the Thames opened to local traffic on 11 January 1864, main-line services commencing on 1 May. On 1 August the Charing Cross Railway was formally absorbed by the South Eastern Railway. The bridge incorporated some 5,000 tons of wrought iron and 2,000 tons of cast iron, and included a 7ft 6in-wide pedestrian walkway on each side. A toll of ½d (¼p) was charged to pedestrians, but the toll was abolished in 1877 and the SER was awarded £98,540 for loss of revenue. Even allowing for the SER's obligation to maintain the walkway and keep it well-lit, it was rather hefty compensation. In 1888, an iron staircase was erected at the cost of £1,901 to give access to the walkway from the Victoria Embankment.

There was a disruption in the usage of the bridge between 5 December 1905 and 19 March 1906 when Charing Cross station was closed after a wall had collapsed and had brought down the roof. Three people had been killed at the station and another three in the adjacent Avenue Theatre where part of the debris had fallen through the roof.

At first there were four tracks across the bridge, but two more were added during the widening of 1877; during the widening, the walkway on the south side of the bridge was dispensed with. Originally, a 130-lever signalbox was mounted on a gantry above the tracks at the western end of the bridge, but that was eventually superseded after the introduction of electric services on 28 February 1926; the replacement overhead signalbox contained a power frame with 107 levers.

After the Grouping the Southern Railway considered truncating the line on the south bank of the river and doing away with Charing Cross Bridge but, of course, the proposals were not acted upon. In 1927, it was proposed to build a double-deck steel bridge which provided space for six railway tracks on the lower (existing) deck with a 30ft-wide roadway and two footways above. Again, however, the proposal was rejected. In subsequent years the interruptions to traffic due to bridge works were minimal, but a major hiatus was caused in 1979 when the bridge's original wrought iron girders were replaced by steel girders. The work, which lasted for six months and cost some £3,000,000, necessitated the diversion of some 400 trains to other stations every weekday. Today, Charing Cross Bridge is a vital component in the network of lines serving Southeast England, although traditionalists might argue that the demise of steam traction at Charing Cross station on 12 June 1961 took away much of the gloss.

1864: Knucklas Viaduct, Knucklas, Powys

One of the very small band of cross-country routes to have escaped the axe is the delightful ex-LNWR Central Wales line. The nature of the terrain crossed by the line necessitated a considerable amount of engineering expertise, and partly due to the slowness of the work, the order of the day was a series of piecemeal openings. The Knucklas–Penybont section opened to goods traffic in October 1864 and to passengers on 10 October 1865. It included Knucklas Viaduct, just to the west of the station of the same name. The 13-arch viaduct, which crossed the Heyope Valley, was built of stone and had castellated embellishments. It was 190yd long and 75ft above ground level.

The Llanwrtyd Wells–Llandovery section of the line opened on 8 October 1868 to complete the through route from Craven Arms. That section included **Cynghordy Viaduct**, built of sandstone with its 18 arches lined with brick. It was 283yd long and carried the line at a maximum height of 102ft above the Bran Valley on a 26-chain curve.

Above:
Knucklas Viaduct, 1864: High over Knucklas village the Knighton banker, '8F' No 48478, assists with the 3.15pm Class H goods from Shrewsbury (Coleham) to Llandeilo Junction on 11 April 1961. The elegant viaduct is still in everyday use, albeit with less-charismatic forms of traction. *Ian Allan Library*

Below:
Cynghordy Viaduct, 1868: A three-car diesel multiple-unit crosses Cynghordy Viaduct, on the Llandovery–Sugar Loaf section of the Central Wales line. *British Railways*

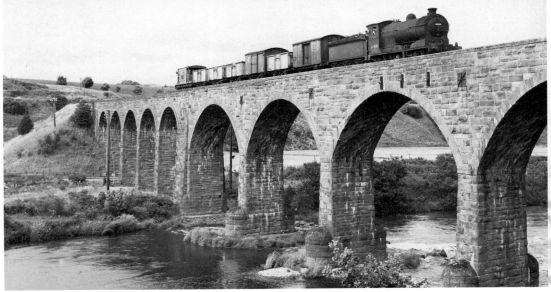

Above:
North Water Viaduct, 1865: With complete justification, the North Water Viaduct on the Montrose–Inverbervie branch now has the status of a listed structure. Passenger services on the branch ceased in 1951 and freight services were withdrawn in 1966. The daily return freight working of 13 July 1961 was entrusted to 'J37' class 0-6-0 No 64598. *M. Pope*

1865: North Water Viaduct, Nr Montrose, Angus

The line along the coast from Montrose to Inverbervie was promoted, somewhat misleadingly, as part of a potential through route to Aberdeen, but was ultimately built as a branch which ran no further north than Inverbervie itself. The branch opened on 1 November 1865 and, between Montrose and St Cyrus, it crossed the North Water of Esk by means of a handsome viaduct. The structure, which was some 200yd long and around 75ft high, had 12 arches, the five over the river being larger than the rest. Built on a curve and on a rising gradient, it was constructed entirely of stone, ie without any brick lining for its arches.

A passenger service was maintained on the branch until 1 October 1951, a daily freight working continuing until total closure on 23 May 1966. On the day before closure a steam-hauled special was laid on, and it was packed to the proverbial gills. In 1990 ScotRail applied to demolish the disused viaduct but the structure was saved by its status as a listed building, its river piers being treated to repairs in 1992/93.

1866: Cannon Street Bridge, London

Designer: Sir John Hawkshaw
Original owner: South Eastern Railway
Cost: £193,000
Type: Lattice beam
Materials: Wrought iron; cast iron
Total length: 235yd
Max height of rails: 35ft above high-water
Spans: 5
Tracks: 5 (later 10)

The South Eastern Railway's first crossing of the River Thames was by means of Charing Cross Bridge, which opened to traffic in 1864. Just two years later the company unveiled its line into Cannon Street station on the north bank of the Thames, the immediate approach to the new station also being by means of a bridge across the river. Like Charing Cross Bridge, that at Cannon Street was designed by the SER's Chief Engineer, Sir John Hawkshaw.

Cannon Street Bridge had five spans supported on four groups of cast iron piers in the river. Each group of piers comprised four columns which were 18ft in diameter at the base and 12ft diameter at the low-water mark. The columns were sunk to a firm bed of London clay and filled with concrete up to the level of the river-bed, above which they were lined with brickwork. The total weight of the 16 columns was 10,500 tons. The superstructure consisted of free-span plate girders for the two shore spans, and continuous plate girders for the three middle spans. The piers and superstructure of the

Above:
Cannon Street Bridge, 1866: As with some of the other railway bridges across the Thames, Cannon Street Bridge was not exactly the most photogenic subject. However, riverside activities often provided a useful distraction, that role being filled here by PS *Crested Eagle* which is taking on passengers at Old Swan Pier. The sight of four steam locomotives on the railway bridge at the same time is very much a thing of the past, this picture having been taken *circa* 1930. *R. S. Clarke/Rail Archive Stephenson*

bridge were ornately finished, the decorative cast iron work on the superstructure allegedly accounting for some 1,100 tons of its 5,300 tons total weight. It has been suggested that Hawkshaw felt obliged to add the embellishments due to the bridge's proximity to the famous landmark of St Paul's Cathedral. Because of the clearances required underneath the bridge, Cannon Street station was built on arches which were intended largely for letting. The floor area of the 'cellars' amounted to 140,000sq ft, and some 27 million bricks were used in the construction.

Although Cannon Street Bridge was given the all-clear by the Board of Trade inspector, Col Yolland, in July 1866, it was not opened to traffic until the station and the spur from London Bridge were completed on 1 September. Initially, the bridge was used by 525 trains each weekday, practically all services between London Bridge and Charing Cross stations calling at Cannon Street station *en route*. For working the shuttle services between Cannon Street and Charing Cross, seven 0-4-4Ts were built for the SER in 1866 at a total cost of £16,800; they were constructed at Canada Works, Birkenhead, to a James Cudworth design and were given Nos 235-241. The last of the seven survived only until 1890.

Cannon Street Bridge had a narrow walkway on each side, but it is believed that it was not originally for public use. In February 1872, however, a proper public footpath across the bridge was opened; it extended from Dowgate Hill (on the north side) to Clink Street (on the south), and a toll of ½d (¼p) was charged. The footpath was, in fact, open only between 5am and 9pm, and was grandiosely described by the *South London Press* on 17 February 1872 as '...a rival to the footway tunnel under the Thames from the Tower to Southwark'.

Because of the ever-increasing traffic into Cannon Street station, it became necessary to widen the bridge to accommodate 10 tracks instead of five. This was undertaken between 1886 and 1893, and increased the width of the structure from 66ft 8in to almost 120ft which, it was alleged, resulted in the widest railway bridge in the world. To support the wider bridge, the formation of each pier was increased from four to six columns, the new columns being added on the upstream side. By 1900 the bridge was used by 783 trains daily, but from January 1917 that figure dropped when the practice of routeing Charing Cross trains via Cannon Street ceased.

Between 1909 and 1913 the bridge was substantially strengthened at a cost of £99,000. Further strengthening work was undertaken prior to the installation of a completely new track layout at Cannon Street station in 1926, the preliminary inspection in 1921 having revealed no evidence whatsoever of settlement in the bridge piers, even after 55 years of intensive use. The new track layout was installed between 3pm on Saturday, 5 June 1926 and 4am on Monday the 28th, during which period Cannon Street station was closed to traffic. Over 1,000 men had worked on a three-shift basis to permit the commencement of electric services from Cannon Street later on in the morning of Monday, 28 February. The new layout was controlled by a 243-lever signalbox; the original box, which had initially housed just 67 levers, had been on a gantry above the rails at the northern end of the bridge but was demolished after the new box had become operational.

Further major track works necessitated the closure of Cannon Street station and the bridge between 2 August and 9 September 1974. This was in connection with a huge scheme to remodel and resignal some 150 miles of line on the approaches to London Bridge, and resulted in Cannon Street Bridge being relaid with just five tracks. The station itself had, during the previous decade, been rebuilt on two levels. By then, the 'economies' of the preceding years had taken their toll on the once-elegant Cannon Street Bridge, some of the ornamentation being almost hidden under functional iron straps, and the railings on the walkway having been enclosed by unlovely corrugated iron sheeting. A degree of restoration work was undertaken in 1986, during which the distinctive towers at the bridge end of the station (which, incidentally, had been built to accommodate water reservoirs) received long-overdue attention.

1867: Barmouth Bridge, Barmouth, Gwynedd

Designer and contractor: Thomas Savin
Original owner: Cambrian Railways
Type: Trestle and drawbridge
Materials: Timber; wrought iron
Total length: 830yd
Max height of rails: 15ft above high-water
Spans: 121
Tracks: 1

The construction of Barmouth Bridge, which crossed the 800yd-wide Mawddach Estuary in North Wales, was started by the Aberystwyth & Welsh Coast Railway, a company that had been incorporated in 1861. In common with several other railways in the area, the A&WCR was worked by the enterprising contractor, Thomas Savin, a man who made a vast but often overlooked contribution to the development of main-line railways in North and Mid-Wales.

In July 1864 Cambrian Railways was formed from four independent local companies and, on 5 July 1865, the A&WCR also entered the Cambrian fold. At the time, the A&WCR's routes were far from complete, and it therefore fell to the Cambrian to finish the works. The line along the south side of the Mawddach Estuary (through Barmouth Junction station) was among the sections to have been finished, but Barmouth Bridge and the line northwards to Pwllheli were still incomplete. The building of the bridge was not without its difficulties as, although the extensive sandbanks of the Mawddach Estuary might seem quite innocuous at low tide, very strong currents are created with tide movements. During the construction work, two labourers were drowned when their boat capsized after being carried out to sea on a fast tide.

The man who masterminded the construction of Barmouth Bridge, Thomas Savin, was not actually in office when the work was completed. Savin had been declared bankrupt in February 1866, his cash-

flow having been hampered by his regular acceptance of shares instead of money. Some viewed Savin's accumulation of shares as a quest for power, but others acknowledged that many of the companies for which Savin had worked had been in no position to settle his fees entirely in cash. For a short while, Savin was unofficially retained by the Cambrian in a consultative capacity but, before long, a proliferation of claims and counterclaims shattered the amicability. There was, however, never any implication of impropriety on Savin's part, and he continued to take an active part in civic affairs in his home town of Oswestry. He became an alderman in 1871, and remained in the area until his death in 1889.

By July 1866 Barmouth Bridge was ready for a locomotive to make the first trial trip, Savin-owned 2-4-0 *Mazeppa* (later Cambrian Railways No 28) taking the honours. A public passenger service was inaugurated across the bridge on 3 June 1867 but this was by means of a horse-drawn carriage. Steam-hauled services did not commence until 10 October when the coast line through Barmouth to Pwllheli was opened for traffic.

The public opening of the bridge could, conceivably, have resulted in a severe case of gastric disorder for one resident of Barmouth. The gentleman in question, a well-known local cynic, had previously expressed grave doubts that a locomotive-hauled train could ever cross the bridge, and his conviction had been so strong that he had publicly vowed to

eat the first locomotive that accomplished the feat. At the grand opening of the bridge, the Cambrian Railways' hierarchy ushered the man to a spot where a decorated table had been prepared, and enquired whether he would like the locomotive baked or boiled.

The opening of the bridge to railway traffic affected local ferrymen who had previously provided the only means of public transport across the estuary. The eventual opening of a footpath across the bridge alongside the railway line hit the ferrymen's pockets even harder, and they subsequently pressed the Cambrian for compensation of £100 per man...the equivalent of four years' income.

Barmouth Bridge was the longest ever built in Wales and, in the opinion of many, the finest structure of its type in the Principality. Its main section comprised 113 spans supported by over 500 timber piles, with an eight-span wrought iron section at the Barmouth end. One of those eight spans took the form of a drawbridge which could be opened to enable shipping to pass through. Prior to sanctioning the use of the bridge, the Board of Trade inspector, Capt Tyler, had opined that the 37 minutes required for two men to open and close the bridge was excessive, and that the cast iron tripod columns under the drawbridge section were potentially vulnerable, a direct hit by an ill-navigated ship being likely to bring down much of the bridge.

The drawbridge section was replaced by a centrally-pivoted swing bridge section during the

major reconstruction work of 1899-1909, other alterations resulting in the original eight-span iron section being reduced to a total of five spans. The signals on the bridge were equipped with purple and white lights, the customary red and green lights being banned in order to avoid confusion with the navigation lights of vessels passing underneath.

The route across the bridge was earmarked for closure in 1967, but was reprieved due to its status as the only feasible means of communication during hard winters when most local roads became impassable. In 1980, however, it looked as if the Teredo worm had succeeded where the post-Beechingists had failed as, during a routine inspection of the bridge, an advanced state of infestation was found in the timber piles. The Teredo ship-worm, which can live only in salt water, has two small shells in its head which it uses for boring into timber where it lays its larvae. The holes start as tiny pin-size borings, but can soon reach ⅛in in diameter and extend for several feet in length. At Barmouth, even new timbers were reduced to a dangerously-infested state within just five weeks.

Despite its destructive nature, the Teredo worm (*Teredo Navales*, or the Naval woodworm) had, many years previously, actually taught Sir Marc Isambard Brunel a thing or two. Sir Marc had been interested in the creature's drilling technique, and had inspected its activities under a microscope. His studies of the worm had led to his idea for the famous tunnelling shield, which he had used to such effect on the construction of the Thames Tunnel.

The tiny, but highly undesirable, little creatures could not be outwitted with adequate speed, and so Barmouth Bridge was summarily closed. In view of BR's much-publicised statement that funds were not available for major maintenance, there were grave doubts about the line's future. To the relief of many, temporary repairs were carried out, cement casings being used to protect the base of the timber piles, and the bridge reopened in May 1981, albeit only to diesel multiple-units. By then, however, it had been announced that the much-needed full reconstruction would indeed be undertaken and, after running up a bill of some £2,000,000, the bridge reopened to locomotive-hauled trains in 1986.

1867: Langstone Bridge, Nr Havant, Hampshire

Designer and builder: Frederick Furness
Original owner: Hayling Railway
Type: Trestle with opening section
Materials: Timber
Total length: 370yd
Max height of rails: 25ft above high-water
Spans: 49
Tracks: 1

The timber trestle viaduct at Langstone on the Hayling Island branch may not rate among the greatest engineering achievements known to mankind, but the charisma surrounding the line itself makes it difficult to ignore the viaduct.

In pre-railway days attempts had been made to develop Hayling Island as a holiday resort, but the efforts had come to little. The London, Brighton & South Coast and the London & South Western Railways arrived at Havant, just to the north of Hayling Island, in March 1847 and January 1859 respectively, but neither company seemed interested in the potential of Hayling Island. It subsequently fell to an independent local company, the Hayling Railway, to promote a branch from Havant to Hayling Island but, in the best traditions of small Victorian railway companies, the HR soon found that it dreams were somewhat optimistic. After opening the first mile of its line as far as Langstone (with a short branch to the quay) on 19 January 1865, the company found itself in financial difficulties.

The HR was rescued by Francis Fuller, a wealthy London businessman who had previously become familiar with the area. Fuller saw no reason why he should not be the one to exploit the undoubted potential of Hayling Island as a holiday resort, and he not only bought extensive tracts of land on the island, but also took financial control of the mortally ill railway company. Under Fuller's guidance, the Hayling Railway completed its line, and it opened to the public on 17 July 1867.

The crossing of the harbour immediately beyond Langstone station was by means of a timber trestle viaduct. Because navigation rights still existed around the island, the viaduct was equipped with a 30ft-long opening span, alongside which was a signalbox. The locking of the signals was such that they could be pulled off only when the span was set for the railway. The regulations for shipping insisted that vessels were not to sail straight through the gap in the bridge, but were to tie up at the mooring posts and be 'warped' through, ie hauled through on ropes attached to a succession of posts.

At the beginning of 1872 the LB&SCR took a lease on the HR, although the latter company retained its nominal independence until the Grouping. A cosmetic change which followed in 1875 was that the railway companies adopted the spelling of 'Langston' (without the 'e'), despite the fact that the name of the community remained unchanged.

The HR was initially worked by the contractor, Frederick Furness, the locomotives including an ex-L&SWR 0-4-2T. In the early LB&SCR period, a Sharp Stewart 2-4-0T (suitably renamed *Hayling Island*) was used but, after that engine's withdrawal in 1890, standard LB&SCR 'Terrier' 0-6-0Ts took over. The 'Terriers' became synonymous with the Hayling Island branch and, in later years, became virtually the only locomotives with light enough axle-weights to be permitted to cross Langstone Bridge. Over the years, the bridge required a degree of attention. Many timbers were replaced in 1902/03 and new trestles, this time on concrete bases, were installed between 1928 and 1931.

The branch's eventual demise was due to a combination of factors. The first of the nails in the coffin came in 1958 when a new road bridge between Langstone and the Island was opened. One outcome was that the relatively small but nevertheless useful amount of freight traffic hitherto monopolised by the branch rapidly defected to the road. The second major nail came in the early 1960s when the age of the Hayling Island 'Terriers' and the blatant lack of suitable replacements started to cause real concern.

The final nail was that, by then, Langstone Bridge was desperately in need of repair, but the estimated cost was in the region of £400,000 and the income generated by the line was insufficient to cover even the interest on such capital expenditure. All in all, the obvious course was to close the branch.

The date of official execution was announced for Monday, 4 November 1963 and, predictably, the workings of Saturday the 2nd and Sunday the 3rd were packed. The viaduct was subsequently dismantled, but the piers on either side of the former opening span were left *in situ* to mark the channel for shipping. Today, these can still be used as a visual guide for tracing the course of the once distinctive structure across the water.

1868: Chester-le-Street Viaduct, Chester-le-Street, County Durham

The NER's line between Durham and Gateshead opened to goods traffic on 2 March 1868 and to passengers on 1 December. Although referred to as the Team Valley branch, that section was later to form a part of the East Coast main line. A major feature of the new line was the viaduct over the Chester Burn and the Pelton Fell road at Chester-le-Street. It had eleven semi-elliptical arches, each of 60ft span, and its stone parapets were carried on brick piers. The line across the viaduct is, of course, still in everyday use, although the town of Chester-le-Street is now served mainly by local trains.

1869: Runcorn Bridge, Runcorn, Cheshire

Designer: William Baker
Original owner: London & North Western Railway
Type: Lattice girder
Materials: Wrought iron; masonry
Total length: 315yd (exc approaches)
Max height of rails: 75ft above high-water
Spans: 3 (bridge only)
Tracks: 2

The crossing of the River Mersey between Manchester and Liverpool presented problems for several pioneering railway companies. Early on, plans for a crossing at Fidler's Ferry were rejected because of the potential problems to maritime navigation, and although powers were obtained in 1846 for a bridge at Runcorn Gap, they were allowed to lapse after the cost of the projected structure proved too great.

Above:
Chester-le-Street Viaduct, 1868: An impressive viaduct - unless you're living in its shadow. An unidentified Class 47 hauls the 15.10 Newcastle–King's Cross over Chester-le-Street Viaduct in March 1971. *M. Dunnett*

Right:
Runcorn Bridge, 1869: The vast scale of Runcorn Bridge can really be fully appreciated only from the riverbank at times of low tide - when the structure is viewed from this angle, the massive sandstone portals at each end seem rather insignificant. This splendid official picture is dated February 1929. *British Railways*

The London & North Western Railway later tried to revive the idea of a bridge at Fidler's Ferry, but the plans were again rejected. It left the LNWR with little option but to build a high-level bridge at Runcorn Gap, and to connect with the Liverpool–Warrington line at Ditton Junction, just to the west of Widnes. As a snippet of total irrelevance, it is believed that the name 'Widnes' came from Danish invaders who gave the name 'Vid Nes' (meaning 'Wide Nose') to the rocky promontory which was later levelled by the building of the railway bridge.

The bridge at Runcorn Gap was designed by the LNWR's Chief Engineer, William Baker (1817–78), and work began in April 1864. It consisted of three wrought iron lattice girder spans supported on sandstone piers, the use of lattice girders for such a lengthy structure being considered, at the time, very advanced. Each of the spans was 305ft long and weighed some 1,700 tons; unusually, they were built up piece by piece *in situ* rather than being prefabricated on the shore and floated into position. The piers, incidentally, had foundations sunk 35ft into the sandstone below the river-bed. At each end of the bridge were arched stone portals with castellated turrets, a plaque over each portal commemorating the designer. The approach to the northern end of the bridge was by means of a 59-arch brick-built viaduct on a 1 in 114 gradient, the rise continuing for some two miles on the south side of the bridge.

An interesting feature of the bridge was that it had an additional thickness of wrought iron plate fitted to parts of the main girders. This was done to disperse possible corrosion from fumes emanating from the chemical works at nearby Widnes but, as things turned out, the prevailing winds usually took the fumes well away from the bridge.

A contractor's train is known to have crossed the bridge on 21 May 1868 but it was the following year before the structure accommodated public traffic, regular goods workings starting on 1 February 1869 and passenger services commencing on 1 April. The route via the bridge shortened the distance between London and Liverpool, but for charging purposes the LNWR was permitted to maintain the mileage of the old route as a pontage allowance. A footpath alongside the main girder of the bridge was provided for pedestrians to replace a centuries-old ferry, and a small toll was charged for using the path.

In the early 1900s the wrought iron components in the bridge's floor system were replaced by steel components, but the main girders have remained largely unaltered to this day. Cosmetically, however, the bridge's appearance is now somewhat marred by the overhead gantries which were installed for the commencement of the full electric services between Crewe and Liverpool on 18 June 1962. By then, the view of the bridge from the east had been somewhat obscured by a new road bridge which had been built alongside.

Returning to the early post-Grouping period, Runcorn Bridge was one of the structures tested by the Bridge Stress Committee, which was established in March 1923 by the Department of Scientific and Industrial Research. The Committee's main aim was to gain a greater understanding of 'impact' stresses on railway bridges, and the effects of a locomotive's hammer-blow were given particular attention. A total of 42 bridge spans (all in England) was tested, those over 100ft in length during 1924 and the smaller spans (including skew arches) during 1925.

A representative cross-section of bridges was tested, the basic categories being:

1) Open bridges, ie those with no ballast, the rails being carried on longitudinal or cross timbers.

2) Bridges with ballast, but no concrete or brickwork.

3) Bridges with floors of concrete or brickwork, or having main or cross girders encased in concrete.

The structures were tested with various types of locomotives ranging from 4-4-2Ts to 2-8-0s, special attention being given to tests involving 3- and 4-cylinder locomotives and also engines working in pairs. The Committee published its 213-page report in 1928. It emphasised the importance of designing engines in such a manner as to reduce the hammer-blow, and stressed the advantages of using three or four cylinders in the construction of heavy locomotives.

1869: Goole Swing Bridge, Nr Goole, Humberside

Designer: Thomas Harrison
Original owner: North Eastern Railway
Type: Swing bridge
Materials: Cast iron; wrought iron
Total length: 277yd
Spans: 7
Tracks: 2

The North Eastern Railway had to overcome considerable opposition before assent was gained for the construction of the line between Staddlethorpe (on the Hull–Selby line) and Thorne (on the South Yorkshire Railway's Doncaster–Grimsby line). Rival schemes had strong support but the NER won the day in the Commons, only to see its proposals rejected in the Lords by a single vote. A re-presentation in 1863 was, however, successful.

The line was opened to traffic on 30 July 1869, one of its major features being the swing bridge across the River Ouse a little to the east of Goole; the bridge itself had, in fact, been formally opened by its designer, the NER's Chief Engineer Thomas Harrison, five months earlier. At the time of its con-

struction, the bridge was the second largest double-track railway swing bridge in the world. An opening bridge had been deemed necessary for access by shipping to and from the town of Selby, which lay up-river. The bridge had five fixed and two opening spans, each of the fixed spans being 39yd long, and made of wrought iron plate girders which were supported on cast iron columns filled with cement. The 83yd-long moveable portion of the bridge consisted of a centre box girder and two solid webbed side girders, connected by transverse girders.

The swing section was supported by a central pillar composed of seven cast iron columns; it was hydraulically operated and swung round on a 30ft diameter turntable, the opening or closing of the bridge being possible in about a minute. The rigidity and security of the tracks were ensured by an arrangement of resting-blocks and locking-bolts at each end of the swing section, while operational safety was achieved by an arrangement whereby the signals on the approaches were activated by the fixing gear. The weight of the swing section was originally quoted as 670 tons, but present-day estimates now quote between 800 and 900 tons. A signalbox was mounted above the rails on the swing section. In May 1933, the section of line between Saltmarshe and Goole became one of the first on the LNER to have colour-light signalling, which resulted in the closure of the signalboxes at each end of the bridge, and also one at Goole.

The difficult tidal conditions on the Ouse resulted in the bridge receiving a fairly regular buffeting from passing vessels over the years. After

Below:
Goole Swing Bridge, 1869: After the bridge was repaired in 1973/74, the first test train crossed the structure on 3 August 1974. This was the scene from the right bank of the River Ouse on the day before. *C. P. Boocock*

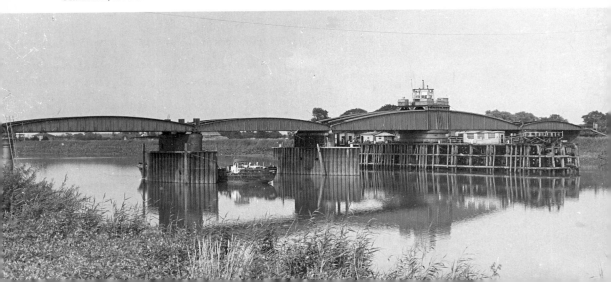

one such incident on 21 December 1973 one span fell into the river after the bridge was struck by a German coaster, but the span was replaced and full normal services across the bridge were resumed on 7 October the following year. Largely because of the battering which the bridge had received, plans were made in 1983 to close the bridge and divert traffic via Selby, but Humberside County Council stepped in with a substantial grant towards the repair of the structure, and it is still in use today.

1869: Solway Viaduct, Cumbria/Dumfries-shire

Designer: John Brunlees
Original owner: Solway Junction Railway
Contractor: Waring Bros & Eckersley
Type: Trestle viaduct
Materials: Wrought iron; cast iron
Total length: 1,940yd
Max height of rails above high-water: 10ft 6in
Spans: 193
Tracks: 1

In the 1860s the extraction of iron ore from mines in West Cumberland increased significantly, and a considerable proportion of the ore was required by the steelworks in Lanarkshire. The ore trains had no option but to use the route via Carlisle, and this prompted two different proposals for a new direct line which bridged the Solway Firth. The scheme which won the day was for the Solway Junction Railway - a line connecting Kirtlebridge (on the Caledonian Railway's line to the north of Carlisle) and Brayton (on the Maryport & Carlisle Railway's main line). The plans were widely ridiculed, but the line was nevertheless built. It opened to mineral traffic on 13 September 1869 and to passengers on 8 August 1870.

The main feature of the line was the 1,940yd-long viaduct across the Solway Firth which, until the completion of the Tay Bridge in 1878, was the longest in Britain. Solway Viaduct was supported on 193 cast iron piers, each comprising five 12in diameter columns which were driven down to boulder gravel some 17-20ft below the bed of the firth. The piers were protected by timber buttresses to prevent damage by the fast tides and shifting sands. During the winter of 1875/76, however, the piers were badly damaged by ice which had formed inside them, but that was little more than an aperitif as, in 1881, ice floes in the Solway demolished 45 of the piers. The repair work cost £30,000. At the time, the ore traffic was more than adequate to justify the cost of repairs, but the boom did not last.

The viaduct's original owner, the Solway Junction Railway, was absorbed by the Caledonian Railway in 1895. The Caley had, in fact, purchased the Kirtlebridge-Annan section of the line in 1873 with an agreement to work the remaining section. Although the SJR was built with only a single track, enough land was purchased for eventual doubling. The first 12 piers at the Scottish end of the Solway Viaduct had been built to double width in order to give a guide for future widening, but no doubling of any part of the line, let alone the viaduct section, was ever undertaken. During the viaduct's relatively brief life, trains passing over it were subjected to a 10mph speed limit, although it is believed that this was, at one time, reduced to 5mph. A further safety precaution was that, if a

Below:
Solway Viaduct, 1869: Until the completion of the Tay Bridge in 1878, Solway Viaduct was the longest structure of its type in Britain. However, the flatness of the land either side of the Solway Firth made it virtually impossible to take a photograph which emphasised the vast length of the viaduct. This mediocre view is included merely for the sake of completeness. *Ian Allan Library*

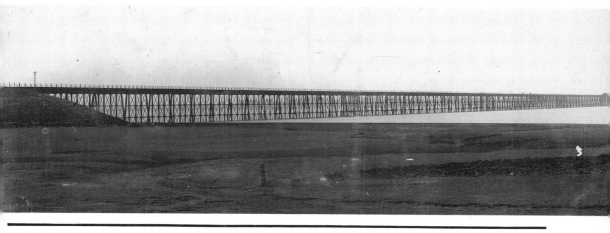

strong wind were blowing, no trains were allowed on to the viaduct until a permanent way gang had walked across and given the thumbs-up.

By the late 1800s the Lanarkshire steelworks were using imported ore, and so the demand for Cumberland ore (which was, by then, close to exhaustion) and the traffic using Solway Viaduct decreased correspondingly. At the start of World War 1 it was estimated that the viaduct would need some £15,500 worth of attention over the following three years, but the lack of traffic, even with the requirements for the war effort, did not justify such expenditure. Instead, the structure was closed on 1 February 1915.

The line nevertheless reopened after the war, but the lack of maintenance to the viaduct in the previous years had been such that, by 1921, a renewed estimate for maintenance put the figure at £70,000. Once again, such an outlay was rejected. The structure was finally condemned in August 1921, the last trains running on the 31st of the month. The viaduct became popular as a highly unofficial footway, particularly on Sunday nights as the public houses in Scotland were closed but their counterparts across the water in England were open. That, perhaps, spoke volumes for the quality of the Cumberland beer as a walk home across the decaying structure in the dark, with the treacherous Solway waters not far below, must have required some nerve, artificially-induced or otherwise.

In the early 1930s the Ministry of Transport considered adapting the rotting viaduct for use as a road bridge, but the estimated cost of £91,500 for work which would have only a limited lifespan was considered far too high. Instead, an abandonment order was issued. The viaduct was demolished between May 1934 and November 1935, the work being undertaken by Messrs Arnott, Young & Co of Glasgow and claiming the lives of three workers who were drowned when their boat was carried out to sea and capsized.

1871: The 'Black Bridge', Bridgwater Docks, Somerset

Designer: Francis Fox (?)
Original owner: Bristol & Exeter Railway
Contractor: Lloyds Foster & Co, Wednesbury (ironwork); Warburton Bros, Bristol (masonry)
Cost: £8,000
Type: Telescopic
Materials: Wrought iron
Total length: 81yd

Max height of rails: 19ft above high-water
Spans: 3
Tracks: 1

In 1862 the Corporation-owned ½-mile-long tramway between Bridgwater station and a wharf on the River Parrett was taken over by the broad gauge Bristol & Exeter Railway. It was later decided to convert the horse-worked tramway to a railway line for use by 'engines of both gauges' and to extend it across the river to the dock, and the line was opened as far as the wharf in November 1867.

The continuation of the line across the River Parrett was, however, not the simplest of matters as the quays up-river of the proposed bridging point were so intensively used that, at times, it was possible to walk from one side of the river to the other across the decks of ships. A railway bridge which prevented access to the upper quays was obviously out of the question, and so the B&ER presented a plan for 'a swing bridge having four openings, the two centre openings being each 50ft span with swivel bridges and the two side openings being each 40ft span'. That proposal was considered too grand and expensive, but the later suggestion of a simpler structure with a swing section on a central pier was also rejected.

The plan which eventually won the day was for a telescopic bridge...a type relatively unusual in Britain. It had three spans, the westernmost span being fixed and supported on pillars in the river. The central span could be rolled eastwards on large wheels, but instead of being rolled over the fixed span on the east bank, the eastern span could be moved sideways and the central span could then occupy the vacated space.

The bridge, which became known locally as the 'Black Bridge', took fifteen months to build and was completed in January 1871, the official opening ceremony for rail traffic taking place in March. Initially, the bridge movements were undertaken by manually-operated winches, but a vertical-boilered steam engine was soon provided, the engine house being alongside the traverser pit on the east bank of the river. The manual winches were nevertheless retained, and came in handy in 1913 when the engine broke down. As for the designer of the bridge, that matter seems to be ill-recorded, but a lack of contradictory evidence might suggest that the credit should go to Francis Fox, the B&ER's Engineer.

The Bristol & Exeter Railway was absorbed by the GWR in January 1876, and the Bridgwater Dock branch remained mixed gauge until the abolition of the broad gauge in May 1892. Apart from routine maintenance, the telescopic bridge required comparatively little repair work for the rest of its life, but during the 20th century its use became increasingly infrequent. The trade at Bridgwater

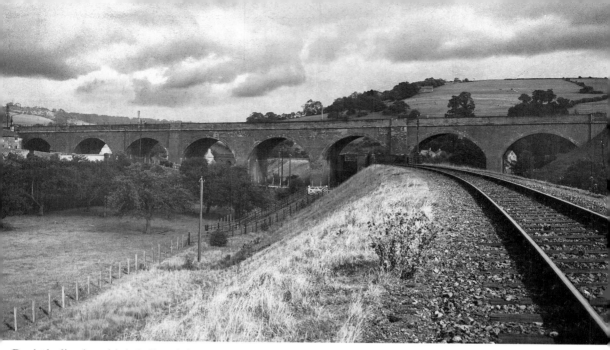

Above:
Midford Viaduct, 1874: Midford Viaduct was one of the most photographed features on the Somerset & Dorset line, but this view is rather different. It was taken on 19 October 1929, and shows the GWR's Hallatrow–Limpley Stoke branch passing underneath the S&D viaduct. This picture was taken looking eastwards, and the arches which carried the GWR Midford–Norton St Philip road are just discernible through the fourth arch from the left of the S&D viaduct. *Ian Allan Library*

Dock declined, and it is believed that the last opening of the bridge took place in June 1957. It had, in fact, been temporarily immobilised during World War 2, the decking which had been laid up to sleeper level having been retained for some time after peace had been restored. The inevitable closure of Bridgwater Dock officially took place on 31 July 1971, and the telescopic section and engine house were dismantled soon afterwards. In 1982, however, the remains of the bridge were rebuilt and a new section laid to carry a road across the River Parrett.

1874: Evercreech Junction–Bath, Somerset/Avon

(various structures, see below)

Original owner: Somerset & Dorset Railway
Consulting Engineer: W.H.Barlow
Contractors: Messrs T & C Walker

The Somerset & Dorset Railway was undoubtedly one of the most charismatic concerns in the country. The company's forerunners started life with the intention of connecting Highbridge on the Bristol Channel to Poole on the English Channel, but its eventual celebrity status was generated by the extension across the Mendip Hills to Bath. Ironically, though, the famed extension proved to be the S&DR's financial undoing.

The Bath extension left the existing line at Evercreech and crossed some challenging terrain, the summit of the line at Masbury being 811ft above sea level, but the line was nevertheless completed in just two years and opened to traffic on 20 July 1874. The route bristled with bridges and viaducts, the first major one (from the south) being the 11-arch **Prestleigh Viaduct** near Evercreech. A little further north, at Shepton Mallet, the line passed across the 317yd-long 27-arch **Charlton Viaduct** and the shorter **Bath Road Viaduct**. The latter was 62ft high to the underside of the main arch and was the highest on the line. Part of it collapsed during a ferocious gale in February 1946 and four new arches had to be built, during which time single-line working prevailed; the renewal work was completed the following summer.

Continuing northwards, **Hamwood Viaduct** (72yd long) carried the line across a deep wooded ravine just to the north of Winsor Hill while, between Midsomer Norton and Radstock, the line crossed the GWR's Radstock–Bristol branch and a

'Marble Arch', acquired by S&DR by 1874: It is believed that the bridge was built by the Somerset Coal Canal Co to carry the tramway from Tyning Colliery over the canal towpath. The restricted clearance underneath the bridge presented an ongoing problem when it came to finding suitably small locomotives for shunting duties at Radstock. The delightful little 0-4-0ST in this 1920s photograph is one of the 'Dazzlers' which were built at the S&D's workshops at Highbridge specially for shunting at Radstock. *H. C. Casserley*

main road on a 128yd-long viaduct known locally as **Five Arches Bridge**. Given the amount of coal traffic in the Radstock area it would have seemed useful for a connecting spur to have been laid between the S&DR and the GWR, but there was no love lost between the two companies and so the chance of an amicable agreement, let alone a transfer arrangement, was more than a trifle optimistic. An illustration of the hostility between the two unneighbourly neighbours is provided by the tale that, in 1881, a stonemason working on the S&DR's bridge was warned that if he should work above the GWR line, the GWR would consider it to be an act of trespass.

Arguably the best-known viaduct on the S&DR's Bath extension was the 168yd-long **Midford Viaduct**. Built of brick and stone, it crossed not only a road, a brook and the remains of the Somerset Coal Canal, but also the GWR's Limpley Stoke–Hallatrow branch (completed in May 1910) which was itself carried across the road partly on a separate viaduct. Part of the GWR branch closed as early as 1925, but the section through Midford struggled on until 14 February 1951. It was, however, not to be forgotten as, in 1953, Ealing Studios used the Midford–Limpley Stoke section for the filming of the comedy classic *The Titfield Thunderbolt*. One of the film's opening sequences, which is undoubtedly ingrained on the memory of every West Country railway enthusiast, shows a train on the S&DR viaduct with another on the GWR viaduct beneath. Although the S&DR's line south of Midford was doubled in 1892/94, the section across the viaduct and all the way northwards to Bath remained single.

Financially devastated by the expenditure on the Bath extension, the S&DR became a joint Midland/London & South Western Railway concern in 1875 and retained its joint status, albeit under new owners after the Grouping, until 1930. Its locomotive stock smacked strongly of Midland/LMSR influence, although the distinctive S&DR Prussian blue livery survived until the late 1920s. In the post-Nationalisation era it seemed as if the Western Region were hell-bent on avenging old GWR scores and the ex-S&D lines were treated not only to minimal investment, but also to changes of timetabling which did little to attract the public. Realists admitted that the line was hardly likely to become a profitable one, but the manner in which it was run down caused considerable ill-feeling among the locals.

Predictably, the line became increasingly sparsely used but closure was nevertheless staved off until 7 March 1966. Nearly 30 years on, substantial sections of the old track bed between Evercreech and Bath are still eminently walkable, and a few sections have even been converted to semi-formal walks. Of the viaducts, those at Bath Road (Shepton Mallet) and Midford remain intact while substantial sections of others still stand.

Before leaving the dear old S&DR completely, mention should be made of one particular under-bridge on the line. Just to the east of Radstock station, a bridge known locally as **'Marble Arch'** carried a tramway from Tyning Colliery across the S&DR line. The tramway crossed the S&DR on the skew and also on a sharp gradient, the consequence being that the arch over an S&DR shunting spur was some 135ft long and left just 10ft 5in headroom. For many years the S&DR kept a trio of diminutive locomotives (two 0-4-0STs and one 0-4-2ST, all known as 'Dazzlers' because of their usually smart liveries) specifically for shunting under 'Marble Arch' and when, in 1929, the little engines were finally deemed past their sell-by dates, the S&DR ordered a pair of Sentinel vertical-boilered 0-4-0Ts. The Sentinels were about the only option which offered a combination of adequate power with minimal height. Before long one of the Sentinels adopted peripatetic tendencies, and the only replacements with suitably low dimensions for 'Marble Arch' duties were ex-Lancashire & York-shire Railway 0-4-0STs. 'Marble Arch' (which, for the record, was officially known as either Tramway Arch or Tyning Bridge) was finally demolished in 1960, thereby bringing to an end a wonderfully idiosyncratic, but somewhat inconvenient, tradition.

Below:
Lydbrook Viaduct, 1874: The impressive scale of Lydbrook Viaduct was, arguably, disproportionate to the importance of the line it carried. This picture was taken in August 1964, eleven years after the line across the viaduct was closed completely and one year before the structure was demolished. *Andrew Muckley*

1874: Lydbrook Viaduct, Lower Lydbrook, Gloucestershire

Designer: G.W.Keeling
Original owner: Severn & Wye Railway
Contractors: Crumlin Viaduct Works Co (ironwork); J.E.Billups, Cardiff (masonry)
Cost: £7,396
Type: Lattice girder
Materials: Wrought iron; masonry
Total length: 130yd
Max height of rails: 90ft
Spans: 3 (plus approaches)
Tracks: 1

The Severn & Wye Railway opened its extension from Serridge Junction to Lydbrook Junction (on the GWR's Ross–Monmouth line) to freight traffic on 26 August 1874. It took three visits from the Board of Trade inspector, the redoubtable Col Rich, before permission was granted for passenger services to commence, the inaugural date being 23 September 1875. The delay was not, however, a major catastrophe for the S&WR as it was primarily a mineral carrier serving the industries of the Forest of Dean although, eventually, the railway company went to considerable length to attract tourists to the area. One aspect of the attention to tourism was the availability of a 'picnic carriage', complete with attendant...a sort of forerunner to the camping coach.

The Lydbrook extension crossed the valley above the village of Lower Lydbrook by means of an extremely graceful viaduct. The pillars were of masonry, but the three spans were wrought iron Warren girders, two of 120ft and the other of 150ft; they were similar to those which had been used in the building of Crumlin Viaduct of 1857, and made

by the same company. In engineering terms the viaduct was not especially noteworthy, but its visual appeal and surroundings nevertheless made it just a little bit special.

The Severn & Wye Railway was purchased jointly by the Great Western and the Midland Railways in July 1894. The sparsely used passenger services between Cinderford and Lydbrook Junction held out until 8 July 1929, although Lower Lydbrook station had been closed to passengers as early as 1 April 1906. For many years, only one or two trains had run through from Lydney to Lydbrook Junction each weekday, the 12-mile trip requiring a tedious reversal at Cinderford and usually taking all of 70mins.

The line remained open for freight traffic but, by then, the days of the heavy iron ore traffic to the South Wales furnaces were all but over. Nevertheless, total closure did not take place until after the viaduct and the Forest of Dean lines had come under Western Region control at Nationalisation. On 1 January 1953, the line was truncated at Upper Lydbrook thereby rendering the section across the little known Lydbrook Viaduct redundant.

For much of the viaduct's life, a strict speed limit of 5mph was imposed on trains crossing it, although the speed limit of the early days had been a breathtaking 6mph. In the later years, motive power consisted almost exclusively of 0-6-0PTs, the last of the ex-Severn & Wye locomotives with their distinctive 'forest' names having been withdrawn way back in 1924. The demolition of Lydbrook Viaduct started on 4 August 1965 and, somewhat insultingly for railway enthusiasts and local historians, the first major stage was regarded by the BBC as 'light entertainment' and given live television coverage. It did not go unremarked that the cost of the demolition was more than double what it had cost to build the viaduct.

1874: Meldon Viaduct, Nr Okehampton, Devon

Designer: William Jacomb
Original owner: London & South Western Railway
Type: Lattice beam
Materials: Wrought iron
Total length: 183yd
Max height of rails: 150ft
Spans: 6
Tracks: 1 (later doubled)

In parts of the West Country, the London & South Western Railway proved to be a constant thorn in the side of the Great Western. The L&SWR wanted access to the 'Three Towns' (Devonport, Stonehouse and Plymouth), and in its quest to reach its target the company gradually extended westwards from Exeter. The section between Okehampton and Lydford (originally spelt Lidford) opened to traffic on 12 October 1874 and, on its route around the northwestern fringe of Dartmoor, had to negotiate some challenging terrain. The line reached a height of 950ft above sea level, the highest point on the L&SWR network, and the crossing of the valley of

Below:
Meldon Viaduct, 1874: Although Meldon Viaduct looked for all the world like one of Thomas Bouch's structures, appearances were very deceptive. Apologies are offered to those who consider that this photograph shows too little of the viaduct, but this superb 1930s picture of 'T9' 4-4-0 No 718 at the head of an Exeter–Plymouth working was rather hard to resist.
C. R. Gordon Stuart/Lens of Sutton. Courtesy: Brian Stephenson

the West Okement River near Meldon was by means of a 150ft-high viaduct.

The design of Meldon Viaduct is usually attributed to William Jacomb (1832–79), a former pupil of Isambard Kingdom Brunel. Jacomb had been appointed as the L&SWR's Chief Engineer in 1869 and was the uncle of J. W. Jacomb-Hood, who occupied the post of Chief Engineer on the L&SWR between 1901 and 1914. Meldon Viaduct was built on a gradient of 1 in 77 (rising towards Lydford) and on a curve of 30 chains radius. The structure had six spans, each 90ft wide, with one lattice beam under each rail, the beams being similar to the Warren girders used in the construction of Crumlin Viaduct in 1857. The superstructure was supported by piers which were formed of four columns, the piers being splayed out towards their bases and, unusually, made of wrought and not cast iron. The contractor engaged for the construction of the Okehampton–Lydford line was Robert Relf & Co and, in the absence of official documentation to prove otherwise, it has been suggested that Relf was also responsible for the building of the viaduct.

In 1879 the viaduct was widened to take a double track, but instead of using elaborate scaffolding to build up from the valley floor, the construction was undertaken mainly by working with cranes from the existing line. The only other major alteration to the viaduct was carried out in the 1950s when the bases of the piers were weighted with concrete 'casings' in order to increase stability. The Exeter–Plymouth line via Okehampton was ultimately transferred to the control of the Western Region and, somewhat predictably, the folks at Paddington saw little use for an alternative to the old GWR route via Newton Abbot. Public services were withdrawn from the Okehampton–Plymouth route on 6 June 1968. A little to the east of the old viaduct is Meldon Quarry, from where of ballast is still hauled to Exeter and beyond.

1875*: Settle–Carlisle, North Yorkshire/Cumbria

(21 principal viaducts, listed overleaf)
Designer: John Crossley
Original owner: Midland Railway
Contractors: Settle to Dent Head (17¼ miles): J. Ashwell, Kentish Town (taken over by Midland Railway's own labour force in October 1871)
Dent Head to Kirkby Stephen (17 miles): Benton & Woodiwiss
Kirkby Stephen to Newbiggin (14½ miles): Joseph Firbank & Co
Newbiggin to Carlisle (25 miles): Eckersley & Baylis

The most famous surviving railway route in England is, without doubt, the Settle & Carlisle line. Built across magnificently bleak moorland, it is the stuff of legend and, justifiably, it has been the subject of countless books and magazine articles. Therefore, it is somewhat superfluous to dwell at

Below:
Ribblehead Viaduct, 1875: The length of the viaduct and its location in one of England's most magnificently bleak landscapes is clearly evidenced here. Early evening sunlight illuminates a Class 47-hauled Glasgow–Leeds train on 16 May 1972. Note the more substantial construction of every sixth pier of the viaduct. *J. H. Cooper-Smith*

Miles	Name	Date Completed	Length	Height	Spans	Width	Span Material/Type
2¼	Marshfield	1871			4	29ft 9in	Masonry
2¼	Church	1871			6	5 x 30ft / 1 x 37ft 8in	Masonry with skew span
4¾	Sherrif Brow	1872	58yd	55ft	3	30ft 0in	Masonry; skew
7¼	Little	1872	55yd	25ft	3	37ft 8in	Masonry; skew
15	Ribblehead	1875	440yd	165ft	24	45ft 0in	Masonry
16½	Dent Head	1875	177yd	100ft	10	45ft 0in	Masonry
17½	Arten Gill	1875	220yd	117ft	11	37ft 8in	Masonry
22½	Moorcock	1875	227yd	50ft	12	44ft 3in/ 45ft 0in	Masonry
23	Lunds	1875	103yd	63ft	5	45ft 0in	Masonry
26	Ais Gill	1875	87yd	75ft	4	45ft 0in	Masonry
34	Smardale	1875	237yd	130ft	12	45ft 0in	Masonry
34¾	Crosby Garrett	1872	110yd	55ft	6	43ft 0in	Masonry; skew
37	Griseburn	1875	142yd	74ft	7		Masonry and brick
40¾	Ormside	1875	200yd	90ft	10	45ft 0in	Masonry and brick
45	Long Marton	1874	108yd	60ft	5	43ft 0in to 45ft 0in	Masonry and brick
49	Crowdundle	1874	86yd	55ft	4		Masonry
54¾	Dodds Mill†	1875	134yd	60ft	7	44ft 7in	Masonry and brick
56½	Eden Lacy††	1875	137yd		7	45ft 0in	Masonry
62¾	Armathwaite	1874	176yd	80ft	9	44ft 7in	Masonry
64½	Dry Beck	1875	139yd	80ft	7	44ft 4in	Masonry and brick
66½	Cotehill†††	1875	91yd	60ft	4	46ft 10in/ 46ft 6in	Masonry and brick; slight skew

Distances are those from Settle Junction
* The line itself opened in 1875, but some of the viaducts had been finished earlier (see list).
† Also known as Little Salkeld Viaduct; †† Also known as Long Meg Viaduct; ††† Also known as High Stand Gill Viaduct

length on the history or the working of the line. Despite the line's eventual celebrity status, in the earliest days it warranted no more than the customary brief entry in *Bradshaw's Shareholders' Guide*:

'By 29 and 30 Vic, cap 223 (16th July 1866), the Midland was authorised to construct a line from Settle to Hawes, Appleby and Carlisle. Length 78 miles, Capital £1,650,000 in shares, £550,000 on loan. Midland to use Citadel station at Carlisle, and North Eastern at Hawes and Melmerby to make use of portions of Midland'.

The Settle–Carlisle line was constructed by the Midland Railway in order to provide a much-needed independent connection with its Scottish allies, the North British and the Glasgow & South Western Railways. The London & North Western Railway subsequently offered the Midland access to its route via Ingleton and Tebay, and this easier option prompted the Midland to seek abandonment of the plans for the Settle–Carlisle line. The preliminary work on the line was therefore put on hold, but Parliament refused to sanction the abandonment and so, in 1869, work on the Settle & Carlisle venture commenced in earnest.

The engineering of the line was masterminded by John Crossley (1812–1879), who had succeeded Charles Liddell as the MR's Chief Engineer in 1858. In view of the daunting terrain traversed by the line, extremely heavy works were required and these included numerous bridges and viaducts. Although structures such as Ribblehead and Dent Head viaducts are, these days, spoken of by railway enthusiasts who have never even visited the line, the name of their creator, John Sidney Crossley, remains remarkably unfamiliar to most.

Up to 7,000 men were employed on the construction of the Settle–Carlisle line at any one time. The mass influx of workers was far more than the local communities could accommodate, and so shanty towns came into being. The largest was near Ribblehead and was known as Batty Wife Hole, after a nearby limestone shaft; it was large enough to warrant its own church, school, hospital, public houses, library and post office. Others were christened Inkerman, Sebastopol, Salt Lake City, Jericho and Belgravia...names inspired by topical events or grim humour at the conditions.

A contemporary account of life at Batty Wife Hole emphasised the self-sufficiency of the community:

Above:
Dent Head Viaduct, 1875: An unidentified Class 45 hauls a Leeds–Glasgow train across Dent Head Viaduct on 2 March 1974. Looking at the landscape, it's no wonder that the Settle–Carlisle line attained legendary status. *J. H. Cooper-Smith*

Below:
Arten Gill Viaduct, 1875: Arten Gill is, perhaps, one of the less well-photographed viaducts on the Settle–Carlisle line. On 19 March 1966, 'Black 5' No 45112 heads south across the viaduct with a mixed freight train. *John Clarke*

'It resembled the gold diggers' villages in the Colonies. Potters' carts, drapers' carts, milk carts, green-grocers' carts, butchers' and bakers' carts, brewers' drays, and traps and horses for hire, might all be found, besides the numerous hawkers who plied their trade from hut to hut.'

More recently, an entertaining description of life in the shanty towns was given by T. J. Hunt in the June 1963 issue of *Railway World*:

'....The navvies brought to the fells a flavour of the Wild West towns. They wore shirts, short tight knee-breeches and woollen stockings. They ate vast quantities of beef - some of which was driven into the district on the hoof - and drank far more than was good for them. The comparatively high wage, 10s (50p) a day, attracted them, keeping them shivering but defiant in one of the wettest, windiest localities in England.'

It took six long years to complete the Settle–Carlisle route, and the first goods trains ran over the entire length of the line in August 1875. Passenger services commenced on 1 May 1876, the first Midland Railway Anglo–Scottish express leaving St Pancras at 10.30am with, remarkably, no ceremony whatsoever. The branch to Hawes took a little longer to complete, traffic not commencing until 1 August 1878. Four days later, the Settle & Carlisle's unsung engineer, John Crossley, died at the age of just 65.

There were several differentials between the various viaducts on the line. One was that different types of stone were used, Dent Head Viaduct, for example, being built of blue limestone, Eden Lacy Viaduct of red sandstone, and Arten Gill of 'Dent marble' (a dark grey limestone). Some of the viaducts across rivers, particularly those towards the southern end of the line, had their cutwaters built right up to parapet level which gave them a somewhat 'fortified' appearance. The larger viaducts usually had some of their piers built to more substantial dimensions, every sixth pier of Ribblehead Viaduct, for example, being 18ft thick instead of 6ft. The idea behind this was that if one span should collapse it would not precipitate the fall of the entire structure.

Of the many viaducts, Moorcock was not among the original plans. It had been intended to cross Dandry Mire at Moorcock by means of an embankment, but the contractors could only watch helplessly as seemingly endless loads of earth simply sank without trace in the moss. Eventually, it was decided that a viaduct would be the only sensible alternative, and so the site was drained and borings were made to find a solid base.

The Settle–Carlisle route became an integral part of the Midland Railway empire, and remained well

used by the LMSR after the Grouping. The working of the line, particularly during hard winters, might have caused problems to the operators but it only added to the route's charismatic appeal for enthusiasts. Over the years a number of the smaller bridges required replacing, but the viaducts have been subjected to little more than routine maintenance. In the cost-conscious 1960s the first serious threats to the line's future were voiced, but the line was saved. Since then the possibility of closure has never been entirely absent, BR's accountants being quick to cite the expenditure required to maintain the line, particularly the viaducts. Today, the line is an obvious choice for the operators of steam-hauled specials, but it is rather sad that most of those who flock to the route to witness such workings would ask 'John Crossley...who's he?'

1875: Medina Drawbridge, Newport, Isle of Wight

The railway between Newport and Ryde on the Isle of Wight opened on 20 December 1875. Almost immediately to the east of Newport station, the single-track line crossed the River Medina on what appeared to be an ordinary three-span girder bridge. However, appearances were deceptive as one of the spans could be tilted up and then drawn back into a cavity under the track bed. The mechanism involved chains, rollers and a 10cwt counterweight, and it took a minimum of three men to open the bridge.

The bridge was built by Messrs Vospers of Gosport and had three spans, each 26ft 6in wide. Before long it was widened to accommodate a second track, this being necessitated by the opening on 1 June 1879 of the Newport–Sandown line which ran parallel to the Ryde line for a short distance after leaving Newport. In the early days the bridge had to be opened several times daily and so a signalbox was provided specially, the bridge mechanism being interlocked with the lever frame and instruments. A bridge movement required clearing

the lines for a distance of 2¼ miles towards Ryde and 4 miles towards Sandown, and it required considerable organisation to avoid delaying services on the two single-track lines.

As the years progressed, the need to open the bridge became less frequent as larger vessels used berths down river. In later years a bridge opening was such a rare event that the drawbridge section invariably required considerable coaxing before it would budge. The Newport–Sandown line closed on 6 February 1956, and the side of the bridge which had carried that track was dismantled in 1963. The single-track Newport–Ryde line across the bridge remained open only until 21 February 1966.

1876: Wylam Bridge, West Wylam, Northumberland

The Scotswood, Newburn & Wylam Railway (which later became part of the NER) completed its line in October 1876 with the opening of the section between North Wylam and a point known as 'The Hagg' (on the south bank of the River Tyne), where it connected with the Newcastle–Carlisle line. Originally, the intention had been for the

SN&WR to cross the Tyne at Wylam by means of a girder bridge supported by three piers, but it had been considered that there was a very real danger of at least one of the piers penetrating old coal workings thereby causing adjacent pits to be flooded. Instead, the crossing of the Tyne was made by means of a delightful wrought iron bridge which had an arched rib and suspended decking. The arch actually comprised three ribs, their rise being 48ft; the decking was 240ft long and 30ft wide and was supported by 19 cross girders. Interestingly, the Tyne Road Bridge at Newcastle (completed 1928) was of similar design to Wylam railway bridge, albeit somewhat larger.

Wylam Bridge cost £16,000 to construct. It was an early example of an 'elastic arch' bridge, and was designed by William George Laws, who later became Chief Engineer for the City of Newcastle Corporation. A contemporary comment about the bridge was that it '...presented the appearance of lightness and grace rather than strength, but nevertheless came satisfactorily out of the unusually severe tests to which it was subjected'. It was certainly one of the most pleasing-looking railway bridges in the area and, after the line across it closed on 11 March 1968, was subsequently converted for use as a public footpath. The path, incidentally, forms part of a semi-formal walkway and, along its route, it passes the cottage in which George Stephenson was born.

1878: Tay Bridge, Wormit–Dundee, Fife/Angus

Designer: Thomas Bouch
Original owner: North British Railway
Contractors: Work started by Charles de Bergue, completed by Hopkins, Gilkes & Co, Middlesbrough.
Cost: £350,000
Type: Lattice girder
Material: Wrought iron; brick
Total length: 3,456yd
Max height of rails: 77ft above high-water
Spans: 86
Tracks: 1

By the early 1870s the North British Railway considered the bridging of the Firth of Tay to be an absolute necessity. At the time, the company's best Edinburgh–Dundee services took almost four hours, the only real alternative involving the tedious use of ferry crossings. The contract for the eagerly-awaited bridge was let in 1871 to Charles de Bergue but, due to illness, he relinquished the contract in 1874 and the existing works were taken over by the well-known Middlesborough-based firm of Hopkins, Gilkes & Co. Unfortunately, as things turned out, the 'new' contract failed to contain precise specifications as to materials and workmanship, and this contributed to the Tay Bridge becoming the scene of one of the worst disasters in British railway history.

The bridge was designed by Thomas Bouch, whose original intention was for a lattice girder structure supported by brick piers, but the preliminary design was subjected to several alterations. One such alteration was introduced after the first ten piers of the central section had been built, as had been intended, of brick - the rest of the piers

took the form of 31ft-diameter wrought iron cylinders. The central section, under which shipping to and from Perth was to pass, comprised eleven spans of 245ft and two of 227ft. When completed, the bridge was subjected to three days of rigorous testing by the Board of Trade Inspector, Maj-Gen C.S.Hutchinson and, with the proviso of a 25mph speed limit, the structure was passed. It opened for traffic on 1 June 1878. A year later, Queen Victoria travelled across the bridge and subsequently knighted its designer, but Thomas Bouch did not have too long to bask in the glory of his newly-endowed knighthood.

Within a few months a number of ties in the cross-bracing were found to have worked loose, but this information was kept from Bouch who had been retained in the capacity of Superintendent. It was later suggested that Bouch's lax execution of his duties made it all too easy for the contractors to conceal defective workmanship. Bouch was, however, informed about vertical cracks which had appeared in several of the piers. Somewhat mysteriously, he ordered that the piers be bound with wrought iron hoops, and seemingly chose not to tackle the real problem which was that the Portland cement which had been poured wet into the columns was, in fact, bursting them. This was just one of several inexplicable lapses, the awful consequences of which were seen on the evening of 28 December 1879.

On that evening, a ferocious westerly gale was blowing. The 5.20pm stopping train from Burntisland to Dundee, hauled by Wheatley 4-4-0 No 224 and comprising five carriages and a van, left Wormit station at 7.14pm and set out across the bridge on the last leg of its journey. As the train entered the central section of the bridge, a tremendous gust of wind blew along the Firth of Tay, bringing down the girders and, with it, the train. Seventy-five lives were lost.

When the locomotive was found three days later its regulator was wide open and the reversing lever was in the sixth notch, the conclusion being that the crew had had no advance warning whatsoever of their impending fate. The locomotive was finally raised the following April and, remarkably, was repaired and restored to traffic. With its newly acquired nickname of 'The Diver', it survived until 1919. A report on the raising of the locomotive in *The Scotsman* newspaper of 16 April 1880 clearly suffered from unreliable sources, as it commented that: 'It is stated that about £50 will cover the expense of the repairs'. The final repair bill was, of course, somewhat higher. There have been many stories about carriages from the train being washed up in Norway and even being restored and converted for use on a 3ft 6in gauge line, but although it seems that a door from a first-class coach reached the Norwegian shore, it is on record that all of the rolling stock that went down with the bridge was accounted for within less than a month.

As for the ultimate fate of the rolling stock, a letter published in the October 1974 edition of the *Railway Magazine* explains a small part of the story. Mr Cedric P. Sabine of Aberdeen enquired:

'I should be most interested if any of your readers know of the whereabouts of three walking sticks made from the carriages of the train from the Tay Bridge disaster. These were presented to the driver, fireman and guard who, having finished their shift, were supposed to be travelling on the ill-fated train as passengers. However, due to spending too long in a local hostelry, they missed the train and were thus saved. The sticks have ebony handles and a plate just below inscribed "A relic of the Tay Bridge, 28.12.1879, presented to [name]".'

During the official inquiry into the tragedy, much was revealed about the slipshod practices which had crept into the design and construction work. To the astonishment of the commissioners, Bouch admitted that no allowance had been made for wind speeds and pressures, despite the fact that American and French engineers allowed for pressures of 50-55lb/sq ft when designing bridges. Bouch tried to wriggle free by arguing that the force of the gale had blown the train against the girders, the over-turning of the last two coaches fracturing one of the girder ties and bringing down the bridge. While there was evidence to suggest that the coaches had indeed overturned on the bridge, Bouch's ill-considered line of defence effectively admitted that the design of the bridge was such that the fracture of one tie could result in its complete downfall.

The summing-up was made by Mr H. C. Rothery, the Board of Trade's Commissioner of Wrecks:

'The conclusion, then, to which I have come is that the bridge was badly designed, badly constructed and badly maintained, and that its downfall was due to inherent defects in the structure, which must sooner or later have brought it down.'

Although the contractors, Hopkins, Gilkes & Co, were heavily criticised for the work undertaken at their Wormit foundry, the real blame was heaped on Sir Thomas Bouch. Remarkably, or even callously, the North British Railway seemed reluctant to terminate Bouch's employment after the BoT report was issued, but public and Parliamentary opinion soon held sway and Bouch's unwilling resignation was accepted.

Bouch's health declined rapidly, and he passed away in October 1880 having spent the period since the inquiry in seclusion at Moffat. It has often been suggested that the real culprits were the contractors but, many years earlier, suspicions had been voiced

Right:
The 'Spider Bridge', 1878: It can be clearly seen how the unique 'Spider Bridge' got its name. This picture was taken at Crewe North Junction before 1906, the locomotive works being in the distance to the left of the taper-corner signal cabin. The locomotive on the right, incidentally, is a 'Special Tank' engaged on empty stock shunting in Manchester Sidings. *Courtesy: LNWR Society*

that Bouch's interests lay more with his bank balance than with giving his clients quality workmanship and value for money. There were some who considered that Bouch died of a 'broken heart', but it must be asked whether a man with a heart would have attempted to retain his job after being held responsible for such a tragedy.

The North British Railway soon got cracking with plans for a new Tay Bridge but, not altogether surprisingly, Parliament expressly forbade the use of the old foundations and, furthermore, refused to sanction any building work with which Bouch was involved. A replacement bridge was eventually built alongside the old one, and opened to traffic in July 1887.

1878: The 'Spider Bridge', Crewe, Cheshire

Elsewhere in this book, mention has been made of three suspension bridges which carried main-line railways in Britain. There was, in fact, a fourth railway-carrying suspension bridge, but it was built to carry an 18in gauge line. The line in question was part of the system at Crewe Works, the LNWR's Locomotive Superintendent, John Ramsbottom, having come up with the idea of an internal narrow gauge railway to aid the movement of parts and materials throughout the constantly-expanding site.

Construction of the narrow gauge system started in 1861, and the network eventually comprised five miles of track. From 1862 purpose-built locomotives were used, a total of seven diminutive 0-4-0Ts being constructed by 1875. One of the locomotives, *Pet*, a veteran of 1865, was eventually saved for

Right:
Clyde Bridge, 1879 (widened 1905): If one looks very closely, the River Clyde is just about discernible under the array of civil engineering. The original railway bridge (now dismantled) is the one with cross girders (behind), the nearer bridge being that which was brought into use in 1905. The only locomotive activity is provided by a Fairburn 2-6-4T. The date of this picture is believed to be *circa* 1952-54. *Ian Allan Library*

preservation and, at the time of writing, lives at the Narrow Gauge Museum at Tywyn.

The LNWR was famed for its self-sufficiency, virtually every piece of its hardware and ancillary equipment being built at Crewe Works. As many of the items were required elsewhere on the LNWR network, the narrow gauge works system was extended to Crewe station so that the equipment could be loaded on to passenger trains for onward transportation. The narrow gauge railway was carried over the running lines to the north of the platforms by means of the Spider Bridge, the main span of which was of suspension construction. The bridge was alternatively known as 'Midge Bridge', the origin of that name being, it is believed, because one of the first narrow gauge locomotives to use the line into the station was named *Midge* .

The main-line railway traffic through Crewe increased during the late 1800s, and it became necessary to replace the signalbox at the north end of Crewe by a newer and larger box. The new box was built around the section of the narrow gauge line

which led to the Spider Bridge, the narrow gauge locomotives and trains actually passing through the box. The narrow gauge system was abandoned in 1929, but the Spider Bridge remained in use as a footbridge until being demolished in 1939.

1879: Clyde Bridge, Glasgow

Until the 1870s the Caledonian Railway's Lanarkshire services terminated at South Side station, while Coast trains shared Bridge Street station with the G&SWR. It was an unsatisfactory situation and so, in 1873, the Caley obtained authorisation to build an extension beyond Bridge Street station to a new terminus on the north bank of the River Clyde. The proposed bridge across the Clyde was subject to certain conditions, the Clyde Navigation Trust stipulating that the structure should carry no more

than four tracks, while Glasgow Corporation insisted on a maximum width of just 75ft.

The extension across the bridge into the new Central station opened to traffic on 1 August 1879. By the late 1890s over 480 trains worked across the bridge each weekday, and although the station facilities had already been enlarged, a major reconstruction was, by then, considered essential. Against considerable opposition, permission was granted for the addition of a second bridge to be built over the Clyde on the west side of the original structure.

In common with its older neighbour, the new bridge had three spans over the river and quays (albeit with the headroom above the high-water mark reduced from 32ft to 21ft) and two across the roadways on each side. However, the appearance of the two structures differed, the old bridge being built of wrought iron lattice girders whereas the new one was of steel web girders. Furthermore, the rail level on the old bridge was up to 3ft lower than that on the new bridge, and so the old structure was re-floored to bring its rail level up to that of the new structure.

The new bridge was 234yd long and varied in width from 114ft at its southern end to 205ft at the northern end, seven tracks entering the bridge from the south and nine leaving to the north. The extra width provided by the new approach enabled Central station to be enlarged from nine to 13 platforms. The new bridge was brought into use in March 1905 and the Caley's one-time terminus at Bridge Street was closed on 1 March of that year.

The reconstruction of Central station was completed in 1906; underneath the remodelled station, the covered section of Argyle Street was so expansive that it became known as the 'Highland man's umbrella'.

The original bridge over the Clyde was strengthened and re-floored in 1926/27, the strengthening work including the fitting of cross girders between the parapets. By the late 1950s, however, significant weaknesses had reappeared and so the structure was subjected to loading limits with double-heading being prohibited. A major resignalling scheme, which was completed at the end of 1960 in connection with the proposed electrification of South Side services, enabled greater use to be made of the newer bridge and, consequently, the role of the old bridge dwindled. A further resignalling programme of 1966 enabled the tracks across the old bridge to be dispensed with completely, and the structure was subsequently dismantled. The newer bridge is, of course, still in use today.

Below:
Monkwearmouth Bridge, 1879: Apart from the fact that 'K1' class 2-6-0 No 62005 never wore an LNER number, this could possibly pass as a pre-Nationalisation picture. It was, in fact, taken on 22 October 1978. *Ian S. Carr*

1879: Monkwearmouth Bridge, Sunderland, Tyne & Wear

The NER's line across the River Wear into a new station at Sunderland opened on 4 August 1879, the crossing of the Wear being by means of Monkwearmouth Bridge. The bridge, which was designed by Thomas Harrison, had transverse wrought iron girders between two bowstring box girders, the latter being stiffened with open webs. It stood 86ft above the high-water mark and, excluding the three stone approach arches at each end, was 106yd long. Monkwearmouth Bridge was among those used for tests by the Bridge Stress Committee in 1924 and, in common with its then neighbour, the Queen Alexandra Bridge of 1909, the locomotives used during the tests were ex-GCR and former LNWR 4-6-0s, and an ex-L&YR 0-8-0.

1879: Severn Bridge, Sharpness, Gloucestershire

Designer: G. W. Keeling
Original owner: Severn Bridge Railway
Contractors: (bridge) Hamilton's Windsor Iron Co, Garston; (approaches) Vickers & Cooke, London; Griffith Griffiths, Yorkley
Cost: bridge £190,000; approaches £90,000
Type: Bowstring girder with swing section
Materials: Wrought iron; cast iron; masonry
Total length: 1,387yd (including approaches)
Max height of rails: 70ft above high-water
Spans: 35 (inc western approach viaduct)
Tracks: 1

Today, the very mention of the Severn Bridge can cause near apoplexy among motorists whose journeys along the M4 motorway involve peak-time crossings between England and Wales. The original Severn Bridge, however, carried a railway and not a road, and was some 10 miles up-river from the existing motorway bridge.

In a reversal of usual contemporary practice, one of the backers for the proposed railway bridge across the Severn was the Gloucester & Berkeley Canal Company. At the time, most canal companies viewed the railways as a massive threat, such fears usually being very well founded, but the Gloucester & Berkeley was actually hampered by a lack of local railways. At the southern end of the canal at Sharpness, larger vessels often had to leave the dock in ballast as there was no satisfactory means of transporting bunker fuel to the isolated site. This had a serious knock-on effect at Gloucester, at the other end of the canal, where many traders desperately needed a more efficient outlet at Sharpness. Importantly, an integral part of the railway bridge scheme was a branch to Sharpness Docks, which meant that coal from the Forest of Dean, on the opposite side of the River Severn, could be transported for bunker fuel.

Apart from the canal company, the backers of the bridge scheme were the Midland Railway and the Severn & Wye Railway, the latter company having a network of predominantly mineral lines in the Forest of Dean. The Great Western Railway was invited to subscribe, but declined. The Midland took responsibility for constructing the branch from Berkeley Road, on the Gloucester–Bristol main line, to Sharpness, but the specially-created Severn Bridge Railway Company was granted the necessary powers to construct the bridge and also an extension connecting with the Severn & Wye Railway at Lydney.

Construction of the Severn Bridge was put in hand in 1875, but the task was not an easy one as the River Severn was 3,550ft wide at the chosen point of the crossing. Furthermore, the estuary has the second highest tidal range in the world - in 2¼ hours, the tide at the site of the bridge can rise or fall by 30ft. The ferocious tides prevented the floating of pre-erected bridge spans to the site, as had been done by Brunel with the Royal Albert Bridge at Saltash and, consequently, much of the work had to be undertaken literally on site above massive timber stagings. The perilous nature of the Severn tides was evidenced early on when partly-erected pier cylinders were washed away in 1876, some scaffolding meeting a similar fate two years later.

The bridge was, in effect, four different structures in sequence. The main section across the Severn comprised 21 spans supported by piers of cylindrical cast iron columns, some of which were embedded into rock over 70ft below the high-water mark. Of the 21 spans, two were 327ft wide and provided 70ft clearance for the main tidal channel of the Severn at high water, the other 19 spans being considerably smaller. The bridge incorporated some 3,600 tons of cast iron and 3,500 tons of wrought iron. The second section of the bridge was over the canal at Sharpness, and comprised a 196ft-long opening section supported by a masonry pier; it was turned on a ring of conical rollers, power being provided by a steam engine located across the top of the bridge. The swing section weighed some 400 tons. The two other sections of the Severn Bridge each comprised a viaduct (one on each approach) built from Forest of Dean stone. At the time of its opening, the Severn Bridge was second only to the Tay Bridge in length.

Above:
Severn Bridge, 1879: In common with some other bridges and viaducts featured in this book, the size of the Severn Bridge was rather grand when compared to the traffic it accommodated. This delightful period view also shows Severn Bridge station, on the west bank of the river. *Bucknall Collection/Ian Allan Library*

Below:
Severn Bridge, 1879: A coaster sailing along the canal from Sharpness to Gloucester passes underneath the opening section of the Severn Bridge on 6 April 1965, some 4½ years after the bridge was abruptly closed to railway traffic. *B. J. Ashworth*

The bridge was ceremonially opened to railway traffic on 17 October 1879 and, as had been anticipated, the Severn Bridge Railway formally amalgamated with the Severn & Wye Railway. The Midland Railway's use of running powers over the bridge was, perhaps, not of tremendous benefit, but head-office was aware that any powers which stole a march on the GWR were well worth maintaining. The branch between Berkeley Road and Sharpness had, in fact, been built by the Midland (opened to freight on 2 August 1875 and to passengers on 1 August 1876), but became MR/GWR property in 1894 when those two companies jointly took over the then-bankrupt Severn & Wye Railway.

The GWR used the Severn Bridge intensively during a short period in 1881 after a fire had caused extensive damage to the pier at Portskewett (near Chepstow), from where ferries plied to and from New Passage (near Pilning). The New Passage–Portskewett ferry crossing was an integral part of the GWR's Bristol–South Wales route until the opening of the Severn Tunnel in 1886. Regular GWR usage of the Severn Bridge, however, did not start until 1923, Bristol–South Wales trains being routed via the bridge on Sundays when maintenance work was being carried out in the Severn Tunnel.

Although it had originally been intended to build a double-track bridge, accommodation was for only a single-track. The weight restrictions for the bridge prevented the use of anything heavier than GWR 'Dean Goods' 0-6-0s, '2021' class 0-6-0STs/PTs, and lightweight MR 0-6-0s, double-heading being strictly forbidden. Nevertheless, on one occasion during the interwar period, the 56-ton bulk of an 'Aberdare' class 2-6-0 was mistakenly routed across the bridge, apparently without any detriment to the structure. During World War 2 the GWR made repeated requests for the '4200' class 2-8-0Ts and '7200' class 2-8-2Ts to be allowed across the bridge, but the LMSR wouldn't entertain such ideas.

After Nationalisation, control of the bridge passed to the Western Region. The WR seemed to thumb its corporate nose at the old LMSR restrictions by readily permitting '4300' class 2-6-0s and '2251' class 0-6-0s on to the bridge, those two types having been banned by the LMSR. In 1956 the WR undertook tests to see how much strengthening the bridge would require to permit the regular passage of far heavier trains, 'Castle' class 4-6-0s Nos 5018 *St Mawes Castle* and 5042 *Winchester Castle* being carefully monitored as they crossed the bridge with a test train of ballast wagons.

The outcome of the tests with the 'Castles' was that strengthening was authorised, but it was never carried out. On the foggy night of 25 October 1960 a runaway oil barge collided with one of the piers,

and two spans were brought down. For a considerable time it was debated whether the necessary repair work was an economic proposition, but the disintegration of the railway system in the Forest of Dean in the mid-1960s rather pre-empted matters. Inevitably, demolition of the bridge was ordered, work commencing in 1967 and being completed in May 1970. The Gloucester firm which undertook the demolition had to hire a 400-ton floating crane, the *Magnus II*, from a German company, the hire fee being £1,050 per day.

Despite its length, the Severn Bridge was one of Britain's lesser-known structures, that no doubt being due to its lack of main-line status. Apart from the Sunday diversion of Severn Tunnel trains, the only passenger trains to use the bridge regularly were the Berkeley Road–Lydney Town locals, of which there were rarely more than seven or eight a day. Even in the freight league, the mineral 'exports' of the Forest of Dean which were transported via the bridge were hardly intensive. The scale of the Severn Bridge was, to be honest, disproportionate to the importance of the local railways.

1879: Harringworth Viaduct, Nr Harringworth, Northamptonshire/ Leicestershire

The Midland Railway promoted the line between Kettering and Melton Mowbray mainly to provide an independent outlet for traffic between Rutland and the south. The route took advantage of two existing lines, and the two new sections which were required to complete the 'new' line were opened to goods traffic on 1 November 1879 and to passengers on 2 February 1880. Through expresses between St Pancras and Bradford started to use the new route from 1 June 1880.

On the newly-built southern section between Glendon and Manton, the railway was carried 60ft above the River Welland (which then marked the border between Northamptonshire and Rutland) and the LNWR's Rugby–Peterborough line by means of a splendid viaduct. Designed by the MR's Chief Engineer, John Underwood, it had 82 arches, each of 40ft span, and was built of blue and red brick. With a length of 1,275yd, it was claimed to be the country's longest brick-built railway viaduct.

Harringworth Viaduct, 1879: On 14 August 1983 the 8.30am Sheffield–St Pancras was diverted via the Oakham–Kettering line and consequently crossed Harringworth Viaduct, which is dubiously claimed to be the country's longest brick-built viaduct. *A. Taylor*

1881: South Esk Viaduct, Montrose, Angus

The line between Arbroath and Kinnaber Junction (on the Caledonian's line to Aberdeen) was opened for local goods traffic on 1 March 1881, but passenger trains did not commence until 1 May 1883. One of the reasons for the delay in the commencement of passenger services was that, after the fall of the Tay Bridge, the line had little purpose as part of a long-distance through route. Another reason was that trouble was experienced with the South Esk Viaduct, which spanned the north arm of Montrose Basin.

The viaduct was built of wrought iron to a design of Thomas Bouch - it was the last Bouch-designed structure to be completed. In December 1880, one year after the fall of Bouch's Tay Bridge, the viaduct was inspected for the Board of Trade by Col Yolland, one of those who had helped to officiate at the Tay Bridge inquiry. From the outset, Col Yolland was distinctly unimpressed by the fact that the viaduct had not been built in accordance with the original specifications and, as he had learned a thing or two about Bouch-designed structures, he subjected the viaduct to very stringent tests over a 36-hour period. At the end of the tests, the viaduct was distorted throughout its length. That could have been the final straw in Bouch's tattered reputation but, perhaps mercifully, Bouch had died two months previously.

The viaduct was demolished, and a new one was constructed in its place. The replacement structure had 15 bowstring spans, and was supported by pairs of cast iron columns filled with concrete. Local folklore has it that the 'new' South Esk Viaduct was a small-scale prototype for the second Tay Bridge. The viaduct was built to carry only a single track; the rest of the Arbroath–Kinnaber Junction line was also single-track but was built with future

Left:
South Esk Viaduct, original viaduct completed 1881: This bowstring girder viaduct replaced a Bouch-designed structure which had been tested to destruction by the Board of Trade Inspector. It crosses what is now the only outlet from Montrose Basin. On 5 August 1972, a Class 47 was photographed hauling the London–Aberdeen sleeper. *Derek Cross*

doubling in mind. One contemporary description of the line as a whole was that it was '...a local railway built to main-line standards'.

Despite its inauspicious beginnings, South Esk Viaduct went on to have a long and useful life although, today, the section of line between Montrose South and Usan, on which the viaduct is located, is the only single-track section on the East Coast line. In the late 1970s work commenced on replacing the viaduct's timber decking by new steel decking, and the old-style bridge rails were replaced by ballasted flat-bottomed rails. In two operations between 1989 and 1991, the viaduct was shot-blasted and repainted.

A very short distance to the south of South Esk Viaduct, the railway crossed the southern outlet of Montrose Basin by means of a curving 17-span brick-built viaduct, which was constructed on a gradient of 1 in 88. The outlet under the viaduct has now been filled in, part of the site being used for a roundabout on the A92 trunk road, and Rossie Island (which separated the two outlets of Montrose Basin) is an island no more. In recent years the brick viaduct has been treated to a degree of repointing and some of the original bricks have now been replaced.

1883: Staithes Viaduct, Staithes, North Yorkshire

Designer: John Dixon/Thomas Harrison
Original owner: North Eastern Railway *
Type: Lattice girder viaduct
Materials: Wrought iron; cast iron
Total length: 233yd
Max height of rails: 152ft
Spans: 17
Tracks: 1
* Work started by the Whitby, Redcar & Middlesbrough Union Railway

In May 1871 the Whitby, Redcar & Middlesbrough Union Railway ambitiously started work on its line in northeast Yorkshire in anticipation of opening up beds of iron ore between Loftus and Whitby. The line was difficult to construct, and the frequency of landslips and cliff falls was such that the WR&MUR's corporate coffers were virtually exhausted long before the line was finished. In 1875 the North Eastern Railway took a lease on the financially ailing WR&MUR and set about completing the line.

Initially, the NER had cause to wonder about the real worth of its acquisition. It had already become evident that the anticipated volume of iron ore traffic would prove very disappointing and, furthermore, the quality of the engineering work along the

unfinished route had blatantly been sacrificed in the name of economy. Indeed, a section between Sandsend and Kettleness had actually fallen into the sea, and the NER wisely chose to reroute the line a little inland rather than have it perched almost on the edge of unsafe cliffs.

It seems that, under NER auspices, the contractors worked around the clock to finish the line, but the practice of lighting bonfires along the route to permit night work did not amuse the folks at Trinity House. On one particular instance, the skipper of the brigantine *Colina* mistook the bonfires on the cliff-tops between Sandsend and Whitby for the lights of Whitby, and the vessel ran ashore. Consequently, the NER was ordered to shield the bonfires from the view of shipping.

Prior to the NER's recommencement of the work the company's engineer, Thomas Harrison, had carried out an inspection of the existing works, and the line's viaducts, in particular, had come in for hefty criticism. In order to examine the viaducts Harrison had ordered that holes be cut in the metal piers, and he had found that a number of the piers had been filled, not with cement, but with gravel, while others were decidedly out of perpendicular.

Harrison later described the task which he had inherited:

'I have never seen work so thoroughly scamped, with the viaducts and ordinary bridges so badly designed and as badly executed as to be in a dangerous condition. Over £30,000 had been spent on putting the viaducts in a proper state and the roadway for the permanent way over the viaducts was of the flimsiest character and such as no Government Inspector would under any circumstances have passed. All the bridges with the exception of one were so defective and in such a dangerous state that three were obliged to be taken down and rebuilt before the contract was let, and plans had to be prepared for rebuilding or strengthening others, and nearly every abutment of the viaducts had to be taken down and rebuilt.'

The line eventually opened on 3 December 1883, and was worked by the NER until being formally taken over in 1889. Among the bridges and viaducts along the route the best-known was, arguably, that at Staithes. Built to a design of John Dixon, who had worked as an assistant to both George and Robert Stephenson, it comprised six 60ft spans and eleven 30ft spans. It had been virtually finished in 1875 but, after the NER had stepped in, the structure had been substantially strengthened by having its piers braced together by longitudinal lattice beams. In later years a wind gauge was installed at one end of the viaduct, and if gales off the North Sea reached a certain velocity, train services across the viaduct were suspended. The wind gauge was ultimately found a home at the National Railway Museum. Among the other principal viaducts on the line were **Upgang**, and **East Row**.

At its northern end, the Whitby line made an end-on junction with what had started life as the

Left:
Staithes Viaduct, line opened 1883: The original viaduct was almost finished when the Whitby–Loftus line was taken over in 1875 by the North Eastern Railway, but it had to be substantially strengthened before being allowed to carry revenue-earning trains. The longitudinal lattice girders were part of the strengthening work. *E. E. Smith*

1884: Hewenden Viaduct, Nr Thornton, West Yorkshire

Construction of the Queensbury Lines in the West Riding of Yorkshire presented the Great Northern Railway with considerable headaches. The nature of the terrain necessitated extensive engineering works and, at the time, the GNR had to watch the pennies very carefully. The Thornton–Keighley (Ingrow) line, for example, required the construction of hefty viaducts at Thornton, Hewenden and Cullingworth. The second of those, Hewenden Viaduct, was near Denholme which stood 877ft above sea level and was, in fact, the highest point on the entire GNR system.

Hewenden Viaduct was 343yd long and built on a curve; it had 17 brick arches, each of 50ft span, and stood 123ft at its highest point. During its construction, shifting sands played havoc with attempts to find a solid base on which to build and, consequently, the stone piers had to be sunk all of 62½ft. The section of line across the viaduct

Cleveland Railway, that company's intention having been to transport iron ore to the Tees where it could be shipped across to Bell's Ironworks at Port Clarence. The former Cleveland Railway line had been completed by the NER and had opened throughout in 1867. It included the impressive **Kilton Viaduct** across Kilton Beck to the north of Loftus (named Lofthouse until 1874). Designed by James Brunlees, the 13-span viaduct was 226yd long and 150ft high and was built of wrought iron girders supported by stone piers. It was, however, a comparatively short-lived structure as it was replaced in 1911 by an embankment containing some 720,000 tons of spoil. That move had been necessitated by the undermining of the viaduct's foundations by ironstone workings.

The Middlesborough–Whitby route as a whole became famous for its splendid sea views. To the chagrin of enthusiasts, not to mention many locals, passenger services south of Loftus were withdrawn on 5 May 1958, the line later being closed completely and the viaducts subsequently dismantled. However, in 1973 the line was reopened to serve British Steel at Skinningrove and the Cleveland Mining complex at Boulby, the potash traffic from the latter reaching 700,000 tons annually in the mid-1980s.

Below:
Hewenden Viaduct, 1884: The structure was built to carry the Great Northern's Thornton–Keighley line, and was close to the highest point on the GNR network. 'N1' class 0-6-2T No 69434 of Bradford shed (then 37C) hauls the 4.18pm Keighley–Bradford train across the viaduct on 14 May 1955, the line closing to passenger traffic just nine days later. *J. C. W. Halliday*

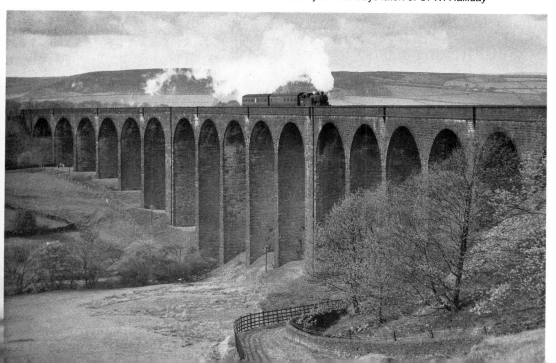

opened on 1 May 1884 and was closed completely on 17 July 1961, passenger services having been withdrawn in May 1955. When this author last visited the area in 1988, the viaduct was still standing.

1885: Esk Valley Viaduct, Whitby, North Yorkshire

The rugged coastline between Scarborough and Whitby might have great visual appeal, but the local topography presented all sorts of problems for those who planned, constructed and later operated the Scarborough & Whitby Railway. When the line was eventually completed the S&WR made the most of the area's attractions, the company's Official Guide containing this flowery offering:

'The Scarborough and Whitby line has opened out the country and made it accessible in all its virgin loveliness. The line runs through pleasant and undulating pasture lands at either end, winds in and out amongst the gorse and heatherclad hills, dips into wooded dales, skirts the edge of a wild moor, climbs the highest cliff on the Yorkshire coast, runs round one of the bonniest bays in the Kingdom, and over a portion of its course is perched on the brow of a cliff against which the waves carelessly break.'

The S&WR started work on the line in June 1872, but the company was in financial trouble long before the route was completed. However, the enthusiasm and financial assistance of local businessman W.H.Hammond did much to save the company from an early demise, although compromises had to be reached concerning the original plans for a completely independent line. One such compromise was a working agreement with the North Eastern Railway, which worked the line from its opening on 16 July 1885, and this necessitated a connection with the NER at Whitby. The connecting line required the construction of not only a 260yd tunnel under Falsgrave Road, but also the well-known 305yd-long red-brick viaduct carrying the line 120ft above the River Esk on 13 arches.

The NER purchased the S&WR outright in 1898. The route between Scarborough and Whitby became renowned for its scenery, but locomotive crews and the railway company's operating department held a different opinion as the ferocious gradients, which peaked at 1 in 39 near Robin Hood's

Left:
Esk Valley Viaduct, 1885: A Middlesbrough–Whitby diesel multiple-unit passes under the disused viaduct on its approach to Whitby in August 1970. The disused line leading up to the viaduct can just be seen under the right-hand arch. *M. Dunnett*

Bay, provided a perpetual challenge. In 1930 the LNER submitted its new twin-unit Sentinel steam railcar *Phenomena* to tests on the line but although that unit was found permanent employment at South Blyth, twin-engine single-car Sentinels became a regular feature on the Scarborough–Whitby route until the 1940s. The closure of the Scarborough–Whitby route across the Esk Valley Viaduct on 8 March 1965 was one of the most unpopular of all the disputed decisions of the post-Beeching era.

1886: Tochieneal–Garmouth, Morayshire/Banffshire

(principal structures featured below)

The Great North of Scotland Railway finally received authorisation for its Moray Firth Coast Line in July 1882, the line having been opposed by the Great North's regular sparring partner, the Highland Railway, which had proposed a rival route. The last section of the line to be completed was that between Tochieneal and Garmouth, freight traffic commencing on 5 April 1886 and passenger services on 1 May. The line had been costly to construct, due largely to the need for two major viaducts.

One of the two structures was the **Spey Viaduct**, between Garmouth and Fochabers-on-Spey (renamed Fochabers in 1893, Fochabers & Spey Bay in 1916, and Spey Bay in 1918). The Great North had anticipated constructing a rather modest structure across the Spey estuary, but local landowners had persuaded Parliament to enforce the building of a large viaduct so as not to interfere with the salmon fishing. The resultant structure took some three years to construct. The main span of the viaduct took the form of a graceful 350ft-long bowstring arch, which was the largest span on any single-track railway in Britain. It was flanked on either side by three plain truss girder spans, each nearly 100ft long, the total overall length of the structure being 947½ft (316yd). The stone piers were founded on solid rock and concreted up to floodwater level.

The design of the viaduct was credited to the Great North's Civil Engineer, Patrick Barnett (1837–1915), although the design work was undertaken in collaboration with Messrs Blyth & Cunningham. The stone work was executed by John Fyfe & Co and the ironwork by Messrs Blaikie Bros of Aberdeen, both concerns having had long associations with the Great North. Despite the cost of construction, the Great North was delighted with the finished product, particularly its stability under

Above:
Spey Viaduct, 1886: The elegance of 'Barnett's Monument' is very evident in this undated picture. *Bucknall Collection/Ian Allan Library*

flood conditions. Somewhat ironically, though, the River Spey subsequently altered its course and now flows under the easternmost spans.

The second major feature of the Coast Line was **Cullen Viaduct** which was also rather more substantial (and costly) than the Great North had originally intended. The reason for the construction of such a large viaduct was explained by the Chairman, William Ferguson, at the half-yearly shareholders' meeting on 17 September 1885:

'The works at Cullen were imposed upon us by Parliament to meet objections by the advisers of the late Earl of Seafield to our passing between his house at Cullen, and the sea. Instead of a picturesque and graceful viaduct over a small part of the park at Cullen House, which would have added much to the natural beauty of the landscape there, and preserved the links at Cullen untouched, we have built two expensive and unsightly viaducts of four and six arches, and then crossed the links first by a lofty viaduct 70 feet high of eight arches, and then a huge embankment which cuts the links in two and disfugures the beautiful bay...

'...Instead of works at Cullen Bay, as originally designed, a credit to the engineer, we have been compelled to carry out others which will in all time coming be a "blot on the fair face of nature in a lovely locality" and cause future generations who do not know "the story of their birth" to regard our engineering skills in laying out the line as sadly deficient, though I venture to say the verdict in regard to its execution must be one highly appreciative of that skill. I sympathise with Mr Barnett in having to construct such a line.'

The Earl of Seafield's obstructiveness was not entirely due to his concern for the views from his estate. A glance at *Bradshaw's Shareholders'*

Guide of a few years earlier reveals that the Rt Hon Earl of Seafield just happened to be a director of the Great North's old enemy, the Highland Railway.

Known almost anonymously as 'Underbridge 923', the eight-arch viaduct at Cullen was, despite the fears of the Great North's directorate, eventually regarded as one of the finest masonry works in the area. Its piers, some of which were founded 20ft below ground level and laid on concrete bases, were hollow, the limestone blocks being filled with rubble. The arches were built of red bricks set in cement, with a ring of ashlar on each side, and the parapets were of blue limestone, topped with a coping of freestone. Some of the stone came from the contractor's quarries at Stirling, the limestone coming from Burghead and being hauled to the site by traction engines which apparently caused considerable damage to the local roads. During construction, work was delayed for over a month after the formwork of the fifth arch had been blown down in a storm. It is estimated that the final bill for the viaduct accounted for some £34,000 of the £305,870 which it cost to build the entire 26 mile-long railway line.

Construction of the four-arch viaduct at Cullen was also delayed, the culprit in this case being the Town Council which objected to the width of the arch over Seafield Street. The problem of narrowing the thoroughfare was circumvented by the provision of two smaller arches over the pavements. The third viaduct at Cullen, the six-arch structure over Castle Street, was constructed without any significant hiccups, but in December 1887 two of its arches were brought down by the subsidence of the

Above:
Cullen Viaduct, 1886: Despite the Great North's initial dissatisfaction with having to build a substantial viaduct at Cullen, the structure eventually became a very popular feature of the attractive town. Unfortunately, this delightful period picture is undated. *Bucknall Collection/Ian Allan Library*

adjoining embankment. Several shops were demolished by the rubble but, fortunately, nobody was killed. The structure was not rebuilt in its entirety, the two collapsed arches being replaced by a new embankment, and a third semi-collapsed arch being filled with concrete. The contractor pulled out all the stops during the rebuilding work, and the viaduct reopened to traffic on 7 January 1888. The bill for the remedial work was £2,408.

The Moray Firth Coast line remained in use until 1968, the last services operating on 4 May, and the Spey Viaduct and the three structures at Cullen were all left to stand. The Spey Viaduct, which had become known as 'Barnett's Monument' (after its designer), is now used as a public footpath, and two of the three viaducts at Cullen are still in reasonable condition. The exception is the Castle Street Viaduct which, in the late 1980s, was showing signs of excessive settlement, but its future was safeguarded by its status (in common with the other viaducts) as a listed structure.

1887: Tay Bridge, Wormit–Dundee, Fife/Angus

Designer: W. H. Barlow and C. Barlow
Original owner: North British Railway
Contractor: Tancred & Arrol, Glasgow
Cost: £1,000,000 (inc approaches)
Type: Lattice girder
Material: Wrought iron; brick
Total length: 3,570yd
Max height of rails: 77ft above high-water
Spans: 85 (including approaches)
Tracks: 2

One of the few good things which could be said about the original Tay Bridge was that, during its short operational life between June 1878 and December 1879, it proved the usefulness of a direct railway across the Firth of Tay. Consequently, the North British Railway soon planned a replacement of the original structure but, even at the early stages, things were not exactly simple.

The first plans for the replacement bridge were prepared by Sir James Brunlees, but as they incorporated the use of the original foundations, the plans were rejected by a Parliamentary Select Committee. The NBR turned to W.H.Barlow, who had been one of the officials at the inquest into the collapse of the old bridge. Barlow enlisted the assistance of his son, Crawford, and proposed an entirely new double-track bridge 60ft up-river of the remains of the original single-track structure. A major obstacle was the Board of Trade's stipulation that '...all obstructions interfering with the navigation caused by the old bridge be removed...', and that ruled out Barlow's plans to use the old structure as a staging during the construction of the replacement.

A compromise with the BoT was eventually reached whereby all but five of the old piers could be retained to the level of their cutwaters, the others having to be removed to a level of 15ft below the low-water mark. This saved a great deal of time-consuming and costly work but it was, however, of

Above:
Tay Bridge, 1887: The impressive approach to Dundee from the northern end of the second Tay Bridge was captured in this 'carriage window' picture, taken from the 10.10am Edinburgh service on 1 April 1965. Despite the interest value of this photograph, it is sincerely hoped that readers do *not* follow the photographer's example of putting one's head at risk and thereby inconveniencing those who would have to clear up the ensuing mess.
Anthony A. Vickers

little use for the construction of the new bridge. A later edict from the BoT reversed the earlier decree, and the confused NBR then found itself compelled to retain all of the original piers to cutwater level.

Including its approaches the new bridge was, to a certain extent, several structures in series. On the southern approach, the lines from Wormit and St Forts approached the Tay Bridge on 50ft-span brick arches, the two lines converging immediately at the start of the 'proper' bridge. The southern section of the Tay Bridge itself comprised one span of 118ft, 10 of 129ft and 13 of 145ft. The central section (the new 'high girder' section), under which shipping had to pass, had 11 spans of 245ft and two of 227ft; when viewed on the level, the 1 in 114 drop in the northbound direction which commenced at pier 32 was clearly evident. Northwards from the 'high girder' section, there was one span of 162ft, 11 of 129ft, 24 of 71ft, and one of 56ft. There were eight further land spans on the curving approach to Dundee, these being known as the Esplanade Spans. From the south, they consisted of a pair of wrought iron skew spans on brick piers, four 66ft girder spans on cast iron columns, a 108ft-span girder section on brick piers and, finally, a short brick arch linking the new bridge with the old line into Dundee Tay Bridge station. Later, Dundee Esplanade station was built, partially on the Esplanade spans.

The new bridge was, at 3,570yd in length, 114yd longer than its predecessor; of the new structure, 2,799yd was in a straight line. Mindful of the fate of the earlier Tay Bridge, the designers had conducted extensive tests to assess the effects of wind pressure, the first time such tests had been conducted for the construction of a British railway bridge, and the resultant structure was built to withstand pressures of 56lb/sq ft. Furthermore, each pier cylinder had been tested to a load of 33% above the maximum working load. The bridge looked far more substantial than Bouch's spindly structure, the feeling of solidity being enhanced by twin-piers connected at their tops by a wrought iron box-girder, and with a reinforcing brace just above the high-water mark.

With the exception of just two spans and, of course, the central 'high girder' section, the girders from the old bridge were reused for the new structure; they formed the outer pair of each span, with new intermediate girders between them. As partial consolation for the £1,000,000 which it had cost to build the new bridge, the North British Railway

Left:
Tay Bridge, 1887: The 1 in 114 drop of the northern section of the Tay Bridge is clearly evident. This 'preservation special', hauled by 'A4' class 4-6-2 No 4498 *Sir Nigel Gresley*, operated on 20 May 1967. *John R. P. Hunt*

was permitted to regard the structure as 10 miles in length for the calculation of fares and freight charges, the old bridge having been reckoned at 6 miles. It was, however, pointed out that the NBR would save £50,000 each year by not having to pay the Caledonian Railway for the conveyance of through traffic via Perth.

The new Tay Bridge opened to passenger traffic on 20 June 1887, and entered the history books as the last of the great wrought iron railway bridges. In marked contrast to the previous Bouch-designed bridge, the replacement stood the test of time remarkably well, the first major overhaul not being required until 1953. This involved the renewal of the expansion bearings, some of which weighed over four tons, but as engineers had occupation of the bridge only for short periods at weekends, the task was not finished until 1965. When that had been completed, work started on a five-year programme to replace sections of the flooring.

During the work flocks of starlings nesting under the bridge presented a regular hazard to the men, the problem being so great that, at one stage, it was even considered using falcons as an 'anti-starling' measure. The problem was eventually solved by the use of gas-operated detonators but, as an additional precaution against over-bold starlings, men working on the bridge were issued with lifejackets which inflated automatically on impact with the water.

The Tay Bridge is, of course, still in use today as an integral part of the Edinburgh–Dundee–Aberdeen main line, although Esplanade station at its northern end and the line diverging to Wormit at the southern end have now gone. Esplanade station was closed to passengers on 2 October 1939, the War Department having requisitioned the premises, and the Wormit line was closed on 5 May 1969.

1890: Forth Bridge, Queensferry, Linlithgowshire/Fife

Designers: John Fowler and Benjamin Baker
Original owner: Forth Bridge Co (joint North British/North Eastern/Great Northern/Midland Railways)
Contractors: Tancred, Arrol & Co
Cost: £3,000,000
Type: Cantilever and lattice girder
Materials: Mild steel; granite
Total length: 2,766yd
Max height of rails: 156ft above high-water
Spans: 23
Tracks: 2

As early as 1805 plans were in hand to bore a pair of road tunnels under the Firth of Forth. That

Above:

Forth Bridge, 1890: The Forth Bridge is, understandably, one of the most-photographed structures in Britain. However, few photographs manage to illustrate the vast scale of the bridge as well as this one, the houses at North Queensferry being positively dwarfed by the steel monster. The date is 17 July 1965, and the locomotive hauling the 2.25pm Edinburgh–Dundee (SO) is 'A3' class 4-6-2 No 60052 *Prince Palatine.*
C. E. Weston

scheme came to nothing, but the challenge of constructing a means of communication across or under the Forth continued to attract engineers. In 1818 an iron suspension bridge was proposed by James Anderson, the design being for a somewhat flimsy structure. A comment on Anderson's proposed design was made by W. Westhofen in the 28 February 1890 issue of *Engineering* magazine: '...so light indeed that on a dull day it would hardly have been visible, and after a heavy gale probably no longer seen on a clear day either'.

Two designs for railway bridges across the Forth later appeared, an 1860 proposal being for a lattice girder bridge between Blackness Castle and Charlestown, and a proposal of 1873 being for a suspension bridge roughly in the same position as the structure which was eventually built. Work on the suspension bridge commenced in 1879, but went no further than the construction of a solitary pier. The abrupt cessation of work was occasioned by the collapse of the Tay Bridge as, without a crossing of the Tay, a bridge across the Forth would

be of little use. Furthermore, the designer of the suspension bridge across the Forth was one Thomas Bouch who, after the Tay Bridge disaster, was decidedly *persona non grata.*

However, the building of a new bridge across the Tay resulted in a revival of the plans to cross the Forth. The company administering proceedings was the jointly-owned Forth Bridge Co, which had been specially incorporated in 1873 for the later-aborted suspension bridge crossing. Various schemes for tunnels and suspension bridges were considered, but the proposal which won the day was that for a massive cantilever bridge.

Work started in June 1883, and necessitated negotiations with the Admiralty who owned the small island of Inch Garvie on which the four piers of the central tower were to rest. The eventual outcome was that the Forth Bridge Co purchased the island outright for £4,300. The bridge had three towers, their main steel tubes being 12ft in diameter and rising to a height of 361ft above the high-water mark. The towers were connected by lattice girder sections, the resultant span between each of the towers being 1,710ft. The approaches at each end were by means of lattice girder sections supported by high granite piers, the span of most of those piers being 168ft. Mindful of the fate of the Tay Bridge, extensive wind-pressure tests were con-

Right:

Forth Bridge, 1890: If it weren't for the group of people in the mid-distance, the sheer size of the Forth Bridge might not be as obvious. This picture was taken inside the Queensferry cantilever. *G. J. Jackson*

Above:
Forth Bridge, 1890: Canon Treacy was clearly lifted both spiritually and physically in order to take this splendid picture of Thompson 'A1' 4-6-2 No 60160 *Auld Reekie* crossing the Forth Bridge with a freight train. *Eric Treacy*

ducted, and the Forth Bridge was designed to withstand a pressure of 56lb/sq ft.

The sheer scale of the Forth Bridge needs no emphasising, but it is nevertheless worth repeating some oft-quoted facts and figures. The main towers and cantilevers incorporated 50,958 tons of steel, some 8,000,000 rivets, and the workforce peaked at 4,600 men for whom a purpose-built 'town' was established on the south shore. Sadly, though, 56 men were killed during the bridge's construction. After the bridge was opened it became considered lucky to throw a coin out of the window of the train, and it was noted that maintenance staff were among those who did nothing to dispel the superstition as, on a good week, a very close inspection of the structure could result in staff retrieving up to £1 each.

The first train, an engineers' special, crossed the bridge on 22 January 1890. The formal opening of the bridge took place on 4 March when, in a howling wet gale, the Prince of Wales (later King Edward VII) ceremonially drove home the final rivet. The opening day special, hauled by the NBR's Holmes 7ft 4-4-0 No 602, was driven across by the Marchioness of Tweeddale and, as if to round off the occasion, the bridge's designers, John Fowler (1817–1898) and Benjamin Baker (1840–1907), had knighthoods conferred on them. There was, however, one major fly in the ointment. Although the construction of the bridge had kept to schedule, the North British Railway had apparently disregarded the matter of approach lines and, on opening day, the only approach open to traffic was the single-track branch via Kirkliston. The double-track main-line approaches at both ends were not ready until 2 June.

Although the Forth Bridge Co was jointly owned by four railway companies, the traffic across it was worked by the North British Railway; the Midland Railway's interest in the bridge's construction was due to its through-traffic agreement with the NBR. As early as 1895, 45,228 trains with a total weight of 13,455,641 tons crossed the Forth Bridge, the figures of the early 20th century sometimes nearing 15,000,000 tons annually.

With two of the greatest railway bridges in Britain to its credit the NBR stole a march on its arch-rival, the Caledonian Railway, the NBR's Edinburgh–Aberdeen route of 130 miles being 29 miles shorter than the Caley's. However, the popularity of the new route via the Forth and Tay bridges resulted in a degree of corporate foot-shooting, as Waverley station in Edinburgh soon became hopelessly congested. The NBR had little option but to rebuild the station completely, and although the work commenced in 1892 it was not completed until 1900. The final bill for the reconstruction of Waverley station and its approaches came to over £1,500,000 which, no doubt, caused near apoplexy for the company's Chairman, George Wieland, to whom the word 'expenditure' was foreign.

The Forth Bridge retained its status as the world's largest cantilever bridge until December 1917, when the Quebec Bridge over the St Lawrence River in Canada was opened. Throughout its life, the Forth Bridge has been subjected to minimal alterations, and that speaks volumes for the soundness of the original design. The centenary of the bridge was celebrated in October 1990 and was marked by a highly-impressive illumination of the entire structure. It is a well-known fact that the painting of the bridge used to be a permanent job, a team of up to 29 men taking three years to apply a total of almost 10,000gal of paint and then starting the task all over again. More recently, though, just four men have been employed on the painting work, the use of diesel-powered sprayers enabling paint to be applied at the rate of 1.8gal per minute.

At present, there is room for vague doubts concerning the future of the Forth Bridge. At the time of writing, the future of Britain's railway network itself is attracting heated debate, and so it cannot be completely ruled out that the Edinburgh–Dundee route via the Forth and Tay bridges might be sacrificed in the name of economy. To most people, such a move would be unthinkable, but in view of the current ethos of 'profitability above all else', nothing can be completely discounted.

1890: Hawarden Bridge, Nr Queensferry, Clwyd

The Manchester, Sheffield & Lincolnshire Railway (which later became the GCR) made several proposals for lines to cross the River Dee near Chester, but none of the plans came to fruition. It took an independent company, the Chester & Connah's Quay Railway, to achieve the task, although financial assistance was forthcoming from the Wirral Railway and the Wrexham, Mold & Connah's Quay Railway, the latter having a close allegiance with the MS&LR. The crossing of the Dee, which promised to provide a highly useful new route to Birkenhead, was initially intended to be by means of an iron swing bridge, but the Board of Trade insisted on a swing span of no less than 140ft. This necessitated a revision of the plans, a steel structure being designed instead.

The bridge was designed by Francis Fox and the contractors were John Cochrane & Sons. It had a swing section of 287ft which was, at the time, the longest swing span in Britain. The swing section could be opened or closed in just 40secs. There were also two fixed spans, each of 120ft, on the approaches. The final bill for the construction was £55,862 plus a further £6,850 for the hydraulic machinery. The bridge was ceremonially opened by

Mrs Gladstone, the wife of the former (and future!) Prime Minister, on 3 August 1889 but traffic did not commence until the following year (goods: 16 March, passengers: 3 August) as the connecting lines were not ready. In 1924 Hawarden Bridge halt was opened at the north end of the bridge, mainly to serve the workers at the nearby John Summers steelworks.

1891: Ouse Bridge, Selby, North Yorkshire

Designer: Harold Copperthwaite
Original owner: North Eastern Railway
Contractor: Cleveland Bridge & Engineering Co
Type: Swing bridge
Materials: Wrought iron; cast iron
Total length: 80yd
Spans: 2
Tracks: 2

The first bridge carrying the railway across the River Ouse at Selby was that of the Hull & Selby Railway, which opened its line on 13 February 1840. Because Selby was an active port, an opening bridge was necessary and so the structure took the form of a twin-span cast iron bascule bridge. The bridge was almost 64yd long and, when raised, allowed a clear waterway of 45ft in width; raising and lowering was by means of a quadrant and rack worked by hand, but each operation could be accomplished in under a minute.

As the railway traffic grew, the old bascule bridge became increasingly hard-pressed to cope, particularly after 1871 when it accommodated East Coast main line traffic as well. However, it was not until 1888 that firm plans were put in hand for a new bridge. As river traffic still had precedence over rail traffic, the replacement was required to

Left:
Ouse Bridge, 1891: The bridge's last bout of rebuilding was undertaken in the late 1960s, the cabin being raised by 3ft 6in to permit the erection of overhead wires. This official picture was taken after the raising of the cabin had been completed but, for various reasons, electrification did not take place. *British Railways*

have an opening section, and so the Chief Engineer of the NER's Southern Division, Harold Copperthwaite, proposed a swing bridge. Built on the east side of the original structure, it was brought into use in February 1891.

Selby's new swing bridge was made of wrought iron plate girders and had two spans, one of 43yd length and the other of 37yd. The longer span was supported by a pier which was formed by a cluster of nine iron cylinders, the central one 7ft in diameter and the others 6ft; the span was set off-centre on the pier in order to provide a clear waterway of 60ft width. The bridge was hydraulically-operated, the movements being controlled from a cabin perched above the girders of the opening section.

The lines either side of the bridge were eventually quadrupled, but the bridge remained double-track. The problems of a bottleneck were partially reduced by a carefully considered points layout on either side of the bridge, the most concise description of which was, arguably, given by the late Ken Hoole in Volume 4 of *A Regional History of the Railways of Great Britain*. Mr Hoole explained that the signalbox was at the south end of the bridge and, in the 'down' direction, the fast and slow lines diverged immediately after crossing the bridge. The point blades were on the south side and the frogs on the north, thus avoiding a complicated system which would have been necessary had the points been on the north side.

Nevertheless, congestion was not totally eliminated as the line across the bridge was, before long, used by some 140 trains each weekday. In order to provide a long-term cure to the area's traffic problems, the NER opened a new line between Selby (Brayton East Junction) and Goole in 1910. Eventually, though, the gauntleting of 'up' traffic across the bridge was abolished when the slow line was altered to join the fast line north of the bridge by means of spring points, a further change coming in 1960 when electrically operated points were installed at the north end of the bridge.

In the late 1960s the bridge's profile was altered by the raising of the cabin on top of the girders to provide clearance for overhead electrification. However, the electrification of the route across the bridge was not undertaken. In September 1983 main-line expresses were rerouted via a new avoiding line to the west of Selby, the swing bridge and its obligatory speed restriction thereby being circumvented by ECML services. Today, Selby Swing Bridge is still in use, but only by local trains including those on the Doncaster–Hull and York–Hull routes.

Below:
Ouse Bridge, 1891: The 1.52pm Hull–Leeds train crosses the Ouse Bridge at Selby on its approach to the station on 19 August 1982. *W. A. Sharman*

1891: Eyemouth Viaduct, nr Eyemouth, Berwickshire

The privately-promoted Eyemouth Railway opened its 3-mile line from Burnmouth to Eyemouth on 13 April 1891. The ER's bank balance was not exactly overflowing and, during the construction of the line, it had been suggested that the expense of bridging the Eye Water could be saved if the line were to be truncated short of Eyemouth. However, the 'into Eyemouth' lobby won the day, and a delightful viaduct was built to carry the railway into the town. The viaduct was 60ft high and had six wrought iron lattice girder spans, each 50ft wide; it was supported by brick-faced concrete piers.

Much of Southeast Scotland suffered terribly during and after the storms of 11/12 August 1948, and the viaduct's centre pier collapsed after being undermined by the floodwater. Many locals felt that the cost of repairs would be used as an excuse to close the line, but the fears proved unfounded and work was put in hand. Fortunately, the girders of the viaduct had not been brought down by the collapse of the pier, and so they were temporarily secured by ties and wedges while the work progressed. The work also involved attention to another pier, the foundations of which had been badly scoured by the rushing water. New concrete foundations, 12ft below the river–bed, were laid, and new cutwaters were added to the eastern side of the piers. After almost a year's work on the viaduct, the Eyemouth line reopened on 29 June 1949. However, the revival lasted for less than 13 years, passenger services being withdrawn on 5 February 1962.

1894: Craigendoran–Fort William, Dunbartonshire/Perthshire/ Inverness-shire

(principal structures listed overleaf)

Original owner: West Highland Railway
Engineers: Formans & McCall, Glasgow

The promotion, surveying, construction and operation of the West Highland Railway is the stuff of legend. The line, which was officially opened throughout on 11 August 1894, crossed some of the most inhospitable countryside in Britain on its route of just under 100 miles. The WHR was worked by the North British Railway from the outset, and was formally absorbed at the end of 1908.

Name	Length	Spans	Type/Notes
Craigenarden	132yd	8 x 36ft	Blue whinstone; concrete arches
Glen Falloch	142yd	1 x 118ft; 6 x 46ft	Lattice girder; concrete piers founded on rock
Crianlarich (1)	63yd	5 x 35ft	Lattice girder; over Oban line
Crianlarich (2)	95yd	2 x 55ft; 4 x 40ft	Lattice girder; over River Fillan
Auchtertyre	100yd	1 x 101ft; 4 x 50ft	Lattice girder; ashlar piers; on curve of 12ch radius
Horseshoe (1)	106yd	5 x 60ft	Lattice girder; on curve of 15ch radius
Horseshoe (2)	192yd	9 x 60ft	Lattice girder
Rannoch	228yd	9 x 70½ft	Lattice girder; partly on curve of 12ch radius

The WHR was engineered by the firm of Formans & McCall of Glasgow, which had been founded in 1828 and had been responsible for the building of many of Scotland's early railways. The contractors were Messrs Lucas & Aird, a London-based concern but with strong Scottish connections. The contractors made it known that they wished to employ local labour as much as possible, but the area through which the railway was to pass was hardly the greatest centre of population in the universe. Consequently, in order to adhere to their preference for Scottish labourers, they offered to pay the fares of suitable applicants who were penniless and, by 1890, over half of the workforce comprised men who had been given paid passages. It seems that the contractors had made the right decision, as contemporary reports frequently remarked on the hard-working qualities of the navvies.

As could be expected, the route of the WHR had a fair representation of bridges and viaducts. Many were lattice girder structures supported by granite piers, and the task of their construction was given to Alexander Findlay & Co of Motherwell. In all, the route boasted 19 structures of three spans or more, 102 bridges of one or two spans, and more than 200 cattle creeps of various sizes. The bridges and viaducts incorporated a total of some 4,000 tons of steel.

Despite a degree of standardisation with the materials used for the bridges and viaducts, the variation in conditions from site to site precluded a standard design. For example, **Glen Falloch Viaduct** (across Dubh Eas, three miles north of Ardlui) had its piers founded on rock but built up in layers of concrete 9in thick. During construction,

Below:
Horseshoe Viaduct, 1894: This unusual picture was taken looking backwards from the tender of '5MT' 4-6-0 No 73078. The locomotive is piloting a 'Black 5' on the 5.45am ex-Glasgow in March 1957, and the train of somewhat mixed stock is crossing the larger of the two viaducts on the Horseshoe Curve. *Ian Allan Library*

Above:
Rannoch Viaduct, 1894: Rannoch Moor is one of the most wonderfully bleak parts of the British landscape. Apart from the crew of Class 37 No 37151 (crossing Rannoch Viaduct with the early morning freight to Fort William) and minimal evidence of human life at Rannoch station (in the distance), there are no discernible signs of civilisation whatsoever in this picture taken in August 1984. *M. M. Hughes*

access to the upper sections was by means of a pre-carious-looking 'service' bridge partly suspended from the sides of the gorge. The use of a temporary service bridge was preferred to the use of staging, the latter being deemed too difficult and costly due to the height of the viaduct and the danger from floodwater. The steel for the viaduct was shipped to the pier on Loch Lomond and transported over-land to the site. Glen Falloch Viaduct has the longest span and greatest height of any WHR structure, but one often forgotten fact is that the level of the rails on the viaduct is, at 144ft high, only 12ft less than that on the world-famous Forth Bridge.

To the north of Tyndrum, different techniques were employed for the two viaducts on the **Horse-shoe Curve**. The curve, incidentally, had been constructed in preference to the expense of build-ing a direct line between the slopes of Ben Odhar and Ben Doran and, with it, a massive and extremely costly viaduct. One of the viaducts on the curve had nine spans and the other had five. The girders of the former were hoisted into posi-tion by cantilever lifting tackle, but those of the latter were assembled on site, fitted on to booms, and then wheeled out together over the piers in the manner of a train.

The longest structure on the line was **Rannoch Viaduct**, built across the bed of a vanished river. A viaduct at that spot had been necessitated by the boggy nature of the ground, as the alternative of infilling to a depth of up to 20ft for well over ½ mile was out of the question. To prepare the foundations for the piers of the viaduct the soft

moss was extracted down to the level of firm boul-der clay; the piers were then constructed, the gran-ite coming from Cruach Rock cutting, less than a mile to the north. In common with Glen Falloch Viaduct, that at Rannoch also carried a footway. The only arched viaduct on the line was **Craige-narden Viaduct**, on Loch Lomondside, a stone-built structure being preferred to a girder structure from deference to the beauty of the local land-scape. As a finishing touch, the parapets of the 54ft-high viaduct were topped with mock crenella-tions.

On the short branch to Banavie, the bridge car-rying the line over the River Lochy was unusual in that its decking was attached half-way up the main girders, this enabling economies to be made in the provision of wind bracing. The Lochy bridge was supported by cylindrical cast iron piers which, above the high-water level, were finished in masonry. A similar structure with a span of 84ft (the longest single-span bridge on the line) was used to carry the railway over the River Nevis, near Fort William.

The Glasgow-Fort William line soon attained, and permanently maintained, a place in the Premier Division of 'Britain's best loved railways'. It is, of course, still in use today. The southern section of the route now also carries traffic to and from Oban, by means of a connection which has been laid at Crianlarich between the former WHR line and the ex-Callander & Oban Railway from Stirling, the latter having closed abruptly in September 1965 after a landslide in Glen Ogle. In the early days the C&OR was worked by the Caledonian Railway, and it cannot go unremarked that, despite the rivalry between the Caley and the North British (which worked the WHR), the stone used for the piers of the WHR viaducts at Crianlarich was transported from Ben Cruachan by the C&OR. Some rivalries, it would appear, could be forgotten when revenue was at stake.

1897: Cross Keys Swing Bridge, Sutton Bridge, Lincolnshire

Designer: J.A.McDonald
Original owner: Midland & Great Northern Joint Railway
Type: Swing bridge
Materials: Cast iron; wrought iron
Total length: 96yd
Max height of rails: 16ft above high-water
Spans: 4
Tracks: 1

The Midland & Great Northern Joint Railway had a localised, but far from inconsiderable, network of lines in Norfolk, Cambridgeshire and Lincolnshire. At the Grouping in 1923 the M&GNR was vested jointly in the LMSR and the LNER, but everyday matters on the M&GNR changed comparatively little and the company's air of independence was maintained. That, however, came to a halt in October 1936 when the company was taken over completely by the LNER. Almost immediately the LNER seemed as if it were set on dispensing with all aspects of the M&GNR's individuality; British Railways took over where the LNER left off and, as early as 1959, most of the network was closed to passenger traffic. To a great extent, the story of the

Below:
Cross Keys Swing Bridge, rebuilt 1897: This was the third bridge at the site, and the second to carry both the railway and the road. The notice on the left-hand side of the bridge states that 'No locomotive or vehicle with a load exceeding 16 tons in weight shall pass over this bridge'. The picture was taken on 27 May 1937, by which time the bridge's latter-day owners, the Midland & Great Northern Joint Railway, had been taken over by the LNER. *H. C. Casserley*

M&GNR paralleled that of the Somerset & Dorset Joint Railway but, with all due respect to devotees of the former, it did not really achieve the same nationwide celebrity status of the latter.

Because of the geographical area in which the M&GNR was situated it might be thought that bridges were somewhat uncommon beasts as significant undulations in the local landscape are a rarity. The M&GNR might not have had to negotiate precipitous ravines but it had to cross countless rivers and waterways and, even excluding culverts, the company's network included some 250 bridges, a few of which were distinctive lattice girder structures.

The best-known was, arguably, Cross Keys Swing Bridge, which crossed the River Nene near Sutton Bridge on the King's Lynn–Spalding line. The structure which survived until the demise of the line in 1965 was, in fact, the third bridge on the site, the first being a road bridge (opened 1850) and the second a combined road/rail bridge which was completed in November 1864 by the Lynn & Sutton Bridge Railway, one of the M&GNR's eventual constituents. Initially, the L&SBR had been obliged to purchase the road bridge for £22,500, but the company was later permitted to adapt the structure for rail and road traffic.

The third and final bridge at Cross Keys was opened on 18 July 1897. Designed by the Midland Railway's Engineer, J. A. McDonald, built by Messrs Handysides & Co and costing £80,000, it was a 168ft 6in-long lattice girder bridge which pivoted asymmetrically on a pier made of cast iron columns. The clearance to shipping was some 95ft in width, movements being controlled from a cabin which straddled the swing section, and judging by contemporary Working Timetables, it appears that an average of five swing movements were required daily during summer, but just one or two each day during winter. The eastern approach to the bridge was by means of two plain girder spans, one of 70ft and the other of 50ft. The M&GNR Joint Committee charged tolls to road vehicles using the bridge, but the income was inadequate to cover the maintenance of the approach roads. That situation was solved in 1902 when responsibility for the approach roads was assumed by the local council, the tolls subsequently being surrendered by the M&GNR.

The line across the bridge was closed completely at the end of April 1965, a little over six years after the withdrawal of passenger services on the old M&GNR west of King's Lynn, and the bridge was later converted for road use. Recently, the overhead

Below:
West Lynn Bridge, original bridge built 1864: The second of three ex-M&GNJR structures to be featured crossed the River Ouse at King's Lynn. Here, ex-LMSR '4F' 0-6-0 No 44231 hauls the 8am (SO) Chesterfield–Yarmouth Beach train across West Lynn Bridge on 30 August 1958. *Hugh Ballantyne*

Above:
Breydon Viaduct, 1903: The distinctive structure had a
170ft-long swing section. It fell into disuse in 1953 and
was dismantled nine years later.
Ian Allan Library

control room and the end braces have been raised to
provide more headroom for heavy lorries.

In the M&GNR's hall of fame, Cross Keys
Swing Bridge was closely followed by **Breydon
Viaduct** which carried a single-track line across the
neck of Breydon Water near Great Yarmouth.
Breydon Viaduct was of girder construction and
consisted of five spans: three of 170ft in length, one
of 111ft, and a swing section of 170ft. The swing
span was turned centrally on ball-bearings and
rollers, power being supplied by an 11hp gas-pow-
ered engine. The structure, which was opened on 13
July 1903, was designed by the M&GNR's Chief
Engineer, William Marriott, and cost £65,131 to
build.

Because river traffic had priority it was normal
practice for Breydon Viaduct to remain in the open
position, the bridge being swung only when a train
was due and reopened to shipping immediately the
train had passed. The installation of new track cir-
cuiting in 1928 enabled block working to replace
the old tablet system across the viaduct. Rail traffic
across the viaduct ceased on 21 September 1953
after the cost of essential repairs to the structure
had been deemed uneconomical. The structure was
finally dismantled in 1962.

A substantial number of the M&GNR's bridges
were constructed from rolled iron joists, and many
of the company's older bridges were eventually
replaced by such structures. During the 1880s
William Marriott used some of the rolled iron joist
bridges to conduct experiments with concrete, the
tests including the coating of the iron sections with
Portland cement in order to minimise rusting and
also reduce the need for repainting. The procedure
came in for some criticism, the most frequently
heard grumble being that a coating of concrete prevented an examination of the iron underneath.

However, the partial removal of some concrete
coatings as much as twenty years later revealed no
deterioration whatsoever in the ironwork underneath. Understandably, the use of concrete coatings
was subsequently stepped up.

One of the structures to receive Marriott's attention was **West Lynn Bridge**, which comprised
three central spans, each of 117ft, and two end
spans, each of 70ft. In his excellent book *A Guide
to the Midland & Great Northern Joint Railway*,
Nigel Digby explains that the bridge had given
trouble ever since it had been built by Waring &
Eckersley in 1864 and, by the time Marriott took it
in hand, the main girders had to be unbent as much
as two inches from their buckled condition.

1898*: Aviemore–Carr Bridge–Inverness, Inverness-shire/Nairnshire

(principal structures listed below)
Designer: Murdoch Paterson
Original owner: Highland Railway

The Highland Railway completed its 35-mile long
'Direct Line' between Aviemore and Inverness in
1898. The company had not particularly wished to
lash out on building a line across such challenging
terrain, particularly as the shorter route meant a
corresponding reduction in fares. However, it had
been felt that the line was necessary to pre-empt a
rival company from opening up an alternative route
to Inverness.

The first section of the Direct Line to open was
that between Aviemore and Carr Bridge, the unveiling being on 8 July 1892. The Carr Bridge–Daviot
section was not completed until 19 July 1897 and
the final link between Daviot and Inverness was not
ready until 1 November 1898. As could be

Viaduct	Length	Height	Spans	Type
Slochd Mhuic		100ft	8 x 37ft 6in	Masonry viaduct
Tomatin	445yd	143ft	9 x 130ft plus 2 masonry arches	Lattice girder on masonry piers
Culloden	600yd	128ft	1 x 100ft; 28 x 50ft	Double-track masonry viaduct

* Sections of line opened in 1892 and 1897

expected from the landscape traversed by the line, the civil engineering works were substantial.

The most notable engineering feature of the Direct Line was Culloden Viaduct, which carried the railway high above the wide valley of the River Nairn. Costing over £70,000 to build, it was (and still is) the longest masonry railway viaduct in Scotland. When the foundations for the piers of the viaduct were being sunk on the north side of the River Nairn, firm rock was reached only 5-6ft below the surface. Naturally, it was anticipated that similar rock would be found at roughly the same depth when sinking the foundations for the south river pier, but excavations to a depth of 15ft revealed no such rock. Consequently, the section of the viaduct between the river and the south abutment were founded on boulder clay or gravel.

A description of the viaduct was included in the report of the ceremonial opening of the line on 29 October 1898, which appeared in the *Inverness Courier* on 1 November:

'...the valley of the Nairn is crossed by means of a splendid Viaduct, from which we have a charming view of valley and river. The Viaduct, which is 1785 feet in length, maintains both the west-ward curve and the steep ascent of the route. The bridge is constructed of red sandstone, found in the vicin-

ity, and it stands from 130 to 140 feet above the bed of the river. There are 28 stately arches. The one in the centre, through which the river flows, has a span of 100 feet, and the others have a span of 50 feet each. The piers gradually taper from their bottom, and are 6 feet 6 inches thick at the spring of the arch. The loftier ones are 15 feet thick at the base. Each pier is set on a foundation of concrete cement and, at intervals of 9 feet, there is a concrete binding 3 feet in depth...On the top of this long and well-proportioned structure, the train passes between parapets, 4 feet 6 inches high and topped with finely-dressed coping.'

The man behind the engineering of the Direct Line and the design of its bridges and viaducts was Murdoch Paterson. He had originally been first assistant to Joseph Mitchell, the unsung engineer who in the

Below:

Tomatin Viaduct, 1897: The Highland Railway's 'Direct Line' between Aviemore and Inverness was engineered by Murdoch Paterson, but it perpetuated the Joseph Mitchell tradition by having exceptionally fine bridges and viaducts. Tomatin Viaduct crossed the River Findhorn, and here Class 47 No 47430 is seen with the up 'Clansman', the 11am Inverness to Euston, on 15 August 1986. *W. A. Sharman*

1850s and 1860s had been responsible for the design of some outstanding bridges and viaducts for the Highland Railway's constituent companies. Mitchell and Paterson had become partners in an independent firm of consultant engineers, with the HR as one of their clients, but the partnership had been dissolved in 1867 after Mitchell's retirement. The HR had subsequently appointed two engineers, John Buttle and Peter Wilson, but the former had hastily resigned in 1868 after it had been discovered that the railway company had, quite unwittingly, been financing the construction of his new home. The other engineer, Peter Wilson, had died at the end of 1874 and, the following year, Murdoch Paterson had been appointed as the HR's Resident Engineer, the title of that post being changed in 1893 to Chief Engineer.

Culloden Viaduct came to be regarded as Paterson's greatest work but, sadly, he passed away in 1897, the year before it was opened. It has been suggested that Paterson had overseen much of the construction from his temporary home at the stationmaster's house at Culloden...the assumption therefore being that the house had been completed (possibly for Paterson's benefit) long before the station was built.

Farther south on the Direct Line, the route crossed the River Findhorn by means of another impressive viaduct. The *Inverness Courier* of 1 November 1898 commented:

'As we leave Tomatin, we are on the look-out for the Findhorn Viaduct, the second great structural feature of the Aviemore Railway. But before we come to it we cross a fine stone bridge over the roadway. From 40 to 60 feet high, and with 9 arches of 36 feet span, it would be a large piece of work if it were not quite so near to its bigger brother.

'The Viaduct across Findhorn Valley and river, of which it commands magnificent views, is 1335 feet in length, and its maximum height is 140 feet. It has a rise of 1 in 60 from north to south. The superstructure is of steel, resting on native granite piers, of massive and towering proportions, which have their foundations on immense blocks of concrete, those in the river bed being also supported by deeply-driven wood piles. The Viaduct has a graceful curve of a half-mile radius.'

Continuing southwards, the line negotiated Slochd Summit and passed across yet another viaduct. The *Inverness Courier* continued:

Below:
Culloden Viaduct, 1898: In pouring rain, Class 47 No 47593 heads north over the magnificent Culloden Viaduct with the 10.03am Glasgow to Inverness service. *W. A. Sharman*

'....the great and gloomy Pass of Slochd is reached. It is colloquially known to the railway as "The Slochd". Its ancient reputation for throat-cutting and highway robbery might be commended to the author of "John Splendid". The valley of the Alt Slochd Mhuic is crossed by the railway at a height of 107 feet by a picturesque structure of stone piers and arches, consisting of 8 spans of 37 feet 6 inches each. The viaduct is built of granite, and arched with freestone, while the coping of the parapets is also of freestone, the contrast between the two kinds of stone having a bright and pleasing effect.'

The other major structure on the line was the bridge across the River Dulnain, near Carr Bridge. By the time the special train reached that bridge there was a hint that the reporter from the *Inverness Courier* was running out of superlatives. His simple description of the structure was '...a handsome bridge, formed of a continuous steel girder of 180 feet span, resting on abutments, and centre-pier of granite. On the bridge the line is 56 feet above the bed of the river.'

Having quoted extensively from the *Inverness Courier* of 1 November 1898, it cannot go unremarked that the paper's other scoops of the day included 'The Ross-shire Sheep Poisoning Case', a meeting of the Fortrose Choral Union, and a report from Bonar Bridge about the 'Difficulty as to Library Site'.

The Direct Line cost almost £1,000,000 to construct which, considering that the Highland Railway built it primarily as a blocking measure, was a very hefty outlay for a line the company didn't really want. However, the line became a favourite among railway enthusiasts and remains so to this day, the impressive viaducts having been treated to little more than routine maintenance throughout their lives of almost 100 years. No doubt the Highland Railway Society will have something special in hand for the line's centenary in 1998.

1899: Annesley–London (Marylebone)

(various structures)

Original Owner: Great Central Railway
GCR Engineers: Alexander Ross (1890-1896);
Charles Rowlandson (1896-1911)
Contracts:
No 1: Annesley-East Leake (19m 44ch); Logan & Hemmingway, Market Harborough; £668,451
No 2: East Leake-Aylestone (16m 36ch); Henry Lovatt & Co, Northampton; £548,835
No 3: Aylestone-Rugby (15m 69ch); Topham,

Jones & Railton, Westminster; £281,589
No 4: Rugby-Charwelton (15m 77ch); T.Oliver & Son, Horsham, Sussex; £513,308
No 5: Charwelton-Brackley (12m 32ch); Walter Scott & Co, Newcastle-upon-Tyne; £470,000 (contract 5 and 6 combined)
No 6: Brackley-Quainton Rd (12m 61ch); Walter Scott & Co, Newcastle-upon-Tyne
No 7: London-Marylebone (1m 7ch); J.T.Firbank, London Bridge: £699,972

The last new main line to reach London was that of the Great Central Railway. The forerunner of the GCR was the Manchester, Sheffield & Lincolnshire Railway, the change of corporate title being assumed on 1 August 1897 when construction of the London extension was at an advanced stage. The London extension started at Annesley North Junction, about ¼mile beyond the south portal of Annesley tunnel in Nottinghamshire, and terminated at Marylebone station. The first sod was cut near St John's Wood on 13 November 1894, and the inaugural passenger trains worked from Manchester to Marylebone on 9 March 1899, public services on the line commencing on 15 March.

The line gained a considerable fan club but, sadly, such popularity did not prevent the line succumbing to the old railway adage of 'last in, first out', and it was closed to through traffic on 3 September 1966. Because of the nature of its route, the GCR's London extension required extensive engineering works which included a considerable number of bridges and viaducts. With respect to all GCR devotees, none of the bridges and viaducts were, in themselves, particularly innovative, but their sheer weight of numbers (and, in a couple of cases, their scale) certainly warrants their inclusion in this book.

Contract No 1 necessitated the construction of 75 bridges and the use of some 10,000 tons of steel and ironwork. The section included **Newstead Abbey Bridge**, near Annesley, an ornamental cast iron structure which carried the line over the carriage drive to Newstead Abbey (once the residence of Lord Byron). The use of cast iron was perhaps surprising as that medium had, by then, been somewhat disgraced. The bridge was removed after the closure of the line.

The first sizeable structure was **Bulwell Viaduct**, 2½ miles south of Hucknall Tunnel. It was 420yd long, had an average height of 44ft, and comprised 26 spans, some of which were on the skew; the 'straight' spans were 34ft 3in wide - the standard width adopted for many arches on the line. The viaduct was built in a little over 12 months and consumed some 6,500,000 bricks, its southern end crossing the Midland Railway's Mansfield line. After the closure of the line the viaduct was demolished, the rubble being spread over the adjacent

Above:
Nottingham Viaduct, 1899: The span carrying the GCR line across the Midland station dominates this classic period picture. *S. W. A. Newton Collection/Leicestershire Record Office*

Below:
Wilford Bridge, Nottingham, 1899: 'K3' class 2-6-0 No 1824 hauls a Scarborough–Leicester train across Wilford Bridge on 16 August 1947. *T. G. Hepburn/Rail Archive Stephenson*

land which, at the time, was earmarked for development under the banner of Springfield Park.

A little to the south, **Nottingham Viaduct** was some 550yd in length and comprised 53 arches and 12 steel bridges; the largest of the steel structures was of lattice girder construction and had three spans, the first of 50ft, the second of 170ft (over the Midland Railway station) and the third of 104ft. On leaving central Nottingham, the line crossed **Trent Viaduct**, which was 277yd long and comprised 14 spans. Starting from the northern end, the viaduct consisted of a girder span of 66ft over the Trentside Boulevard, three brick arches each of 32ft 3in span, three pairs of 112-ft span lattice girders (for the passenger and goods lines separately) over the River Trent and, finally, seven arches each of 32ft 3in span. The track was quadrupled from Arkwright Street station over the viaduct, and then reverted to double track on its exit. After the line closed, extensive redevelopment wiped away most traces of the route through central Nottingham, Trent Viaduct being demolished in the late 1980s.

Contract No 2, which consumed some 75 million bricks, took the line across the valley of the River Soar no less than ten times. From the north, the section included **Loughborough Viaduct**, an elegant structure built in brindle brick facing with red backing in lime mortar. It was 160yd long, 50ft high and had 11 spans. Before entering Loughborough, the line crossed the Midland Railway's Trent–Leicester line and the Leicester–Loughborough canal by means of a skew girder bridge of four 40ft spans. The next engineering work of note was **Swithlands Viaduct** which, in fact, comprised two structures, one of ten arches and the other of five (all fifteen being of 30ft span), and a plate girder bridge of 40ft span carrying the line over a reservoir. Of those structures, Swithlands Viaduct was saved and, with a single track, is now part of the preserved line between Loughborough and Leicester.

Arguably the most expansive part of Contract No 2 was **Leicester Viaduct**, which carried the line through the city on a succession of bridges and viaducts for a distance of over one mile. The elevated section started at Harrison Street and included a fan-shaped skew span across Northgate Street, further skew spans over the River Soar, a 19ft span above Braunstone Gate, and twin lattice girder spans of 43yd over the Old River Soar. The construction of the railway through Leicester was a costly business, not only because of the lengthy raised section, but also because the railway company had to build 300 new houses at Newfound Pool and on the Bow Bridge Estate to replace older houses which had had to be demolished to make way for the line. Many of the brick arches in Leicester survive today, although the girder spans were taken down for scrap in the 1980s. The final

work of note in that section was **Aylestone Viaduct**, which comprised four spans of 41ft 6in and a 90ft-span lattice girder bridge over the Grand Union Canal. The author is informed that Aylestone Viaduct is still *in situ* as part of the Great Central Way.

Contract No 3 involved slightly fewer bridges and viaducts. Apart from a 65ft-span plate girder skew bridge carrying the railway over the LNWR's Leicester–Nuneaton line to the north of Whetstone, and a 29ft plate girder bridge over the Midland's Leicester–Rugby line near Cosby, the major feature was **Whetstone Viaduct** a 152yd-long structure which carried the line across the valley of the River Sence on 13 arches, each of 30ft span.

Contract No 4 included **Oxford Canal Viaduct** which comprised two spans of 91ft, one of 90ft, and one of 120ft, each span being made up of four parallel girders. To the south was **Rugby Viaduct**, which had 14 brick arches (one of 14ft span, the others of 26ft) followed by a steel bridge made up of two plate girders (58ft and 75ft span), three lattice girder spans (105ft, 165ft and 105ft), and a plate girder span (40ft). The lattice girder spans of Rugby Viaduct, which crossed the LNWR main line and sidings, eventually came to be known as 'The Birdcage'. The LNWR had an agreement with the GCR whereby the latter had to provide and maintain, at its own expense, a signal gantry on the eastern side of the viaduct. The gantry was replaced by colour light signals in 1939. Apparently, the two girders above the ex-LNWR line were still *in situ* in 1990, the rest of Rugby Viaduct having been removed and the area redeveloped.

The other works of note included in contract No 4 were **Willoughby Viaduct**, which was 186yd long and had 13 arches, **Staverton Viaduct**, 119yd long and consisting of nine arches, and **Catesby Viaduct**, which was 159yd long and had 12 arches. All three of those structures crossed the River Leam at various points, their arches being built to the standard width of 34ft 3in.

Contracts Nos 5 and 6 included **Helmdon Viaduct**, one of the structure's nine standard arches crossing the single-track Northampton & Banbury Junction Railway, and the 252yd-long **Brackley Viaduct** across the River Ouse. The latter was originally intended to comprise 22 standard spans, but difficulty was encountered with movement of the ground at the south end, and so two plate girder spans, each of 35ft, replaced the last two arches. Some of the foundations incorporated limestone which had been excavated from a nearby cutting. Apparently, Helmdon Viaduct was still standing in 1986, albeit in need of attention, whereas the area once occupied by Brackley Viaduct now forms part of the A43 Brackley bypass. When Brackley Viaduct was demolished the solidity of the structure presented considerable problems for the demo-

Above:
Brackley Viaduct, 1899: The two plate girder spans at
the south end of Brackley Viaduct are clearly evident.
An unidentified 'Black 5' crosses the viaduct with the
14.38 Marylebone–Nottingham semi-fast on 27 March
1965. *Brian Stephenson*

lition firm, and the extensive use of explosives
caused much annoyance to the locals. It took a year
to demolish the viaduct and clear the site.

The London end of the line included two structures of note. The first was **Loudoun Road Bridge**,
the existing Metropolitan Railway bridge having to
be reconstructed and widened at the GCR's
expense. The new structure, a 118ft-long three-span
girder bridge, carried the GCR and the Metropolitan Railway side by side over the LNWR, some
350yd west of Primrose Hill Tunnel. The reconstruction work necessitated the removal of the eastern extremities of Loudoun Road (later renamed
South Hampstead) station on the LNWR line. The
other major structure in the area was **Regent's
Canal Bridge**, a 400ft-wide girder bridge which
carried 14 tracks across the canal. The London end
of the old GCR line is, of course, still in use.

1900: Deveron Bridge, Rothiemay, Aberdeenshire/ Banffshire

The Great North of Scotland Railway was projected
as a through route between Aberdeen and Inverness. Its first 39-mile section from a temporary terminus at Kittybrewster (on the outskirts of
Aberdeen) to Huntly opened in September 1854, an
extension to Keith opening in October 1856. The
connection to Inverness was provided by the Highland Railway, whose line to Keith opened throughout in August 1858.

The most impressive engineering feature of the
Great North's line was a masonry bridge of five
skew arches over the River Deveron at Rothiemay
station (two miles from Rothiemay village). The
bridge was unusual in that it effectively consisted
of five narrow bridges side by side, but staggered
and on skew piers. Between 1880 and 1900 the
Great North doubled its main line between Dyce
Junction (6½ miles from Aberdeen) and Keith, and
this necessitated an improved alignment at Rothiemay, which was effected by the replacement of
the old viaduct by a modern girder structure.

The new bridge was built alongside the old one.
It was designed by the Great North's Engineer-in-Chief, Patrick Barnett, and the contract for the steel
and ironwork was awarded to Messrs Findlay & Co
of Motherwell. The bridge comprised two main lattice girder spans, each 212ft 6in long and 25ft wide.
The abutments and retaining walls were of stone,
over 2,500 wagon-loads of the material being
required, and the foundations were sunk to a depth
of 9ft below the water-level of the river. Construction took a little over 18 months, during which time
an average of 80 men were employed on the foundation and stonework at any one time.

When completed, the new bridge was subjected
to tests involving eight locomotives - a weight of
some 750 tons in all - but the maximum deflection
was no greater than ¾in. The new alignment across
the bridge was brought into use for public traffic on
30 April 1900, a special train having run the previous evening. Although redundant, the old stone
bridge was left to stand alongside its replacement
until being demolished in 1978. During World War
1, it had been laid with a light railway track so that
timber for the war effort could be transported from
the nearby forests to Rothiemay station.

Following widespread service reductions under the Beeching 'economies' of the 1960s, the ex-Great North main line via Deveron Bridge was, apart from one short section, singled in 1970. The future of the line itself was not really threatened, and today it hosts a relatively frequent train service between Aberdeen and Inverness.

Deveron Bridge is one of several former Great North of Scotland Railway bridges and viaducts to be featured in this book. That is rather apt as, at the time of writing, the GNSR Association is celebrating its thirtieth birthday and currently has its highest ever membership figure. The Great North was the smallest of Scotland's five main-line locomotive-owning companies, and its charismatic nature is reflected by the present-day enthusiasm for the long-since-departed company.

In its early days, however, the Great North was not viewed with such reverence. The great railway writer, Ernest Ahrons, opined:

'Once upon a time this was a shocking railway. A really very, very shocking railway. Why it was ever allowed to be called a railway at all passed comprehension.

'Its stopping trains could not even be dignified with the title "slow". They set the pace of a glacier, only the glacier would probably have got there first. But one thing the Great North did thoroughly well - it charged "express" fares for the privilege of a passage on its glaciers; and these express fares were of an exceeding magnitude.'

In fairness, though, Ahrons emphasised that, at the time he was writing (the early 1900s), things had changed from 'bad to excellent'.

1901: Glenfinnan Viaduct, Glenfinnan, Inverness-shire

Designer: Simpson & Wilson, Glasgow
Original owner: West Highland Railway
Contractor: Robert McAlpine & Sons, Glasgow
Cost: £18,904
Type: Arch viaduct
Materials: Concrete
Total length: 416yd
Max height of rails: 100ft
Spans: 21
Tracks: 1

The West Highland Railway opened its line to Fort William on 7 August 1894. Before long, thoughts turned towards extending the line to the west coast of Scotland, principally to serve the fishing communities, and after much deliberation it was decided that Mallaig Bay offered the best prospects for the terminus of the proposed extension.

After considerable legal wrangling, the Mallaig extension was eventually authorised and the first sod was cut in January 1897. Because of the delay in gaining assent for the line, the original contractor

Below:
Deveron Bridge, new structure built 1900: The twin bridges across the River Deveron at Rothiemay were photographed in 1937. The elegant old bridge of 1856 was replaced by the girder structure (visible behind) in 1900 and, despite its redundancy, remained *in situ* until 1978. *Bucknall Collection/Ian Allan Library*

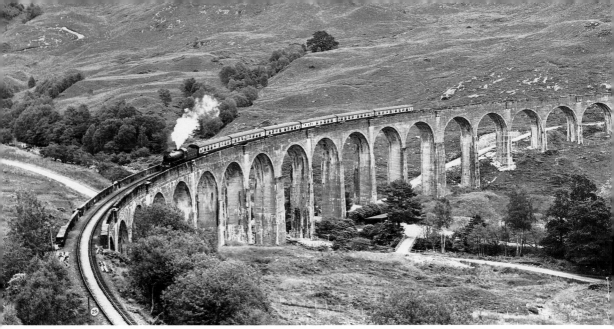

Glenfinnan Viaduct, 1901: 'Concrete Bob' McAlpine did his reputation a power of good with the construction of Glenfinnan Viaduct. The Fort William–Mallaig route, which crosses the viaduct, is now an understandably popular venue for steam-hauled specials, and our old friend, the confusingly-numbered 'K1' 2-6-0 No 2005, was photographed on such a working on 11 August 1987. *W. A. Sharman*

had to pull out and the firm of Robert McAlpine & Sons was hired instead. McAlpine had started his working days as a brickie's labourer but had later set up his own small business. He had entered railway folklore by walking across Rannoch Moor in January 1889 when the route of the Fort William line was being planned. McAlpine was highly enthusiastic about the large-scale use of concrete, a relatively new medium which had previously been used in Britain mainly as an auxiliary material.

As far as is known, the first large-scale use of concrete had been in Switzerland, where a bridge with a 60ft span had been built in 1874, but McAlpine positively welcomed the opportunity to construct a series of concrete bridges and viaducts on the Mallaig line to show Britain that the material could be used on a far larger scale. 'Concrete Bob', as McAlpine was known in the civil engineering world, was quick to point out that concrete did not rust; nor did it require regular repainting. Furthermore, the budget for building the Mallaig line was somewhat slim and the use of concrete for the building of the bridges and viaducts was, according to McAlpine, likely to save anything up to 30% in construction costs. Besides, the local stone was described as 'virtually unworkable'.

McAlpine had almost a free rein to show off his beloved concrete, and the standard pattern for the bridges on the Mallaig line incorporated spans of 50ft. The most famous of all the structures on the line was undoubtedly Glenfinnan Viaduct, which had 21 arches and was built on a curve of just 12 chains radius. The method of construction was to pour the concrete into timber formwork, a pair of ½in-thick steel plates being inserted at the crown of each arch to deal with the eventuality of settlement. However, no significant settlement has ever occurred.

Today, the aesthetic appeal of concrete is often disputed, but the Scottish author J.J. Bell had no hesitation in describing Glenfinnan Viaduct as 'a thing so delicate that the fairies might have built it'. One uncorroborated story which has been passed down over the years concerns a horse and cart which fell inside one of the hollow piers before the superstructure had been built. The story goes that the removal of the deceased beast and the cart was impossible, and their remains are still buried inside the pier.

Among the other concrete structures on the Mallaig line was **Loch nan Uamh Viaduct**, which had eight 50ft arches, but after Glenfinnan Viaduct the most celebrated structure on the line was undoubtedly **Borrodale Bridge**. McAlpine originally intended to cross Borrodale Burn by building piers in the stream, but the owner of the Arisaig Estate would agree only if the piers were clad in granite. That was ruled out because of the cost, and so McAlpine bridged the burn with a single arch of 127ft 6in (42½yd) span and a pair of side spans of 20ft each, the side spans being dressed in stone at the insistence of the landowner. The bridge over

Walnut Tree Viaduct, 1901: To the best of this writer's knowledge, no regular passenger services were ever scheduled via the line across the elegant Walnut Tree Viaduct. This working of 31 July 1965 was a special organised by the Swansea Railway Circle, the locomotive in charge being '5600' class 0-6-2T No 6643. *P. L. Simpson*

Borrodale Burn was, at the time, the longest concrete span in the world. During the five years prior to its construction only three large-scale concrete bridges had been built anywhere in the world (all road bridges designed by the German engineer, Leibrand) but, in the 11 years after the building of Borrodale Bridge, no less than 52 sizeable concrete bridges were built worldwide. McAlpine had certainly done his bit for the promotion of his beloved concrete.

Work on the Mallaig extension was beset by abysmal weather and labour troubles, the navvies being known to the locals as 'McAlpine's Fusiliers'. The line was eventually opened on 1 April 1901, the first train being the 07.20 from Mallaig which carried passengers who had arrived by steamships from the Isles. The West Highland Railway had been worked from the outset by the North British Railway, formal absorption by the NBR taking place on 31 December 1908.

Over the years, the Mallaig line achieved celebrity status among enthusiasts, not only for its magnificent scenery but also for its locomotives. Today, it is an obvious choice for the operators of steam-hauled specials, but to a certain magazine editor, the name of Glenfinnan Viaduct seems like a jinx. The editor in question has related that, on countless occasions, he has arrived extremely early to secure a prime vantage point for photographing a steam-hauled working across the viaduct but, a few minutes before the train's arrival, a chap wearing a vivid 'day-glo' anorak appears from nowhere and positions himself right on the lineside. The editor's resultant pictures inevitably need extensive (and detrimental) cropping to lose the miscreant in the anorak.

1901: Walnut Tree Viaduct, Taff's Well, Mid-Glamorgan

Original owner: Barry Railway
Type: Lattice girder
Materials: Steel and masonry
Total length: 516yd
Max height of rails: 120ft
Spans: 7
Tracks: 2 (later singled)

In financial terms the Barry Railway was extremely successful but the company was hardly popular among its rivals in South Wales. The Barry arrived comparatively late in the day but grew rapidly, its network expanding largely by the use of ungraciously-given running powers, with much of its traffic initially being won by undercutting its competitors. The descriptions of the Barry Railway included such glowing epithets as 'sordid and greedy', 'parasitic' and, as a reference to its seemingly incessant demands for running powers, 'the spoiled child of Parliament'.

One of the Barry's early uses of running powers was via the Rhymney Railway northwards from Walnut Tree Junction, near Taff's Well. However, the Barry did not view that as a long-term option and set its corporate sights on a new 'cut-off' freight route between its own docks at Barry and the Rhymney Valley. The strategic importance of the new route was that the Barry would gain access via RR metals to the London & North Western Railway at Rhymney Bridge, thereby opening a new avenue for exploitation.

The Barry gained the necessary Act of Parliament for the new route in August 1896 but, although the line was only seven miles long, it was not opened until 1 August 1901. One of the main reasons for the delay was that the Barry had chosen to bridge Nantgarw Gap (near Taff's Well) by means of a viaduct, rather than laying the line through the valley. The decision to build along such an alignment was not extravagance, but necessity. At the time, the narrow pass through Nantgarw Gap was used by the Glamorganshire Canal, the main Merthyr road, a minor road, an industrial railway, and the Taff Vale Railway's Cardiff–Pontypridd main line. There was, admittedly, a narrow space on the eastern side of the valley, but that had already been earmarked for the Cardiff Railway's new line. With such a profusion of communication routes squeezing through Nantgarw Gap, the Barry Railway had little option but to go overhead by means of what became known as Walnut Tree Viaduct.

The expense incurred in constructing the magnificent viaduct was soon recouped. The Barry drew on its expertise at 'poaching' trade from its rivals for diversion to Barry Docks and, in the first seven weeks alone, over 104,000 tons of coal was transported via the new route across Walnut Tree Viaduct. But, of course, the Barry wanted a lot more. The General Manager's report of 27 September 1901 stated that other colliery companies were showing an interest in the new route, but expressed regret that: '...the Tredegar Iron & Coal Co still sends its Barry traffic through the Hands of the Rhymney and Taff Vale Railways to Cogan Junction. The reason for this is that the Manager expects a lower rate to Barry than to Cardiff.'

The Barry Railway was taken over by the Great Western at the Grouping. The mid-1920s saw a significant decline in the South Wales coal trade, but traffic to Barry Docks via Walnut Tree Viaduct still remained reasonably healthy. Eventually, though, Barry Docks were gradually run down, as was the South Wales mining industry, and the route across the viaduct saw less and less traffic. The end was, however, rather abrupt. A fire destroyed Tynycaeau North signalbox in March 1963 and, consequently, the section south of Walnut Tree Viaduct was closed completely at the end of the month. The viaduct nevertheless remained open to traffic until 14 December 1967 to provide access to the dolomite siding at its southern end, the line across the structure having, by then, been singled. The girders of the viaduct were removed in 1969, and the masonry piers were demolished in 1973.

Walnut Tree Viaduct was widely regarded as one of the most elegant structures of its type in the South Wales valleys. To the Barry Railway, however, it was a little more than just a good-looking viaduct on a new 'cut-off' route. Symbolically, its position across Nantgarw Gap had forced the Barry's bitterest rival, the Taff Vale Railway, to look up to it.

Before we leave the Barry Railway, mention should be made of **Llanbradach Viaduct** and **Penyrheol Viaduct**. Both were on another of the Barry's 'cut-off' routes, this time the 2¾-mile line between Penrhos Junction (on the Barry–Bargoed

Right:
Penyrheol Viaduct, 1905: The demolition of railway bridges and viaducts was *not* something unique to the post-Beeching era. After a disappointingly short life, Penyrheol Viaduct was demolished in 1937, and the work was duly recorded by the official photographer. Although the blurring of the falling girder may be scoffed at by present-day amateur photographers who have been brought up on versatile electronic SLRs with shutter speeds of 1/2000sec, it must be remembered that the cameras of the 1930s were cumbersome tripod-mounted affairs with very restricted shutter speeds. *Welsh Industrial & Maritime Museum*

line) and Barry Junction (on the Brecon & Merthyr Railway's Machen–Rhymney line) which opened for coal traffic on 2 January 1905. The larger of the two structures was Llanbradach Viaduct, the construction of which is believed to have accounted for around half of the £500,000 budget for the entire line. The viaduct was 800yd long and stood 125ft above the valley floor. It comprised 11 162ft-wide spans on brick piers, four approach arches, and a steel bridge over the Rhymney Railway. The main part of the viaduct was of lattice girder construction, and the entire structure incorporated some 3,150 tons of steel.

After the Grouping the GWR regarded the line across Llanbradach and Penyrheol Viaducts as superfluous; it was closed in 1926, traffic subsequently being routed via the former Rhymney Railway line. The two viaducts were demolished in 1937, the first of the two to go being Penyrheol. The *GWR Magazine* of March 1937 reported:

'At the present time Penyrheol viaduct is being demolished and the steelwork sold as scrap, for which there is now a big demand. The main girders being 101 feet long, eleven feet two inches deep, and weighing some 35 tons each, are far too unwieldy to lift and load into wagons direct; for this reason, after the decking has been removed, the girders are pushed off the tops of the piers, to fall into the valley below, a distance of some fifty feet. The girders are then cut by oxy-acetelene plant into convenient sizes and the material loaded into wagons by a crane standing on the remaining portion of the bridge on the adjoining line.'

In view of the engineering expertise which went into the construction of Penyrheol and Llanbradach Viaducts, and also their striking appearance, it is extremely sad the two structures had such short lives.

1903: Connel Ferry Bridge, Connel Ferry, Argyllshire

Designer: Sir John Wolfe Barry
Original owner: Callander & Oban Railway
Contractor: Arrol's Bridge & Roof Co
Type: Cantilever
Material: Steel; granite approach arches
Total length: 340yd
Max height of rails: 54ft above high-water
Spans: 1 (plus 8 on approaches)
Tracks: 1

The Callander & Oban Railway completed the line between the communities of its title on 1 July 1880. It was worked by the Caledonian Railway and, to all practical purposes, was part of the Caley's network. The C&OR later proposed a branch from Connel Ferry (6¼ miles north of Oban) to Ballachulish and Fort William, the intention being not only to tap the slate traffic from Ballachulish quarries, but also to fend off rival schemes for through routes which threatened to abstract traffic from the Oban line. Predictably, the West Highland Railway strongly opposed the C&OR's plans, and the outcome was an amended C&OR scheme for a 27½-

Below:
Connel Ferry Bridge, 1903: The distinctive road-and-rail bridge on the Ballachulish branch had the somewhat sensible restriction that road and rail traffic should not be permitted to cross the bridge at the same time. Sadly, this picture is undated but, judging from the vehicles and their registrations, a guess is hazarded at around 1955/56. Answers on a postcard are *not* requested. *Michael E. Ware*

mile branch between Connel Ferry and Ballachulish, and a proposed West Highland branch between Ballachulish and Fort William. The latter proposal was soon dropped, leaving the C&OR in command of Ballachulish, and the branch from Connel Ferry opened to public traffic on 24 August 1903.

The C&OR had been full of optimism for its proposed branch and, at one stage, had even considered working the line itself - how the Caledonian would have reacted is a matter for speculation. The building of the branch presented considerable challenges but, as the line hugged the coast for most of its route, the obstacles were not those usually associated with railways in the Scottish Highlands. The main problems were the crossings of Loch Etive and Loch Creran, and each was tackled differently.

Loch Etive was encountered immediately to the north of Connel Ferry. The obvious point at which to bridge the loch was near its entrance where it narrowed to some 700ft, but the narrowing of the channel and the presence of a rock bar at that point resulted in extremely strong currents, known as the Falls of Lora. In Gaelic, incidentally, *coingheall* (from which 'Connel' was derived) means whirlpool. The currents effectively prevented the construction of piers except in the shallow water near the shores, and completely ruled out the use of staging between the two shores. The only real answer was a cantilever bridge, the steelwork of which could be built out over the water without the need for staging.

The consulting engineer engaged for the construction of the Connel Ferry Bridge was Sir John Wolfe Barry, whose main claim to fame was the building of Tower Bridge in London. His father, Sir Charles Barry, had been credited with designing the Houses of Parliament, but that had not been held against him. The appointment of a mere Englishman such as John Barry for the engineering of an archetypal Highland line was, however, not as mysterious as it might seem, as Barry was the Caledonian Railway's consulting engineer and, perhaps tenuously, he had received his early education at Glenalmond School in Perthshire. The contractor, William Arrol, was hired because of his experience in building the Forth Bridge, the only other significant cantilever railway bridge in Britain.

The centres of the cantilever frames on the Connel Ferry Bridge were 524ft apart, the piers being set into granite masonry on top of solid rock bases. Each of the two landward sections of the cantilever bridge were almost 106ft long, the approach from each bank being by means of a viaduct comprising three arches of 38ft 6in span. Work on the main cantilever section progressed from both ends simultaneously, an arrangement of adjustable bolts enabling the two halves to be aligned accurately when they met in the centre. In all, some 2,600 tons of steel were used in the construction of the bridge.

One of the many interesting features was that, of necessity, a 3in gap had to be left between the rails to allow for expansion, a joint rail being positioned outside the running rails to support the outer halves of wheel treads.

The bridge was inspected for the Board of Trade by Col Yorke, who tested the structure with a train consisting of eight Caledonian locomotives and four 30-ton wagons - about 740 tons in all. He demanded the substitution of broken stone ballast for the gravel which had been laid, but otherwise the bridge was deemed satisfactory. Eight days later, on Friday, 21 August 1903, the Ballachulish branch was ceremonially opened, public traffic commencing on the following Monday.

The bridge was built to carry a road as well as the railway, but the local authority was unimpressed with the railway company's proposed method of charging for road use. Consequently, it was July 1909 before road traffic started using the bridge and, even then, vehicles did not make the crossing under their own power but were loaded on to one of two flat trucks and hauled across by the 'Connel Bus'. That vehicle was a 23-seat road charabanc converted by the Caledonian Railway for railway operation; it made ten trips across the bridge to North Connel every day (including Sundays), four of those trips being extended to Benderloch. During conversion, the 30hp bus (believed to be a Thorneycroft) had been fitted with a high-ratio reverse gear as the lack of turning facilities meant that it had to run backwards on the northbound journeys. The charge for conveying motor cars across the bridge behind the 'Connel Bus' was a whopping 15s 0d (75p).

In 1913 all classes of road traffic were at last permitted to cross the bridge under their own power, and the 'Connel Bus' was rendered redundant. Nevertheless, high tolls continued to be charged for crossing the bridge, the C&OR being fully aware that the only alternative was a 35-mile detour which, during winter months, was often snowbound. Because of the limited clearance on the bridge, no road traffic was permitted when a train was crossing. Gates were used to halt the traffic when required, control being from the gatehouse at the north end of the bridge; electric circuits were connected with the road gates to prevent a train tablet being issued if the gates were not properly closed.

Approximately 9½ miles north of Connel Ferry Bridge, the Ballachulish branch crossed Loch Creran at Creagan Narrows by means of **Creagan Bridge**. Although spring tides created relatively strong currents at Creagan Narrows, the tidal flow was nowhere near that encountered at the Falls of Lora at Connel Ferry, and so more conventional techniques could be used for building the bridge at that point. A lattice girder bridge was therefore constructed to carry the line across Loch Creran; it had a pair of 150ft spans supported by a central pier of rock-faced granite ashlar, the decking being some 40ft above the high-water mark. At each end of the bridge there was a single span built from granite, the parapets being castellated in what has been described as 'Scottish Baronial-style'. The only significant problems encountered during the bridge's construction were the compressed-air work for the sinking of the piers, and the cramped working space on the central pier.

It was originally intended to permit pedestrians to cross Creagan Bridge by means of a footway outside the main girders, and thus avoid a 5-mile trip around the shores of Loch Creran, but the railway company failed to reach an agreement with the local authorities, and the footway was never officially brought into use.

The Ballachulish branch retained a traditional flavour right through LMSR days and into the BR era, although that was due to the weight restrictions imposed on the line rather than sentimentality. Almost until the demise of steam traction, ex-Caledonian '3F' 0-6-0s and '2P' 0-4-4Ts monopolised the workings, Class 26 and 27 diesels taking over in the final years. After a couple of false alarms, the line was closed on 28 March 1966, but a condition imposed by the Department of Transport was that Connel Ferry Bridge should be devoted entirely to road traffic and the tolls should be abolished. During the mid-1950s it had cost 4s 0d (20p) to take a small car across the bridge...that might have been a better bet than the 15s 0d of forty-odd years earlier, but it had still been far from cheap.

1905: Trowse Swing Bridge, Norwich, Norfolk

The original swing bridge across the River Wensum at Norwich was that of the Norwich & Brandon Railway (one of the Great Eastern's eventual constituents), which completed its line on 15 December 1845. A swing bridge had been required as the Wensum was a navigable waterway, and the bridge provided two river openings, each of 44ft. By the turn of the century the single-track section across the bridge had become a troublesome bottleneck. Some 170 trains used the bridge each weekday, and the practice of slowing to 3mph to pick up pilotmen didn't help matters. The solution was a new double-track bridge, and this was installed in 1905, work commencing on the evening of 12 August 1905 and finishing on the morning of 14 August; it was power-operated and had two spans, one of which was navigable. A similar design was also used for the swing bridge which replaced the original Grissell & Peto structure at **Oulton Broad**, near Lowestoft. The Trowse swing bridge was replaced by a new single track swing bridge in the mid-1980s as part of the Norwich electrification scheme.

Below:
Trowse Swing Bridge, renewed 1905: This splendid pre-Grouping picture shows what appears to be a Great Eastern 'Claud Hamilton' at the head of the train crossing the Trowse Bridge. *Ian Allan Library*

Top:
King Edward VII Bridge, 1906: 'The last of the great railway bridges' is a fair description of this famous structure across the River Tyne. Class 45 No 45177 is seen crossing the bridge with the 15.20 Newcastle–King's Cross train on 4 May 1971.
J. H. Cooper-Smith

Above:
King Edward VII Bridge, 1906: On 5 September 1960 the 'up' 'Northumbrian' crosses the King Edward Bridge in the charge of 'V2' class 2-6-2 No 60940. *Colin P. Walker*

1906: King Edward VII Bridge, Newcastle-upon-Tyne, Tyne & Wear

Designer: C. A. Harrison
Original owner: North Eastern Railway
Contractor: Cleveland Bridge & Engineering Co
Type: Lattice beam
Materials: Steel; granite
Total length: 383yd
Max height of rails: 112ft above high-water
Spans: 4
Tracks: 4

The railway traffic in the northeast of England grew steadily as the 19th century progressed. At Newcastle, Robert Stephenson's High Level Bridge of 1849 became increasingly congested and, furthermore, the need for east coast trains to perform a reversing manoeuvre at Central station did little to help the flow of traffic. A second major bridge across the Tyne was the only real solution, and plans were put in hand at the turn of the century.

The design for the new bridge was prepared by Charles Harrison, the nephew of Thomas Harrison who had prepared the drawings for Stephenson's High Level Bridge. Charles Harrison had been appointed as the Consulting Engineer of the NER's Northern Division in 1889, another family member, Alfred, having briefly filled the post after Thomas's departure in 1888. It was decided to site the new bridge about ½ mile to the west of the High Level Bridge; apart from providing an additional four tracks across the River Tyne, this enabled through trains from the south to enter Central station from the west, and eliminated the need for a reversal before continuing the journey to Scotland.

The new bridge had four spans (as opposed to the six of the High Level Bridge), the two centre ones being 300ft, the side span at the north being 231ft and that on the south 191ft. The southern span fanned out at the landward end to permit the laying of a triangular connection with the existing main line between Bensham and Gateshead. The lattice girders were 27ft deep and set 11ft apart, one end of each girder resting on a 'roller bed' to allow for thermal expansion and contraction; the decking carrying the tracks was 50ft wide. In all, the bridge consumed 5,782 tons of steel.

The bridge piers, which took the form of 'triple shafts' above cutwater level, were composed of some 330,000cu ft of Norwegian granite, their foundations being built in caissons sunk through the river-bed into solid ground which, at its deepest, was 69ft below high-water. The original intention had been for the southernmost span to consist of a series of stone arches, instead of a single lattice

span, but the foundation work had revealed that the underlying rock was too badly fissured to be used with safety.

The structure was named the King Edward VII Bridge and, although not completely finished, was formally opened by the Monarch on 10 July 1906. Coincidentally, a little over half a century earlier the King's mother had performed a similar ceremony at the nearby High Level Bridge. Regular traffic started using the King Edward VII Bridge on 1 October, the first train across it being hauled by NER 'Q' class 4-4-0 No 1930.

As a 'pontage' allowance, the NER was permitted to regard the bridge as three miles long for charging purposes, this practice being inherited by the LNER at the Grouping and surviving until Nationalisation. A familiar sight for passengers crossing the bridge was the marker which indicated the former boundary between the counties of Durham and Northumberland (the border being in the middle of the River Tyne) but, sadly for traditionalists, the border disappeared during the local government reorganisation of 1974.

The King Edward VII Bridge came to be regarded as Britain's last great railway bridge. By 1906, the extent of Britain's railway network was approaching its peak and, although many other railway bridges were built (or completely reconstructed) in later years, very few were a vital part of a major new trunk route. Today, the bridge is an integral component in the East Coast main line.

1906: Ashton Swing Bridge, Bristol, Avon

Original owner: Bristol Corporation/Great
**   Western Railway**
Designer and builder: John Lysaght & Co
Cost: £70,389
Type: Twin-level swing bridge
Materials: Steel
Total length: 194yd
Height of rails: 9ft above high-water
Spans: 1
Tracks: 2

Although Bristol was for centuries the second most important port in the country, the docks in the city centre did not receive the luxury of rail connections to the outside world until comparatively late in the day. The Bristol Harbour Railway took four years to build its ¾mile-long line between Temple Meads station and Bathurst Basin; it opened in March 1872 and was extended by ¼mile to Wapping Wharf in June 1876.

During the late 1890s Bristol Corporation announced plans for upgrading some of the older quays, and the Great Western Railway considered that a new route of access to the docks from the south and west would be advantageous. The outcome was the opening on 4 October 1906 of two new spurs into the dock area, both spurs joining the Bristol–Portishead branch at Ashton Junction.

The two spurs diverged a little beyond the north end of a swing bridge which spanned the New Cut. The bridge was one of the very few 'double-deck' bridges in the country, the railway line being carried on the lower deck and a main road on the upper deck. A description of the bridge appeared in the *GWR Magazine* of July 1906:

'This structure was built by the Bristol Corporation, and carries both the railway and high-level road over the River Avon. Its total length is 582ft and it contains some 1,500 tons of steelwork, the swing span alone, which is 202ft long, weighing 1,000 tons. This is worked from a central tower...by hydraulic power, and the bridge is electrically interlocked with the signalboxes on either side to prevent signals being lowered for the passage of a train unless the swing span is firmly secured.'

A swing bridge, or some other form of opening structure, had been necessary as commercial shipping still occasionally used the New Cut for access to Bathurst Basin, although much of the maritime activity on that stretch of waterway was, by then, of the pleasure variety. Messrs Campbell & Co offered a variety of paddle steamer cruises from Bristol Docks, one regular feature of the summer schedules of 1910, for example, being trips to Cardiff for 1s 6d (7½p) return.

Eventually, the paddle steamers started and finished their journeys down-river at a pontoon at Hotwells and, consequently, the use of the New Cut as a commercial waterway diminished, the last recorded movement of the swing bridge at Ashton being in 1936. In 1951 Bristol Corporation obtained powers to fix the bridge and remove the machinery, and the railway line across the bridge was officially closed on 11 January 1964.

The road section on the upper deck was removed during a major road reconstruction scheme of 1966, but the railway on the lower deck was retained, albeit as a single track, and hosted two notable workings in the 1980s. One was a special train of Orient Express Venice-Simplon stock hauled by Class 37 diesels which brought a contingent of VIPs to the World Wine Fair on 12 July 1984, and the other was a 'GWR 150' special the following year, hauled by ex-LMSR 2-6-0 No 46443. Cynics were quick to suggest that BR's retention of the almost unused railway line across the bridge was, at times, financed by unwitting football supporters. The structure provided a quick and easy route for pedestrians *en route* to the Bristol City ground, but

BR sometimes stationed officials on the bridge so that summonses could be issued for trespass. At the time of writing, however, easy access to Ashton Gate football ground is not a problem; it is rumoured that, if one arrives there before 3pm on a Saturday, one might well be picked for the team.

Another railway bridge in the Bristol Docks area warrants a brief mention. The lines of the Bristol Harbour Railway were originally laid with mixed gauge rails, and the 'cut-outs' which had once accommodated the broad gauge rails on the small opening bridge across the entrance to **Bathurst Basin** (next to the Ostrich pub) were clearly distinguishable until very recently.

1908: Calstock Viaduct, Cornwall/Devon

Designer: Messrs Galbraith & Church
Original owner: Bere Alston & Calstock Light Railway
Type: Arch viaduct
Materials: Concrete blocks
Max height of rails: 120ft above high-water
Spans: 12
Tracks: 1

The Bere Alston & Calstock Light Railway was formed to rebuild a locomotive-worked 3ft 6in gauge mineral tramway which served the mining area around Kelly Bray (Callington) in southeast Cornwall. The company's Light Railway Order authorised the conversion of the line to the standard gauge, and also a deviation at its eastern end which connected with the Plymouth, Devonport & South Western Junction Railway at Bere Alston. The light railway company was, effectively, a subsidiary of the PD&SWJR.

The eastern terminus of the old tramway had been at a wharf on the River Tamar at Calstock, but the new alignment of the light railway crossed the Tamar on a viaduct high above Calstock on its route to Bere Alston. The structure was built of concrete blocks and had 12 spans, each 60ft wide. Although it was anticipated that much of the mineral traffic from the Kelly Bray area would be taken to Bere Alston for onward transportation by rail, it was not intended to dispense with the quay at Calstock and so it was necessary for the new line to incorporate access to Calstock Quay, 113ft below the new alignment. This was achieved by means of an ingenious wagon lift on the side of Calstock Viaduct.

The wagon lift enabled trucks to be lowered and raised between the viaduct and the quay. It was designed by Messrs Galbraith & Church and was built almost entirely of mild steel. The cage could

Left:
Calstock Viaduct, 1908: This close-up of the celebrated wagon lift shows the girder section which carried the siding to the top of the lift. It is interesting to note that the wagons are inscribed with the initials of the Plymouth, Devonport & South Western Junction Railway. *Ian Allan Library*

accommodate one 4-wheeled wagon with a maximum weight of up to 20 tons (some sources quote only 15 tons), and it was operated by a steam winding engine which was fixed to the top of the lift framing. Duplicate steel cables, each of which could bear the full load, were provided in case of failure. The siding leading to the top of the lift was carried by steel girders built on to the side of the viaduct, and it is believed that wagons were pushed on to the lift manually.

Over the years the use of the wagon lift decreased, but it remained *in situ* until October 1934 when it was sold and dismantled. The viaduct itself has fared somewhat better, as the Bere Alston–Gunnislake section of the old Callington branch remains in everyday use by passenger trains. As an interesting aside, the conversion of the old tramway to a light railway was overseen by one Holman Frederick (later Lt-Col) Stephens who was, without doubt, the best-known of British light railway engineers.

1909: Queen Alexandra Bridge, Sunderland, Tyne & Wear

Original owners: North Eastern Railway/Sunderland Corporation
Cost: £450,000
Type: Lattice girder
Materials: Steel
Total length: 310yd
Max height of rails: 85ft above high-water
Spans: 4
Tracks: 2

Towards the end of the 19th century, the rail crossing of the River Wear between Sunderland and Monkwearmouth had become extremely congested. Crossing the Wear by road was little easier and so, in 1900, the North Eastern Railway and Sunderland

QUEEN ALEXANDRA BRIDGE, SUNDERLAND.

Corporation jointly proposed a double-deck road/rail bridge across the river between Millfield and Southwick.

Because of the shipping activity at Sunderland, the River Wear Commissioners demanded that the proposed bridge should leave a clear headroom of no less than 85ft and, furthermore, that the river channel should not be obstructed during construction work. Compliance with the demands obviously required a bridge of great size, and also well-considered methods of construction. It is unclear whether a cantilever bridge was considered, but the lattice girder bridge which was constructed was, in fact, built by cantilevering the two halves of the main 110yd-span out from their abutments until they met over the centre of the river.

The bridge was opened by the Earl of Durham on 10 June 1909 and, allegedly to compliment the recently opened King Edward Bridge at Newcastle, was named the Queen Alexandra Bridge. It had taken 4½ years to construct and had cost £450,000, of which £146,000 had been provided by Sunderland Corporation. The main span of the bridge, which was 345ft long and weighed some 2,600 tons, was the heaviest single span in Great Britain and more than three times the weight of the central span of the Forth Bridge. With the three additional 67yd-long spans on the approaches (one on the south side and two on the north), the bridge incorporated a total of nearly 9,000 tons of steel.

Above:
Queen Alexandra Bridge, 1909: Although this picture was taken as early as 1923, the rail deck across the bridge had, by then, already fallen into disuse. Maritime activity is very evident - locals would have to be restrained from commenting about the current state of play on Wearside.
Bucknall Collection/Ian Allan Library

The NER's new route across the bridge was intended for use by freight trains; it provided a connection between Diamond Hall Junction (on the Sunderland–Penshaw line) and Castletown Junction (on the Hylton, Southwick & Monkwearmouth line). Despite the resources that had gone into the bridge's construction, it saw its last rail traffic in 1921. As far as can be determined, the NER did not make a conscious decision to close the bridge permanently, the traffic seemingly petering out instead. Consequently, the precise date on which the last revenue-earning train crossed the bridge appears to be unrecorded.

Nevertheless, the rail deck of the Queen Alexandra Bridge was put to good use in 1924 when it was used for tests by the Bridge Stress Committee. The Committee was concerned with evaluating individual spans, rather than entire bridges, and the structure was the longest and heaviest of the 42 which were tested. The locomotives used during the tests of the Queen Alexandra Bridge were an ex-Great

Central '8C' class 4-6-0 (a class of just two Robinson-designed locomotives which became LNER class 'B1'...not to be confused with Edward Thompson's later 'B1s'), a former Lancashire & Yorkshire superheated 'Q4' (LMS '7F') 0-8-0 and an ex-LNWR 4-6-0 (LMSR '4F' No 8823). Although reference has been made to the 'testing' of the bridge, it should be pointed out that the Bridge Stress Committee was investigating the effects of different locomotive types on different types of bridges, as opposed to testing the bridges themselves.

The road deck across the bridge remained in regular use, and the structure later came under the control of Sunderland Corporation. In view of the Corporation's contribution of less than one-third of the bridge's construction costs, it wasn't a bad deal from their point of view. The rail approaches at either end of the bridge were eventually demolished, but the rail deck was left *in situ*. The road deck is still well used today.

1911: Carmarthen Bridge, Carmarthen, Dyfed

When the South Wales Railway extended its line from Carmarthen to Haverfordwest in January 1854, the line crossed the River Towy (now referred to as the Afon Tywi) at Carmarthen by means of a wrought iron drawbridge. It was one of four opening bridges on the South Wales main line. The eventual replacement for the drawbridge was a steel bascule bridge which opened to traffic on 11 July 1911, the first train to cross it being an Ocean Liner express from Fishguard.

The bascule section of the new bridge had a pair of massive 'Kentledge' boxes as counterweights, these being filled with cast iron blocks and asphalt; the two boxes were braced together in order to provide lateral strength against the winds. When the bascule section was raised, it provided a clear waterway 50ft wide. The design of the bridge was such that minimal effort was required to perform a lifting movement, the power being provided by a low-geared electric motor for which the current was supplied by a battery of accumulators charged by a paraffin engine. The bridge's approach spans were constructed of steel plate girders and were supported by cylindrical cast iron piers at 60ft centres. The decking on the approach spans was steel, but that on the bascule section was timber.

By the late 1940s commercial maritime traffic to Carmarthen Quay had all but ceased, and so a raising of the bridge was, by then, a somewhat rare occurrence. Yachting became a popular pursuit, but

Below:
Carmarthen Bridge, renewed 1911: This fine official picture of the imposing rolling lift bridge was taken in 1928. The counterbalance boxes were filled with cast iron blocks and asphalt. *Courtesy: Cleveland Bridge & Engineering Co*

most yacht-owners happily lowered their masts to pass under the bridge. One owner, however, continued to insist that the bridge be raised specially for him, and it is believed that his demands were heeded until the mid-1960s when a fire caused severe damage to the buildings housing the lifting mechanism. The precise date of the last bridge-lift seems to be unrecorded, but by the early 1970s continuous rails had been laid across the bridge and, therefore, bridge movements were impossible.

1916: King George V Bridge, Althorpe, Humberside

The GCR's Doncaster–Grimsby line was originally carried over the River Trent in north Lincolnshire by means of a 161yd-long swing bridge which had been designed by Charles Bartholomew. That bridge, which was built of iron, was completed in 1864. It comprised five spans, the central one of which could be opened to provide two navigable channels, each 60ft wide. It was an impressive structure but, almost 40 years later, the repairs which it required were extensive enough to be deemed virtually uneconomical. Instead, a new lifting bridge was built on a different alignment, and accommodated a road as well as the railway, the original bridge having had a footpath on each side.

The new bridge opened on 21 May 1916. The initial intention had been for a three-span bridge but, in 1913, a slippage of the east bank had necessitated the addition of a land span. The bridge was designed by the Scherzer Rolling Lift Bridge Co of the USA, and built by Sir William Arrol & Co. From the west, there were two river spans each 135ft long, then a lifting span of 160ft (giving a clear waterway 150ft wide), a track span of 40ft on which the lifting span 'rolled' and, finally, the unplanned-for 70ft-long land span.

Each span had three main girders, the central ones dividing the railway from the road, and the structure was supported by four river piers of steel caissons faced in granite. The lifting span and counterweights weighed all of 3,000 tons. It was powered by two 115hp electric motors and could be raised to an angle of nearly 82° in under two minutes. The sheer quantity of steelwork incorporated in the bridge was such that, even in north Lincolnshire, heat expansion has occasionally caused the structure to jam.

Below:
King George V Bridge, 1916: Class 31 No 31322 makes cautious progress over the bridge spanning the River Trent while hauling a westbound train of mineral empties. The road section of the bridge is behind the fencing on the left while, in the distance, the massive counterweights can be seen towering above the structure. *Philip D. Hawkins*

Motorway construction has been one of the factors behind the ongoing need for new railway bridges. To the southeast of Manchester, the line to Hayfield had to cross the Brinnington–Denton section of the new M66, and so a 2,600-tonne fabricated steel bridge was erected and then slid into place as a complete unit. The bridge was positioned in May 1988, the operation taking just 1hr 40min. *Courtesy: Fairclough Civil Engineering*

The age of railway building has not completely passed, as is evidenced by such systems as the Tyne & Wear Metro and the Docklands Light Railway. Consequently, brand-new railway bridges and viaducts have continued to appear, while others have been necessitated by the construction of, among other things, new motorways. Furthermore, there have been times when old and decaying bridges and viaducts have been deemed past economical repair and new structures have taken their place. As was pointed out in the introduction to this book, it is impossible to describe more than a handful of Britain's 'original' railway bridges and viaducts in a single volume and, similarly, only a very brief selection of modern structures can be included. Here are just a few.

The branch line from Sittingbourne to Sheerness opened on 19 July 1860. It crossed the River Swale by means of Kingsferry Bridge, a combined road and rail bridge which had, of necessity, an opening span. The original opening section was replaced, in 1904, by a Scherzer rolling lift span which, like its predecessor, carried road and rail traffic. The railway company (by then the SECR and, later, the Southern Railway) continued to collect tolls from road users until 1929, when Kent County Council took over the roadway. The bridge suffered severe damage in December 1922 when it was struck by a vessel, and was not reopened to rail traffic until the following November.

After a further maritime mishap in 1954, which once again resulted in the temporary closure of the bridge, the long-term future of the battle-scarred structure was reviewed. The outcome was the construction of a completely new bridge on the west side of the existing one. The new structure, appropriately named New Kingsferry Bridge, is built of concrete and has a central section which can be raised vertically between two pairs of 130ft-high towers. The lifting section is 125ft long and 50ft wide; weighing 465 tons, it is counterbalanced by four 110-ton weights. It can be raised to its full height in just 90sec, the power being provided by electric motors and the machinery being under the towers, some 60ft below high-water level. The two pairs of towers, incidentally, are connected by a service tunnel. The total length of the bridge is 217yd and it cost £1,380,810 to build.

The New Kingsferry Bridge was formally opened by the Duchess of Kent on 20 April 1960. The year before, the Sheerness branch had been electrified, but it was decided not to lay a conductor rail on the lifting section of the bridge as trains were considered to be of adequate length to span the gap between the live rails on either side. When the bridge is lowered after having been opened to river traffic, electrically operated bolts automatically reconnect the signalling circuits and also the return traction current path via the running rails. The bridge is permanently manned, a control cabin in one of the towers having radio and telephone contacts to ship and shore. In contrast to its prede-

Left:
New Kingsferry Bridge, 1960: This official picture of the new bridge was taken from the roadway on the mainland approach, and shows the lifting span partly raised. The railway line is behind the fencing on the right, part of the old bridge being visible behind the railway. *British Railways*

cessors, the new bridge carries the roadway on the western side of the road, this arrangement having been made partly to simplify the realignment work necessitated by the new rail approaches.

A similar style of structure to New Kingsferry Bridge was later opened across **Deptford Creek**, in southeast London. The original lifting bridge over the creek was built in 1838 and, although repaired over the years, was not replaced until December 1963. The old bridge was manually operated, and it took 12 men all of 60min to raise the lifting section whereas the new bridge has an electrically-operated 40-ton lifting section which can be raised vertically in just three minutes. The final work for the installation of the new bridge required an occupation by engineers of less than 48 hours. The structure was designed by the Southern Region's Chief Civil Engineer, A. H. Cantrell, and the main contractors were Sir William Arrol & Co of Glasgow, a firm which has had a long involvement with British railway bridges.

Above:

Deptford Lifting Bridge, 1963: The new bridge provides a sharp contrast to the brick arches of 1838. When this official picture was taken, work was in hand on the final stages of cable laying in conjunction with the Southern Region's scheme to renew power supply equipment and signalling in southeast London. *Courtesy: AEI*

Elton Viaduct, Nr Sandbach, Cheshire

By the time the LMR looked at the civil engineering requirements for the electrification of its main line to Euston, Elton Viaduct (over the River Wheelock on the Crewe–Manchester section) had already been substantially altered. The original viaduct opened in August 1842 and in the late 1930s all but one of the spans were replaced by an embankment. This had been necessitated by abnor-

Elton Viaduct: The first picture shows all too clearly how the original viaduct of 1842 had been affected by subsidence. The second picture, which was taken on 6 May 1963, shows the clever solution. As the new bridge continues to sink, further layers of concrete pipes can be added at the top. *British Railways*

mal subsidence, caused by the extraction of brine from the ground.

BR's pre-electrification solution to the potential problem of raising the remaining span every few years was rather ingenious, even if it did cast doubts about the structure's status as a bridge, let alone that of a viaduct. The bridge span over the river was replaced by an 'embankment' formed of 5ft-diameter reinforced concrete pipes which were placed in layers in a honeycomb fashion. It was calculated that, as the old span had sunk at a rate of 8in per year, the addition of a new layer of pipes would be required every seven years or so to maintain the track level. As a precaution against subsi-

Below:
Lyne Bridge On 15 February 1979, very soon after the distinctive bridge was opened to traffic, 2-SAP unit No 5908 crosses the bridge in a flurry of snow with the 2.24pm Staines–Weybridge service. *Les Bertram*

dence causing the overhead wires to sag, adjustable rugby-style 'goalposts' were erected for additional support.

Lyne Bridge, Chertsey, Surrey

When the car park known as the M25 was under construction, a new bridge was built to carry the Chertsey–Virginia Water line over the motorway. Designed by J. B. Manson, a BR engineer, the bridge was built on a new alignment to circumvent the need for a skew bridge on a daunting angle of 28°. The building of a new alignment provided BR with the bonus that traffic had to be interrupted only twice, once for the connection of the lines and again for the disconnection.

Christened Lyne Bridge, the structure was the first pre-stressed concrete cable-stayed railway bridge in Europe. The bridge is 120yd long, and comprises two spans formed of pre-stressed concrete edge-beams with a reinforced concrete deck between them. Its distinctive feature is a pair of 72ft-high reinforced towers, to which its upper and lower stay cables are anchored. Construction of Lyne Bridge commenced in earnest in April 1977, the work being completed in February 1979.

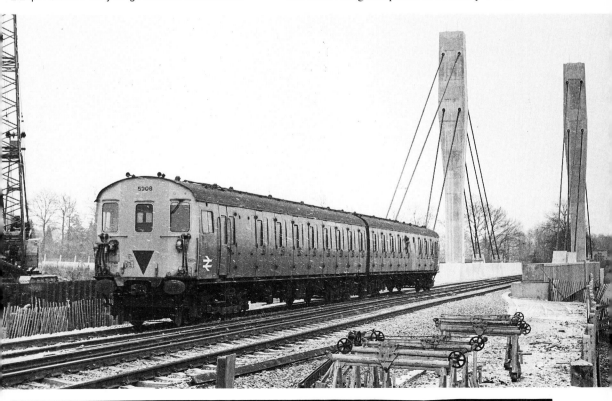

Tyne & Wear Metro bridges and viaducts

One of the largest new works of recent years is the Tyne & Wear Metro, which was conceived with the intention of taking over the British Rail lines and stations north of the River Tyne, and extending south of the river to Gateshead and South Shields. The first section opened in August 1980 and, apart from a later extension to Newcastle Airport, the network north of the Tyne was virtually completed by November 1982. South of the Tyne, the extension across the river to South Shields was unveiled in March 1984.

The best known of the Metro's civil engineering works is the **Queen Elizabeth II Bridge**, which carries the line between the centres of Newcastle and Gateshead. It was opened by Her Majesty The Queen in November 1981. Although a tunnel under the river was considered, that idea was soon dropped, partly on the grounds of cost, and partly because the stations at Newcastle and Gateshead would have had to be very deep underground.

When plans for the bridge were under discussion, the Port of Tyne Authority stipulated that, whatever type of bridge was built, it must not cause obstruction in the river and, furthermore, it must have a

Below:
Byker Viaduct, 1980: This official picture was taken in February 1980, and although the viaduct seems to be virtually completed, the overhead wires have yet to be installed. *Courtesy: Tyne & Wear PTE*

Below:
Byker Viaduct, 1980: This official picture was taken in February 1980, and although the viaduct seems to be virtually completed, the overhead wires have yet to be installed. *Courtesy: Tyne & Wear PTE*

minimum height above high water of 25 metres (81¾ft). This was because, at the time, Dunston Staiths were still being used for the export of coal. Of the three designs which were subsequently considered, two were for cable-stayed bridges with box girder decks while the third was for a through steel truss. The last-named won the day mainly on grounds of cost.

Before construction commenced, a series of drillings was undertaken to confirm that there were no old coal workings directly under the proposed sites for the foundations. Although no workings were found, the faults in the rock on the south bank caused concern and so a casting of concrete with rock anchors was used to 'stitch' the rock together. The building of the north pier was comparatively straightforward, a total of 100 piles being sunk into the existing bedrock. For the construction of both piers, sheet pile coffer-dams were used.

The superstructure of the bridge is a three-span continuous steel through truss. The central span is 179yd long, the entire structure being 384yd long and incorporating some 4,000 tonnes (3,920 tons) of steel. The two rail tracks are carried on timber sleepers which lie on ballast contained in steel troughs. It was calculated that extremes of temperature could cause the bridge to expand or contract by some 150mm (6in) over its total length, and so sliding bearings are provided at the river piers and the north abutment to allow for expansion or contraction. An expansion joint is also installed in the trackwork on the bridge, and is believed to be one of the longest such joints in Europe.

Of the nine other brand-new Metro bridges, **Byker Viaduct** was built on part of the proposed alignment for a recently-dropped east–west motorway. The abandonment of the motorway plans was somewhat convenient as the earlier intention of using two of the four BR tracks between Manors and Heaton (as the old Tyneside electric services had done) had been scuppered, BR having had to make the two 'spare' tracks unavailable because of its own proposed services between Newcastle and Scotland. Byker Viaduct is 895yd long, the central piers being 98ft high. It was the first major bridge in the United Kingdom to be built by cantilevered construction from pre-cast concrete segments jointed together by epoxy resin and stressed together. The two tracks across the viaduct are carried on concrete paving.

Apart from the new bridges and viaducts, a total of 10 former BR structures were renewed for use by Metro trains. One was **Willington Viaduct**, an iron structure dating from 1869 although its timber-built predecessor had been built in 1839 (see p26). Metro found that the viaduct was badly corroded, and so new steel members were used for strengthening, and a thorough blast-cleaning and repainting job was undertaken.

Index to bridges and viaducts

Where dates are given, the relevant bridge or viaduct is discussed in the text. Those marked 'see xxxx' are dealt with in separate entries for a different date. Those without dates are mentioned only briefly (for example in the introduction, or only in photographs).

Below:
Avon Bridge, second rebuilding 1959: Class 47 No 47033 crosses the 'new' Avon Bridge after pulling away from Bath with a Weymouth–Bristol working on 24 February 1975. *Ian Allan Library*

Below:
Ingleton Viaduct, completed 1861: In marked contrast to some other bridges and viaducts, no fatalities or serious injuries were reported during the construction of Ingleton Viaduct. The largely-ignored Lune Valley line, which crossed the viaduct, was closed to all traffic in 1964, this demolition train being photographed in June 1967. *Ian S. Krause*

Above:
Tay Bridge (Perth), rebuilt 1863: A 'B1' class 4-6-0 heads eastwards from Perth with an evening goods for Dundee - the year is believed to be 1965. The train is crossing the water on the east of Moncriffe Island. *W. J. V. Anderson/Rail Archive Stephenson*

Below:
Wye Bridge, rebuilt 1962: On 11 March 1965, 'Modified Hall' 4-6-0 No 6995 *Benthall Hall* crosses the rebuilt Wye Bridge with a northbound freight. *B. J. Ashworth*

Sadly, this sort of fate befell many historic bridges and viaducts. The structure seen disintegrating in this picture carried the Glasgow–Edinburgh line over a series of abandoned locks connecting the Union Canal with the Forth & Clyde Canal at Camelon, near Falkirk. The 120-year-old stone arch viaduct was in need of extensive repairs, and so BR decided instead to straighten the track by building an embankment and a new single-span bridge over a 40ft-wide road. The new alignment can be seen behind the flying debris. *British Railways*

Craigellachie Bridge, 1863: On 26 May 1958 '3P' 4-4-0 No 54473 crosses the elegant bridge over the River Spey on the approach to Craigellachie station. The train had, apparently, originated at Inverness. *T. G. Hepburn/Rail Archive Stephenson*